MODELING AND ANALYSIS USING Q-GERT NETWORKS

A. ALAN B. PRITSKER

Professor, Purdue University
President, Pritsker & Associates, Inc.

Second Edition

A HALSTED PRESS BOOK
JOHN WILEY & SONS
New York - London - Sydney - Toronto

Distributed by:

   Halsted Press, a Division of
John Wiley & Sons, Inc., New York;

and

Pritsker and Associates, Inc.
      P.O. Box 2413
West Lafayette, Indiana 47906

*Library of Congress Cataloging in
Publication Data*

Pritsker, A   Alan B   1933-

   Modeling and analysis using Q-GERT
networks.

   Bibliography: p.
   1. Queuing theory. 2. GERT (Network
analysis)
I. Title.
T57.9.P69 1979   658.4'032   78-71976
ISBN 0-470-26648-1

Printed in the United States of America
10 9 8 7 6 5 4 3 2 1

MODELING AND ANALYSIS USING Q-GERT NETWORKS

To My Wife ANNE

PREFACE

What is Q-GERT? Q-GERT is a network modeling vehicle and a computer analysis tool. GERT is an acronym for Graphical Evaluation and Review Technique. The Q is appended to indicate that queueing systems can be modeled in graphic form. The similarity of the names GERT and PERT is used to indicate that Q-GERT can be used to model projects consisting of sets of activities. In fact, GERT generalizes PERT concepts and Q-GERT augments GERT with the addition of queueing and decision capabilities. A fundamental contribution of Q-GERT is its method for graphically modeling systems in a manner that permits direct computer analysis. The Q-GERT Analysis Program has been developed to provide this computer analysis.

Q-GERT has been designed, developed and used for studying the procedural aspects of manufacturing, defense and service systems. It satisfies the need for a network approach to the modeling of systems that involve procedural, risk and random elements. It provides industrial engineers, business analysts and operations researchers with a graphical vehicle for modeling, analysis and communication. It performs a function similar to that provided by circuit diagrams for electrical engineers, free body diagrams for mechanical and civil engineers, signal flow graphs and block diagrams for systems analysts and PERT/CPM networks for project managers. Q-GERT networks are models of systems that consist of activities, servers and queues. As shown in this book, Q-GERT can be used in conjunction with project management, risk analysis and decision making for solving the problems of manufacturing, inventory and service organizations.

Throughout the book, emphasis is placed on the modeling philosophy inherent in the use of Q-GERT. Basically, Q-GERT supports a systems approach to problem resolution consisting of four steps. First, a system is decomposed into its significant elements. Second, the elements are analyzed and described. Third, the elements are integrated in a network model of the system. Fourth, system performance is assessed through the evaluation of the network model. This book demonstrates how to model systems with Q-GERT and how to use the Q-GERT Analysis Program to obtain system performance measures.

Q-GERT employs simulation procedures to analyze a Q-GERT network, and the Q-GERT Analysis Program can be viewed as a simulation language, much like GPSS. This book contains a user's manual and an operations manual for the Q-GERT Analysis Program. It does not document the internal workings of the Q-GERT Analysis Program. The emphasis of the book is on the elements of Q-GERT that are used in modeling procedural systems. Because of this, the book should be viewed more as a modeling book using a network approach to problem resolution than as a book on the use of simulation.

The main prerequisite required of the reader is a background in probability and statistics. Probability is required in order to characterize the elements of a network. Statistics is required in order to comprehend the outputs of the Q-GERT Analysis Program. No theorem proving nor equation deriving competence is necessary to model or use Q-GERT. The material in the book is primarily at the Senior/Graduate level. It can be used at lower levels to introduce modeling, statistical and simulation concepts. The choice depends upon the level of statistical detail to be included in the course.

The Q-GERT Analysis Program is written in standard ANSI FORTRAN IV. It has been compiled and run on a wide class of computers, and its portability has been demonstrated. The program is available from Pritsker & Associates, Inc., Consultants in Systems Engineering, P.O. Box 2413, West Lafayette, Indiana 47906.

The organization of this book reflects a hierarchical modeling approach that is advocated when using Q-GERT. The underlying network modeling and analysis concepts, and the descriptions of actual applications of Q-GERT are presented in Chapter 1. Chapters 2, 3 and 4 introduce and use basic Q-GERT concepts. The basic Q-GERT concepts are designed to allow the reader to model in Q-GERT without being overburdened with intermediate and advanced concepts. In Chapter 3, procedures are presented for using the Q-GERT Analysis Program to analyze Q-GERT networks that involve only the basic concepts. Chapter 4 presents six examples that illustrate the concepts presented in Chapter 2. The examples demonstrate the use of the Q-GERT Analysis Program as described in Chapter 3. The examples deal with a television inspection and adjustment system; operations in a paint shop; the provisioning and repairing of machines; a conveyor system analysis; sequential maintenance operations and subcontracting; and project management and planning.

Chapter 5 presents intermediate Q-GERT concepts. This chapter completes the description of the symbolism available when developing Q-GERT network models. Chapter 6 presents the additional data input requirements associated with the intermediate Q-GERT concepts. A discussion of statistical distributions is provided. In addition, three Q-GERT network models are formulated and analyzed. These models pertain to a banking system, a truck hauling situation, and shoveling and crushing operations at a quarry.

Advanced Q-GERT concepts which deal with the method for putting FORTRAN inserts into a Q-GERT network model are presented in Chapter 7. The organization of Q-GERT and the locations where a user can insert FORTRAN coding are described. The Q-GERT variable names and a list of subprograms that are available to assist the user in writing program inserts are presented. The use of subroutines for special initial conditions, output reporting and transaction processing are described. Models containing user-written FORTRAN program inserts are presented in Chapter 8. These examples involve the computation of criticality indices in PERT type networks, the incorporation of breakdowns in a job shop environment and the analysis of an inventory control system. Complete descriptions of the programming inserts along with the output reports for these examples are included in Chapter 8.

Chapter 9 includes a description of statistics collection and auxiliary data storage and retrieval subprograms available in the Q-GERT Analysis Program. An example that illustrates how a user can collect statistics at periodic subintervals is presented. Another example demonstrates how to include cost elements in a network model of an industrial sales negotiation process. In Chapter 10, methods are presented for defining, duplicating, editing and linking similar (or identical) subnetworks. An analysis of space experiments is presented to illustrate the concepts. Chapter 11 introduces the concept of resources. Resources are used to control the flow of transactions. Three examples are included in Chapter 11 to illustrate the procedures for allocating resources to transactions.

Appendices are included that describe the inputs and the error messages associated with the Q-GERT Analysis Program.

The plan for this text was to provide a progression from basic concepts to advanced concepts through a structured presentation. At each level, examples are provided that illustrate the concepts presented. This approach requires some duplication with regard to the description of inputs, outputs and networking procedures. The author considers such duplication to be appropriate when learning a new modeling technique. The use of many examples throughout the book is predicated on the belief that modeling is an art, and learning an art is best achieved through experience. Hopefully, the examples presented provide a foundation from which bigger and better models can be built. The reader should not infer from this philosophy that a bigger model is necessarily a better model. The goal of a network model should be that it is useful. Usefulness of a model can be obtained as a fulfillment of any of the following: the model provides for a better understanding of the system; the model serves as a communication vehicle that permits further study of the system; the model can be used to evaluate proposed system configurations; or the model helps to improve or optimize system performance.

Q-GERT has been developed over the last decade. Many individuals have contributed to its design and development. In Chapter 1, the history of GERT and related developments is given and the contributions of specific individuals are listed. With regard to Q-GERT, the following were involved in developing the program and I want to thank them for their efforts and acknowledge their contributions: David Bartkus, Steven Duket, Elliott Sigal, Timothy Townsend and Ware Washam. In particular, the contributions of Elliott Sigal were significant and his assistance over the past three years has been of tremendous value. Also, I want to thank Captain Victor Auterio who has used Q-GERT extensively and has made numerous suggestions for ways to improve it.

In preparing this manuscript, Jerome Sabuda and Anne Spinosa assisted in the running of the Q-GERT Analysis Program and the eighteen examples. Their tireless efforts are sincerely appreciated. At earlier stages of Q-GERT development, Floyd Grant and Mary Grant provided such assistance, and I gratefully acknowledge their support. Throughout the writing of this book, I received numerous suggestions and recommendations for improving it from individuals who took the time to go over the manuscript. These individuals have improved the presentation and helped me to clarify important aspects of the network language. Thanks for this go to: Steven Duket, Caryl Pritsker Du-Brock, Elliott Sigal, Charles Standridge and James Wilson. It is a pleasure to record my appreciation to my wife, Anne, for assisting in putting the manuscript into its final form.

A. Alan B. Pritsker

West Lafayette, Indiana
Revised: August 1978

CONTENTS

CHAPTER

1   Network Modeling and Analysis   1

Model Building,   2
Q-GERT Networks,   3
Applications,   5
Work Flow Analysis of a Property and Casualty
   Insurance Company's Regional Service Office,   7
Evaluation of Air Terminal Cargo Facilities,   7
Risk Analysis of Pipeline Construction,   8
Q-GERT Design Considerations,   8
Modeling with Q-GERT,   9
A Designer's View,   11
Network History Relative to GERT,   11
Organization of the Text,   16
Exercises,   17

2   Basic Q-GERT Concepts   18

A Q-GERT Network of a Single Server Queueing
   System,   19

   Modeling Queues and Servers,   19

CHAPTER

Modeling the Arrival of Transactions, 21
Modeling Departures of Transactions, 23
Combining Modeling Concepts, 23
Collecting Statistical Information, 24
Queue Node Specification, 25
Activity Durations, 26
Q-GERT Execution, 28
Basic Q-GERT Concepts Contained in the
    One Server, Single Queue Network Model, 29

Embellishments to the One Server, Single Queue
    System, 31

Single Queue, Parallel Server System, 31
Initial Transactions at a Q-node, 32
Finite Queue Size, 33
Balking of Transactions, 34
Complex Arrival Process, 36
Accumulating Transactions, 38
Sequential Service Operations and Blocking, 40

Summary of Basic Q-GERT Concepts and
    Terminology, 45
Exercises, 49

3   **The Q-GERT Analysis Program**   **52**

The Basic Q-GERT Analysis Program, 53
Basic Q-GERT Data Input Cards, 55
Free Form Input Features, 56
Examples of Data Input, 62
Run Definition, Stopping a Run and Multiple
    Run Analysis, 66
Statistical Collection and Output, 66

Data Collected on Nodes, 67
Data Collected on Q-nodes, 68
Data Collected on Servers, 70

Illustration of Queue, Server Utilization,

CHAPTER

Blocking and Balking Statistics, 71
Description of Q-GERT Analysis Program Output
Reports, 77

Final Results for First Simulation, 81
Number in Q-Node, 81
Server Utilization, 81
Blocked Time Per Unit Time, 82
Number Balking Per Unit Time, 82
Results for Run i, 83
Final Results for n Simulations, 83
Average Number in Q-node, 84
Number in Q-Node, 84
Average Server Utilization, 84
Extreme Values, 85
Average Blocked Time Per Unit Time, 86
Blocked Time of Server, 86
Average Number of Balking Per Unit Time, 86

Histogram Outputs, 87
Exercises, 88

4   **Examples of the Use of Basic Q-GERT Concepts**   91

Example 1. Inspection and Adjustment Stations
    on a Production Line, 91

Example 2. Paint Shop, 98

Example 3. A Production System Involving
    Machines, Spare Machines and Repairmen, 103

Example 4. A Conveyor System, 107

Example 5. Work Stations In Series, 114

Example 6. Simulation of a PERT Network,   118

Exercises,   129

5   **Intermediate Q-GERT Concepts**   **132**

Attributes of Transactions,   133

   Assigning Attribute Values to Transactions,   133
   Examples of Attribute Assignments,   134
   The Use of Attributes,   136
   Special Procedures for Assigning Attributes,   136
   Data Input of Value Assignments to
     Attributes,   138
   Example Illustrating Special Procedures for
     Assigning Attributes,   138
   Attribute Assignments at Q-Nodes,   141
   Attribute Based Queue Ranking,   142
   Data Input for Ranking Transactions in
     Q-nodes,   143

   Example Illustrating Queue Ranking,   143
   Conditional Branching and the Use of
     Attributes in Transaction Routing,   145
   Data Input for Conditional Branching,   149
   Examples,   150
   Probabilistic Branching Based on Attribute
     Values,   153

Selector Nodes (S-nodes),   154

   Routing Transactions to Parallel Queues,   156
   Selecting From Q-nodes in Order to
     Initiate Service Activities,   157
   Assembly of Transactions Prior to Service,   159
   Selecting Servers,   161

CHAPTER

Example, 162
Parallel Identical Servers Following an S-
  node, 164
Balking from an S-node, 164
Blocking by an S-node, 165
Multiple S-nodes Associated with a Q-node, 166
Data Input for S-nodes, 168

Match Nodes, 170
  Examples of Match Node, 171
Node Modification, 173

Data Input for Nodal Modifications, 175
Examples of Simple Nodal Modifications, 175
Example of Multiple Nodal Modification, 176
Serial Nodal Modifications, 178

Summary of Intermediate Q-GERT Symbols, 180
Exercises, 183

6   Data Input and Examples: Intermediate Concepts   189

Data Input, 189
Selecting a Distribution Type to Represent
  an Activity Time, 196

  Uniform Distribution, 196
  Triangular Distribution, 197
  Exponential Distribution, 198
  Poisson Distribution, 199

CHAPTER

Normal Distribution, 200
Lognormal Distribution, 201
Erlang Distribution, 204
Gamma Distribution, 204
Beta and Beta-PERT Distributions, 204

Truncated Versus Mixed Distributions, 208
Example 7. A Banking System, 209

Example 8. Modeling of a Truck Hauling
  Situation, 216

Example 9. Modeling of Quarry Operations, 222

Exercises, 228

7   **Advanced Q-GERT Concepts: Program Inserts**   **235**

Modeling Strategy, 235
Location of Programming Inserts in Q-GERT
  Models, 236

  An Example, 237

General Form for Coding Function UF (IFN), 238

  User Function Requirements for the Example, 239
  User Function Coding for the Example, 240

CHAPTER

Definitions of Q-GERT Variables,   243

   NDE,   243
   NFTBU,   243
   NREL, NRELP, NREL2,   245
   NRUN, NRUNS,   245
   NTC,   246
   PARAM,   247
   TNOW,   247
   TBEG,   248

Numeric Codes Associated with Function Types,
  Queue Selection Rules and Server Selection
  Rules,   248

Functions Available for Obtaining Samples from Probability Distributions,   248

Function DRAND (ISTRM),   249
Function DPROB (CPROB, VALUE, NVAL, ISTRM),   251

Parameter Changes Required When Using
  Lognormal, Beta, Gamma, Beta PERT or
  Triangular Distributions Directly in
  Function UF,   252
Subroutine UI,   253
Subroutine UO,   254
Special Subprograms for Use When Coding UF,   254

Subprograms Associated with Transactions,   254
  Function GATRB (J),   254
  Subroutine GETAT (ATT),   258
  Subroutine PATRB (ATTR, J),   258
  Subroutine PUTAT (ATT),   258
  Function TMARK (IDUM),   259
  Subroutine PTIN (NODE, TIME, TIMEM, ATT),   259
Subprograms Associated with Q-nodes,   259

CHAPTER

Function CAPQ (NODE),   260
Function RCAPQ (NODE),   260
Function XNINQ (NODE),   260
Function NOFQ (IDUM),   260
Function TINIQ (NODE),   261

User Defined Nodal Modifications: Subroutine
  NODMOD (NOUT, NIN),   261
Subprograms Associated with Activites,   261

Subroutine STARTA (NODE, NACT),   262
Subroutine HALTA (NODE, NACT, REMTI, ATT),   262
Subroutine XTEND (NACT, TIME),   263
Subroutine SNACT (ICA, NACT, REMTI),   263
Function NACTY (IDUM),   264
Subprograms Associated with Service Activites,   264
Function ISTUS (NODE, NSERV),   265
Function TISS (NODE, NSERV),   265
Function REMST (NSERV),   265
Subroutine STSER (NSERV),   266
Subroutine STAGO (NSERV, NODE, TIME, ICATT, ATT),   266

Dummy Subprograms,   267
Restriction on Use of User Subprograms That Can
  Start Activities,   267
Exercises,   268

8   Models Illustrating Advanced Concepts   271

Example 10. Obtaining Activity Criticality
  Indices,   272

Example 11. A Job Shop Environment with Machine
  Breakdowns,   278

CHAPTER

Problem Statement,   278

Example 12. An Inventory Control System,   286

Exercises,   293

9   **User Collected Statistics, Waiting Times and
        Auxiliary Attribute Arrays**   **296**

User Collected Statistics,   297

Collection of Statistics Based on Observa-
  tions,   297
Collection of Statistics for Time-Persis-
  tent Variables,   299
Histograms,   303
Example 13. Statistical Collection of Data for
  Subintervals,   304

Example 14. A Model of Costs Associated with an
  Industrial Sales Negotiation Process,   310

Computation of Waiting Times,   324
Auxiliary Attribute Processing Subroutines,   328
Examples of the Use of Auxiliary Attribute
  Subroutines,   329
Exercises,   332

10   **Q-GERT Subnetworks**   **335**

Q-GERT Subnetworks Input Features,   336
Defining and Duplicating a Subnetwork,   336
Editing Subnetworks,   338
Linking Subnetworks,   341
Data Inputs for Processing Subnetworks,   342
Output Reporting for Subnetworks,   343
User Access to Node and Activity Numbers,   344

CHAPTER

Example 15. Using Subnetworks to Analyze Space
  Experiments,   344

Exercises,   353

11   **Resources In Q-GERT**   **355**

Illustration of Resource Modeling, 356
Defining Resource Types, 358
Allocate Nodes, 359
Free Nodes, 362
Alter Nodes, 364
Short Form for Resource Data Input, 367
Functions for Accessing Resource Information, 368
Subprograms for Performing Resource Operations, 369
Examples Using Resources, 371

Example 16. Modeling Truck Hauling Using
  Resources, 371

Example 17. Oil Tanker Accommodation at a Port,
  375

Example 18. Embellished Inspection and
  Adjustment Stations, 378

Exercises, 385

A Concluding Note   **387**

References and Bibliography   **389**

Appendix 1   Data Input Description   **399**

Appendix 2   Q-GERT Analysis Program Error Messages   **437**

**Appendix 3   Q-GERT Analysis Program Operational
              Information**   **443**

Index   **447**

EXAMPLES

1 **Inspection and Adjustment Stations on a Production Line**   91
Concepts: Sequential Servers; Probabilistic Routing;
Feedback of Transactions

2 **Paint Shop**   98
Concepts: Finite Transaction Generation; Workman Flow
Through Operations

3 **A Production System Involving Machines, Spare Machines
and Repairmen**   103
Concepts: A Network Without Source and Sink Nodes;
Sequential Operations

4 **A Conveyor System**   107
Concepts: A Zero Capacity Q-node; Balking from Q-nodes;
Multiple Use of a Parameter Set

5 **A Production Line Involving Work Stations in Series**   114
Concepts: Balking to Represent Subcontracting; Blocking
of a Work Station

6 **Simulation of a PERT Network**   118
Concepts: Comparison of PERT and Q-GERT Modeling
and Calculations

7 **A Banking System**   209
Concepts: Parallel Servers; Probabilistic Branching from
a Q-node to Represent Two Types of Service;
Selector Node; Balking from an S-node;
Network Modification; Resetting Seed Values;
Eliminating Transient Statistics

8 **Modeling of a Truck Hauling Situation**   216
Concepts: Accumulation of Transactions at a Node;
Assembling of Transactions at an S-node;
Tracing; Disjoint Timing Network; Ending a
Run Due to no Scheduled Events

9   **Modeling of Quarry Operations**   222
    Concepts: Generation of Different Transaction Types;
               Attribute Value Assignments; Conditional
               Branching; Service Times Taken from a
               Transaction's Attributes; Nodal Tracing

10 **Obtaining Activity Criticality Indices**   272
    Concepts: Use of User Functions; Accessing Attributes
               Directly

11 **A Job Shop Environment with Machine Breakdowns**   278
    Concepts: Adding a Value to an Attribute Value;
               Stopping a Service Activity in Progress;
               Putting a Transaction into the Network

12 **An Inventory Control System**   286
    Concepts: Starting an Activity and Stopping Service with
               Program Inserts; User Initialization and
               Output Reporting

13 **Statistical Calculation of Data for Subintervals**   304
    Concepts: Use of Subprograms by the User to Collect
               Subinterval Data

14 **A Model of Costs Associated with an Industrial Sales
    Negotiation Process**   310
    Concepts: Adding Costs to a Project Network; Collecting
               Cost Data; Stopping the Next Scheduled
               Activity Completion

15 **Using Subnetworks to Analyze Space Experiments**   344
    Concepts: Subnetwork Input and Output Illustrations

16 **Modeling Truck Hauling Using Resources**
    Concepts: Use of ALLOCATE, FREE, and ALTER Nodes   371

17 **Oil Tanker Accommodation at a Port**
    Concepts: Specifying a procedure for resource allocation   375

18 **Embellished Inspection and Adjustment Model**   378
    Concepts: Multiple use of a resource: Q-node selection at an
               ALLOCATE node; multiple ALLOCATE nodes
               associated with a Q-node

MODELING AND ANALYSIS USING Q-GERT NETWORKS

Chapter 1

NETWORK MODELING AND ANALYSIS

Models are *descriptions* of systems. In the physical sciences, models are usually developed based on theoretical laws and principles. The models may be scaled physical objects (iconic models), mathematical equations and relations (abstract models), or graphical representations (visual models). The usefulness of models has been demonstrated in describing, designing and analyzing systems. Many students are educated in their discipline by learning how to build and use models. Model building is a complex process and in most fields is an art. The modeling of a system is made easier if: 1) physical laws are available that pertain to the system; 2) a pictorial or graphical representation can be made of the system; and 3) the variability of system inputs, elements and outputs is manageable.

Industrial engineers, managers and administrators, management scientists and operations researchers deal mainly with *procedural* systems. These individuals and their respective fields are attempting to bring order out of chaos with respect to the modeling and analysis of procedural systems. For our purposes, procedural systems can be thought of in terms of information flow and decision making with respect to the implementation of stated or implied policy. Emphasis is placed on improving performance through procedural changes or through new designs regarding scheduling, sequencing, distribution, allocation, layout and similar functions. The modeling of procedural systems is often more difficult than the modeling of physical systems for the following reasons: 1) few fundamental laws are available; 2) proce-

1

dural elements are difficult to describe and represent; 3) policy inputs are hard to quantify; 4) random components are significant elements; and 5) human decision-making is an integral part of such systems.

This book introduces a new technique, Q-GERT, which can be used for modeling and analyzing a class of procedural systems. Q-GERT involves the graphical modeling of systems in a network form. Q-GERT networks provide a vehicle through which information about models of procedural systems can be communicated. Q-GERT networks can be analyzed automatically to provide statistical information about the system under study. This introductory chapter discusses the difficulties involved in modeling procedural systems and how Q-GERT alleviates some of these difficulties.

MODEL BUILDING

Since a model is a description of a system, it is also an *abstraction* of a system. To develop an abstraction, a model builder must decide on the elements of the system to include in his model. To make such decisions, a purpose for model building should be established. Reference to this purpose should be made when deciding if an element of a system is significant and, hence, should be modeled. The success of a modeler depends on how well he can define significant elements and the relationships between elements.

In modeling procedural systems, the specification of the proper elements to include in the model is difficult. It is recommended that a dialog between the model builder and his client be established at the earliest possible time. The model building process should be considered as an iterative one. "First cut" models should be built, analyzed and discussed. The time that elapses between the establishment of the purpose for building a model and the production of outputs of the "first cut" model should be kept as small as possible. In many cases, this will require heroic assumptions and a willingness on the part of the modeler to expose his potential ignorance of the system under study. In the long run, it should pay off, as modeling inaccuracies will be discovered more quickly and corrected more efficiently than would be possible otherwise. Further, discussions that include outputs tend to clarify issues and to promote suggestions. Showing ignorance of system particulars early in a project, say, two to four weeks into a project, is not critical compared to a display of ignorance after working on a project for a year. In fact, it may be impossible to seek assistance after a year since the modeler at that time may be required to defend his model and its outputs.

The design of Q-GERT allows the user to easily modify or extend his model, and allows for hierarchical modeling (18). A network form which can be explained in a straightforward manner is used as the basic modeling vehicle. Thus, simple "first cut" models can be built quickly and complex models can be built from these simple models. In other words, detailed models can be developed from aggregate models. In fact, the first cut models provide the organizational framework from which complex models can be constructed. For example, the embellishment of a model of a one server, single queue system to include multiple queues, multiple servers, and new server selection procedures can easily be accomplished within the Q-GERT modeling framework. Further, the addition of balking from a queue or the blocking of a service station involves only minor network changes as will be illustrated in Chapter 2.

A digital computer program written in ANSI FORTRAN (2) has been developed for analyzing Q-GERT network models. Output performance measures can be obtained immediately following the development of the Q-GERT network model. In the development of Q-GERT, special attention has been given to input and output procedures which permit an analyst to obtain results in a timely manner to enhance communication activities.

The availability of Q-GERT symbols to facilitate the network modeling of procedural systems and the availability of the Q-GERT Analysis Program to obtain timely outputs support the problem solving procedure recommended above.

Q-GERT NETWORKS

Q-GERT employs an activity-on-branch network philosophy in which a branch represents an activity that involves a processing time or a delay. Nodes are used to separate branches and are used to model milestones, decision points, and queues. A Q-GERT network consists of nodes and branches. Flowing through the network are items referred to as transactions. Transactions are directed through the network according to the branching characteristics of the nodes. Transactions can represent physical objects, information, or a combination of the two. Different types of nodes are included in Q-GERT to allow for the modeling of complex queueing situations and project management systems. Activities can be used to represent servers of a queueing system and Q-GERT networks can be developed to model sequential and parallel service systems. The nodes and branches of a Q-GERT model describe the structural aspects of the system. A *process* approach (39,61) is taken in which the flow of a transaction is modeled.

Transactions originate at source nodes and travel along the branches of the network. Each branch has a start node and an end node as shown below.

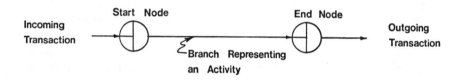

Transactions moving across a branch are delayed in reaching the end node associated with the branch by the time to perform the activity that the branch represents. When reaching the end node, the disposition of the transaction is determined by the node type, the status of the system, and the attributes associated with the transaction. The transaction continues through the network until no further routing can be performed. Typically, this occurs at sink nodes of the network but may occur at other nodes to allow for the destruction of information flow.

Transactions have attribute values that allow different types of objects (or the same type of object with different attribute values) to flow through the network. Procedures are available to assign and change attribute values of transactions at the various nodes of the network.

As transactions flow through the network model, statistics are collected on travel times, the status of servers and queues, and the times at which nodes are released. Thus, a statistical data collection scheme is embedded directly in a Q-GERT network model. The Q-GERT Analysis Program employs a simulation procedure to analyze the network. The simulation procedure involves the generation of transactions, the processing of the transactions through the network, and the collection of statistics required to prepare automatically a summary report as dictated by the Q-GERT network model.

This book describes in detail the characterization of: 1) objects by transactions; 2) activities by branches; and 3) milestones, queues and decision processes by nodes. The input procedures and output reports obtained from the Q-GERT Analysis Program are illustrated throughout the text.

APPLICATIONS

Many applications of Q-GERT have been made. GERT networks have been designed, developed and used to analyze the following situations:

1. Claims processing in an insurance company (66);
2. Production lines (92);
3. Quality control in manufacturing systems (93);
4. Assessment of job performance aids (7);
5. Burglary resistance of buildings (46);
6. Capacity of air terminal cargo facilities (5,25,66);
7. Judicial court system operation (12,23);
8. Equipment allocation in construction planning (48,49);
9. Refueling of military airlift forces (6);
10. Planning and control of marketing research (8,116);
11. Planning for contract negotiations (9);
12. Risk analysis in pipeline construction (36);
13. Effects of funding and administrative strategies on nuclear fusion power plant development (132);
14. Research and development planning (35,84):
15. System reliabilety (16,87,95,138).

A list of titles of papers relating to these GERT applications is given in Table 1-1. The books *Systems Analysis and Design Using Network Techniques* (142) by Gary Whitehouse and *Introduction to Systems Analysis With GERT Modeling and Simulation* (87) by Larry Moore and Ed Clayton describe and summarize many GERT applications. The forthcoming book by Salah Elmaghraby, *Activity Networks,* and a text on networks by Don Phillips should further stimulate the use of networks for modeling systems.

Basically, Q-GERT applications relate to queueing systems analysis or project planning and management. For queueing models, transactions are used to represent people (customers, burglars, operators) and/or items (claims, checks, aircraft). The transactions flow through a network and are processed in accordance with the activities defined on the network. The routing decisions for the transactions are prescribed by the nodes of the network. For project planning situations, information flows through the network and the potential outcomes that result from complex project management decisions are evaluated. PERT and CPM type analyses and complex risk analyses have been performed using Q-GERT (8,36).

Problem statements for three of the applications listed above will now be given to provide a preview of situations in which a Q-GERT analysis was found to be advantageous.

Table 1–1. List of Titles of GERT Application Projects and Articles.

"A Q-GERT Work Flow Simulation of a Property and Casualty Insurance Company's Regional Service Office" (70)
"A GERTS IIIQ Application to a Product Line" (95)
"GERT Network Analysis of Complex Production Systems" (96)
"A Computerized Approach for the Assessment and Evaluation of Job Performance Aids" (7)
"GERT Network Model of Burglary Resistance" (47)
"Q-GERT Simulation of Air Terminal Cargo Facilities" (5)
"Q-GERT Model of the Dover Air Force Base Aerial Port Cargo Facilities" (26)
"Analysis of Criminal Justice Systems Using GERTS IIIQ: A Case Study" (24)
"An Adjudication Research Simulation Model (AASM)" (12)
"An Investigation of the Use of Simulation Networks for Modeling Construction Networks" (48)
"An Investigation of the Use of Simulation Networks for Modeling Construction Operations" (49)
"Aerial Refueling for Military Airlift Forces: An Economic Analysis Based on Q-GERT Simulation" (6)
"The Use of GERT in the Planning and Control of Marketing Research" (119)
"Sales Negotiation Cost Planning for Corporate Level Sales" (9)
"Industrial Buying: A Method for Planning for Contract Negotiations" (10)
"Risk Analysis of a Pipeline Project Construction Schedule" (37)
"Use of the Partitive Analytical Forecasting (PAF) Technique for Analysis of the Effects of Various Funding and Administrative Strategies on Nuclear Fusion Power Plant Development" (135)
"An Application of GERT Network Techniques to the Selection and Management of Research and Development Projects" (35)
"A Stochastic Network Approach to Test and Checkout" (136)

WORK FLOW ANALYSIS OF A PROPERTY AND CASUALTY INSURANCE COMPANY'S REGIONAL SERVICE OFFICE (70)

The work flow system of a regional service office consists of various types of paper work associated with the processing of property and casualty insurance claims through a centralized computer information system. The different types of work are routed through 14 distinct operating units or departments within the regional service office that consists of over 150 personnel. The system was modeled as a complex queueing situation to identify the bottlenecks of the work flow and to assist in investigating the effects of certain managerial decisions. The Q-GERT model aided in estimating the consequences of specific actions contemplated or anticipated by management. The procedural changes investigated were:

1. Changes in the volume of each type of work handled by the regional service office;
2. Changes in the composition and requirements of the work input;
3. Changes in priority rules for the processing of work in the same operating unit;
4. Changes in the pathways of the work flow system;
5. Reallocation of personnel among the different departments; and
6. Changes in total processing times of customer requests due to training programs in specific areas.

EVALUATION OF AIR TERMINAL CARGO FACILITIES (5,26,69)

Managers of the military airlift system need a way of measuring the productive capacity of aerial port cargo processing. Specifically, the managers need to determine the effects of fluctuating demands for airlift cargo on a terminal's ability to meet the demand in a timely manner. Resource utilization is also an important factor.

At a terminal, cargo arrives by truck or by aircraft. The arriving cargo is offloaded and sorted by shipment, type, destination and priority. It is moved to various sorting areas where it is held until some form of consolidation is possible. Once consolidated, it is weighed, inspected and stored. Its status can then be classified as "movement-ready". When movement-ready cargo is selected for a mission, it is transferred to a staging area where it is combined with the other cargo assigned to the mission and defined as a load. The load is then processed by cargo loading equipment and transferred to the aircraft.

The Q-GERT model of this situation was used to answer the following procedural type of questions:

1. Is it worthwhile to introduce automation equipment in ports to improve processing capacity?
2. Where should new equipment be located?
3. How many simultaneous aircraft can a port load?
4. During contingencies, when is it necessary to increase the level of traffic activity, and what additional resources will be required?

RISK ANALYSIS OF PIPELINE CONSTRUCTION (37)

The construction of a pipeline basically involves: 1) preparing a site for laying pipe, 2) laying the pipe, and 3) welding sections of the pipe together. Supporting operations for pipeline construction involve the building, dismantling and moving of campsites, the construction of roads and other transportation facilities, and relandscaping the site. When pipeline construction is performed in Alaska, the adverse weather conditions must be considered when planning the construction project. A Q-GERT network was developed consisting of the pipeline construction activities, camp construction activities and transportation facility development activities. The effects of weather conditions on construction activities were modeled within the Q-GERT framework. A risk analysis was performed using the Q-GERT Analysis Program to determine the probability of completing pipeline construction by specified due dates. A cost analysis was also performed to determine potential overrun conditions.

Q-GERT DESIGN CONSIDERATIONS

Q-GERT has been designed to allow an analyst to model complex procedural systems within a logical systematic framework. This involves the development of network symbols and interconnections that provide the following capabilities:

1. The embellishment and compounding of simple systems to form complex systems;

2. A communication mechanism to facilitate discussion of significant features of the operational system;
3. A means for specifying the data requirements to produce an analysis of the system; and
4. A computer program for obtaining measures of system performance directly from the network model.

It would be nice to say that a deductive procedure was employed throughout the development of Q-GERT. Such was not the case as Q-GERT was developed over a ten-year period with intermediate versions (107,110) providing the springboard for new capabilities. Each new capability was evaluated in terms of a flexibility factor and a confusion factor. Flexibility was desired in order to model more diverse types of systems. However, with every new addition of capability, communication via the network model decreases and the chance for confusion increases. In the current version of Q-GERT, an attempt has been made to eliminate those features which could result in confusion and yet to maintain the features found desirable over a wide range of applications.

MODELING WITH Q-GERT

Figure 1–1 presents an overview of the components involved in a Q-GERT systems analysis. The Q-GERT symbol set is provided by the designer. The analyst brings to the systems analysis a knowledge of the system and the scenarios to be evaluated. Based on the scenarios and the purpose for model building, the Q-GERT symbols are combined into a network form. At this point, discussions can be held and the network revised and embellished.

The next step is to describe the Q-GERT network in a computer readable form. The Q-GERT Analysis Program specifies the procedure for describing the network on data cards.* The data for the Q-GERT Analysis Program describes both the network and the conditions for which the analysis is to be performed. A concerted effort has been made in designing the Q-GERT Analysis Program to minimize this latter type of information. Data elements that describe the activity times and decision processes included in the network must be collected and/or hypothesized by the analyst. By exercising the model with hypothesized data, the modeler can obtain a feel for the precision required during the

* The word "card" is used in a generic sense to mean one line of input. Input to the Q-GERT Analysis Program from a terminal is permissible.

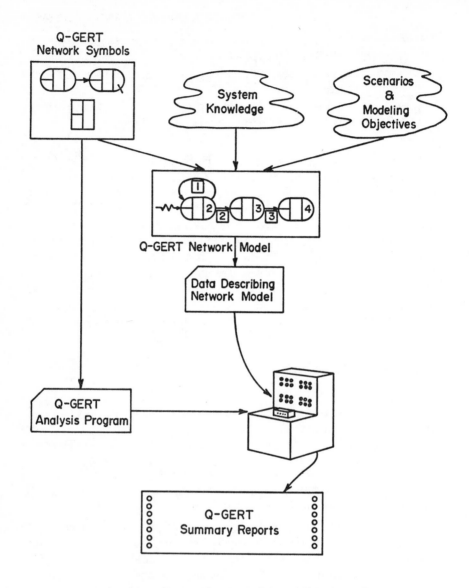

Figure 1-1 Components of Q-GERT modeling and analysis.

data collection phase. Also, preliminary attempts at structural valida-
tion can be made with hypothesized data.

The Q-GERT Analysis Program provides summary reports of the information requested by the analyst. The analyst should use this information for updating the model and for making inferences about the system under study.

A DESIGNER'S VIEW

From the designer's point of view, Figure 1–1 illustrates the types of
problems that need to be considered when developing a network modeling and analysis technique. First, the concepts required to model systems need to be defined. Then symbols need to be designed to portray
the concepts graphically. The procedures for connecting the symbols to
allow an analyst to build networks by integrating the symbols also need
to be provided. Further, concepts need to be included that allow the analyst to embed a statistical collection procedure directly in the network
model. These design problems represent only the first phase in a network designer's project.

The second phase involves the development of an analysis program or
algorithm that can accept network descriptions as data input. Such a
program should be able to analyze the network in accordance with the
analyst's specifications and to produce outputs that can be used in making inferences about the system under study. The requirement for the
design of suitable inputs and outputs for network analysis programs
cannot be overstressed.

NETWORK HISTORY RELATIVE TO GERT

This section provides a brief history of activity networks. Included are
the antecedents to GERT and the past, present and future developments related to GERT. The purpose of the history is to illustrate the
evolutionary nature of a development. Any errors of omission or commission are purely accidental. Not being an historian, and as the devel-
oper of GERT, clearly such errors can arise due to the perspective
taken. As a final introductory note, the non-historically oriented reader
can skip this section on any reading of the book.

A convenient place to start the history is with Gantt charts which
show the time phasing of activities, but which do not provide informa-

tion concerning the sequencing of activities. To show the sequencing of activities, PERT and CPM were developed (3, 83, 137). An extension to these techniques was suggested by Freeman (42) and dealt with the portrayal of alternative networks to represent a project. This was referred to as Probabilistic PERT. Eisner (27) generalized this concept by including a new node type in PERT that graphically portrayed alternative paths in a network. A similar concept was proposed for CPM by Crowston and Thompson (20) and was called Decision CPM. For D-CPM, integer programming techniques were used for treating problems with decision elements in networks.

PERT and CPM are both activity-on-branch network representations. Activity-on-node representations, also referred to as Precedence Diagramming, were introduced as an alternative way to portray precedence activities. Different types of precedence were also proposed that generalized the network forms. Thus, requiring a precedence for a start time or a completion time was suggested. For example, the completion time of activity B was to occur at least ten time units after the start of activity A. Or the start of activity B was to occur ten time units after the start of activity A. This concept generalized the normal precedence relation which states that activity B follows the completion of activity A. This concept was further generalized to allow for activities to be started after a certain percentage of a preceding activity was completed. Other generalizations of PERT and CPM dealt with the adding of costs and resources to the network. None of these additions changed the basic network structure used for modeling.

A significant breakthrough in generalizing the structure of activity networks was made by Elmaghraby (28, 30) when he defined three types of nodes: AND nodes; EXCLUSIVE-OR nodes; and INCLUSIVE-OR nodes. The first GERT developments were built on Elmaghraby's node definitions (101).

Let us start our historical discussion of GERT with the naming procedure. My first choice was SNAP: Stochastic Network Analysis Procedure. This seemed catchy and we could say that with a SNAP a network model can be built. However, in reviewing the literature, I found there was a nuclear program and a star tracking program, both of which were using the acronym SNAP. Thus, there were too many SNAPs around. I confronted my wife, Anne, with this dilemma, and after telling her that I was dealing with a generalization of PERT, she calmly proposed, "Why don't you name it after your mother and call it GERT?" So be it. The choice of Graphical for the letter G rather than Generalized is predicated on the belief that graphical models of procedural systems are useful in and of themselves.

The first research activities on GERT were performed at the RAND Corporation while developing procedures for automatic checkout equipment for the Apollo Program. The first applications of GERT were made on this program with Drezner (25).

Working with Happ and Whitehouse at Arizona State University it was shown that signal flowgraph theory could be used for analyzing networks that contained all EXCLUSIVE-OR nodes, even when the activity times were random variables (102, 103). The GERTE program was developed for analyzing this subset of GERT networks with Nelson (85). Improvements and documentation for the GERTE program were made with Ishmail, and the capability to obtain the first four moments associated with duration times was included in the program by Burns (108). The inclusion of counters and conditional moment generating functions in GERT networks with only EXCLUSIVE-OR nodes was done with Whitehouse (143). The use of Mellin transforms within the GERT framework for studying reliability problems was suggested (101). The development and implementation of this suggestion was carried out by Byers and Skeith. The application of the GERTE type networks to queueing systems analysis was suggested by Whitehouse (139). The development and implementation of the use of GERTE in queueing problems was done by Gallagher (44) and extended by Branson and Shah (11). Sensitivity analyses of GERTE networks were performed by Hill (53) and Raju (115). Time/cost analysis procedures for GERTE type networks were developed by Arisawa and Elmaghraby (4).

Attempts were made to obtain analytic solutions for GERT networks that included INCLUSIVE-OR and AND nodes. For some networks, these node types could be reduced to the EXCLUSIVE-OR type and GERTE analysis procedures employed (101). However, this could only be done for small networks, and in many cases could not be done at all. At this point, a simulation program was written for the general analysis of GERT networks containing the three node types. This program was written in GASP IIA (105), and initiated a whole new trend of thinking.

Since a simulation program was to be used for analyzing GERT networks, a rethinking of the node types and branch types associated with the network could be made. No longer were there restrictions on the symbol set due to analysis procedures. Clearly, this should have been the starting place for the design of the network approach, but it was not. Questions regarding the logical operations to associate with a node and how to specify the logic operations seemed of prime importance. Clearly, an AND and OR logic capability was desirable. With the inclusion of feedback, multiple releases of a node needed to be considered. It also appeared that the first release conditions may be different from the second release conditions which in turn may be different from the third release condition. This complex description was resolved by a design decision to consider the first decision different from all subsequent decisions. This, in some sense, corresponds to the arbitrary dichotomy employed in renewal theory when dealing with delayed recurrent events. The use of the number of incoming activity completions or transactions to prescribe the logic conditions associated with the release of a node permitted a wide variety of logic operations to be associated with nodes. If the number of incoming branches is equal to the number of activity completions required, an AND logic operation is specified. If only one activity completion is specified, an OR logic operation is specified. Majority voting is obtained by specifying the number of activity completions to be equal to a majority of the number of incoming branches. Similar decisions were made with regard to other elements included in GERT networks. These developments will be described in terms of the computer programs that I developed to treat special features. The individuals who worked with me in a design capacity are indicated throughout the discussion.

The original simulation program was called GERTS, for *GERT S*imulation program. GERTS II incorporated: 1) the concept of number of activity completions required to release a node; 2) counter types for activities; and 3) the halting of activities when other activities were completed. GERTS IIIZ allowed setup costs and variable costs to be associated with the activities of the network (107, 113). GERTS IIIQ introduced the concept of a transaction flowing through the system and Q-nodes where the transactions waited for activities (107). GERTS IIIR introduced the concept of resources which specified that an activity could not be started until resources required by the activity were available (107). P-GERTS was developed for simulating generalized activity-on-node or precedence diagramming networks (109).

At this point in the development of GERT, multiple programs existed for analyzing GERT networks with special features. Each program employed the same fundamental set of symbols. Programs were developed from each of these programs, and, hence, a smooth pattern of development is hard to portray. Washam implemented the free form input program for the Q-GERT packages (110). Townsend developed procedures for assigning attributes to transactions and for using the attributes to direct transactions through a network (133). Selector nodes were added for routing transactions to Q-nodes and service activities and also for selecting from among a set of Q-nodes when a server became free. Seum redeveloped Precedence GERT to include Q-nodes and complex branching and queueing procedures (123).

Hogg, Phillips, Maggert and Lesso combined queueing concepts and resource allocation decisions and developed GERTS IIIQR (54, 55, 56). Hebert extended GERTS IIIR by developing procedures for computing early start, early finish, late start, and late finish and criticality indices for resource constrained GERT networks (52). This program is referred to as R-GERT.

Balking from Q-nodes and selector nodes was included. Bartkus implemented the blocking of servers. Sigal implemented multiple server capabilities, and developed subnetwork definition and editing features, nodal traces, and user statistical collection and reporting (127). Subprograms were developed to provide the capability to include program inserts. Duket designed and implemented the match node capability. These developments provided the base for the current Q-GERT Analysis Program which was developed at Pritsker & Associates, Inc. with the help of Floyd Grant, Mary Grant and Jerome Sabuda.

Based on GERTS IIIZ, Vanston developed PAF for studying program management decisions for nuclear fission projects (135). Phillips, Polito, Schulaker and Petersen developed GRASP which extended GERTS IIIZ capabilities for studying reliability problems (98). Sigal incorporated GASP IV concepts into GERTS IIIZ in the development of SMOOTH, a network language for modeling combined discrete and continuous systems (126). Wortman and Duket, working in conjunction with Sigal, Seifert and Chubb, developed SAINT, Systems Analysis for Integrated Networks of Tasks, which builds on SMOOTH and P-GERT concepts (144, 112). SAINT can be used for studying human factors types of problems where sequences of tasks are performed by operators in a resource constrained environment. The environment also can affect, from a psychological point of view, the performance of operators on tasks through the use of moderator functions.

Roberts and Sadlowski have developed INS, an Integrated Network Simulator, which contains new network programming and design concepts (116). INS has a dual flow orientation where both transactions and resources flow through the system. Resource networks are built to represent the sequence by which resources are assigned to activities. INS is currently being used to study ambulatory care systems.

As a summary to this section, the GERT family tree is shown in Figure 1-2. The Q-GERT Analysis Program is the final result of the development cycle. It includes many of the features described above but some have been deleted, for example, halting of activities, counter types and activity costs. New additions are user written program inserts, user statistics collection and subnetwork generation and editing. The user-written inserts provide a means for adapting the Q-GERT Analysis Program to meet the specialized needs of the user population.

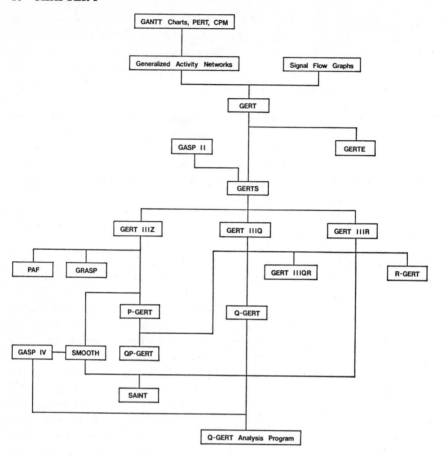

Figure 1-2   The GERT family tree.

ORGANIZATION OF THE TEXT

This book has been written in a hierarchical fashion. First, basic Q-GERT concepts and symbols are presented in Chapter 2. Inputs and outputs based on these concepts are described and illustrated in Chapter 3. Six models using basic Q-GERT concepts are then presented in Chapter 4. Intermediate Q-GERT concepts are described in Chapter 5 that allow for increased flexibility in model building and analysis. The basic and intermediate Q-GERT presentations include all the graphical features of Q-GERT. In Chapter 6, three examples are used to illustrate Q-GERT modeling using all the graphical concepts.

A third level of Q-GERT is presented that involves non-graphical modeling and analysis methods. These advanced Q-GERT capabilities involve the building of FORTRAN based models that can be inserted by the analyst directly within the network structure. To support the advanced concepts, advanced input and output techniques are available. Chapters 7 through 10 of this book describe these advanced Q-GERT methods.

A fourth level of Q-GERT involves resources which are described in Chapter 11. Resources are entities that are allocated to transactions at various nodes of a network. By presenting Q-GERT in this hierarchical fashion, the direct advantage of network modeling is obtained quickly, yet the increased flexibility that accompanies direct user modeling is made available.

EXERCISES

1-1. Define the following terms: modeling; network; network modeling.

1-2. Describe and characterize a procedural system. Give an example of a procedural system and discuss policies relative to the system and the procedures for implementing the policies.

1-3. List five structural (modeling) limitations of PERT/CPM.

1-4. Given two parallel activities, describe how to compute the expected time to complete the two activities if the activity times are random variables. Suppose that only one of the two activities needs to be completed, describe how to compute the expected time to complete one of the two activities. Suppose that the probability of performing activity 1 is p_1, and the probability of performing activity 2 is $p_2 = 1\text{-}p_1$, describe how to compute the expected time to perform activity 1 or activity 2.

1-5. Why is Q-GERT considered to be a hierarchical analysis technique?

1-6. Why is it necessary to prescribe a purpose for performing a systems analysis? Can you give an example of a discipline that does not adhere to this approach?

1-7. Define the types of statistics you would consider useful in an analysis of a procedural system.

1-8. List six advantages of Q-GERT.

1-9. Explain the difference between GERT modeling and GERT analysis.

Chapter 2

BASIC Q-GERT CONCEPTS

As an introduction to Q-GERT network modeling, let us consider a one server system in which a single line of items forms before the server. The server of the system has a status: busy or idle. The server status changes as system conditions change. The server is busy when he is processing an item, otherwise he is idle. The items flow through the system. They arrive, possibly wait, are served, and depart the system. Such a sequence of events, activities and decisions is referred to as a *process*. Entities that flow through a process are called *transactions*. Thus, items are considered as transactions. A transaction can be assigned attribute values that enable a modeler to distinguish between individual transactions of the same type or between transactions of different types. For example, the time a transaction enters the system is an attribute of the transaction.

Q-GERT provides a framework for modeling the flow of transactions through processes. The framework is a network structure consisting of specialized nodes and branches that are used to model servers, queues for servers, activities and transaction flow decisions. In short, a Q-GERT network is a graphical representation of a process and the flow of transactions through the process.

A Q-GERT NETWORK OF A SINGLE SERVER QUEUEING SYSTEM

To illustrate the basic concepts and symbols of Q-GERT, we will construct a model of an inspection process in the manufacturing of transistor radios. In this system, manufactured radios are delivered to an inspector at a central inspection area. The inspector examines each radio. After this inspection, the radio leaves the inspection area. Although we could model the entire manufacturing process, we are only interested in the operations associated with the inspection of radios. Therefore, we concern ourselves with the following three aspects of the system:

1. The arrival of radios to the inspection area;
2. The buildup of radios awaiting inspection; and
3. The activity of inspecting radios by a single inspector.

This is a single server queueing system. The radios are the system's *transactions*. The inspector is the *server*. The *service activity* is the actual inspection, and the buildup of radios awaiting service is the *queue*.

A pictorial diagram of this inspection system is shown below:

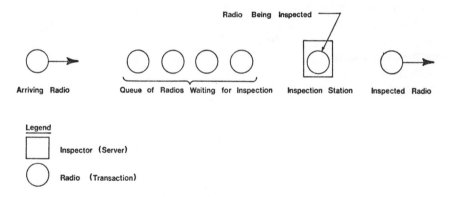

Modeling Queues and Servers

Let us build a network for this one server system. The passage of time is represented in a Q-GERT network by a *branch*.* Branches are the graphical representation of activities. Clearly, the service operation (the inspection of the radios) is an activity and, hence, is modeled by a

*The degenerate case is allowed where the branch represents the passage of zero time.

branch. If the service activity is ongoing, that is, the server (the inspector) is busy, arriving transactions (radios) must wait. Waiting occurs at Q-nodes. Thus, a one server, single queue system is depicted in Q-GERT by a Q-node and a branch as follows:

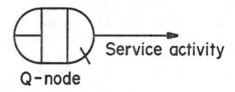

In our example, radios wait for service at the queue. When the inspector is free, the server takes a radio out of the queue and performs the service activity. The procedure for specifying the time to perform the service operation will be discussed later. A wide variety of service time distributions are available for use in Q-GERT.

Since there may be many Q-nodes and service activities in a network, each is identified numerically. Nodes are given node numbers and activities are given activity numbers. In addition, service activities are assigned a value to indicate the number of parallel services allowed by the branch, that is, the number of possible concurrent processings of transactions. For our example, we assign: the number 10 to the Q-node; the number 3 to the service activity; and, since we only have a single server, a 1 to the number of parallel servers represented by activity 3. The notation shown below is the procedure for labeling the elements of the network.

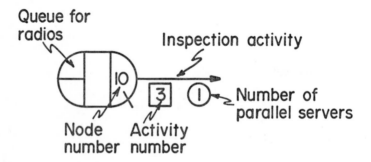

The node number is put on the right hand side of the node. The activity number is put in a square below the branch and the number of parallel servers is put in a circle, again below the branch. A Q-node has a "hash" mark in the lower righthand corner to indicate that it represents a queue.

Modeling the Arrival of Transactions

Turning our attention to the transactions (the individual radios), we must somehow model the arrival of radios to the system. Suppose we know the time between arrivals of radios (or at least the distribution of the time between arrivals). Then the arrival process can be modeled by a branch representing the time between successive arrivals. Each arrival begets the next arrival. This can be modeled by a node that has two branches emanating from it: a branch routing the arriving transaction to the server; and a branch returning to the node that causes the next arriving transaction to be generated. A graphical representation is shown below.

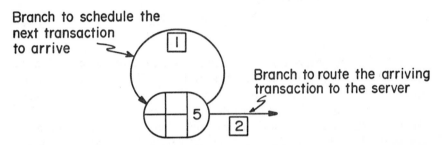

Branch to schedule the next transaction to arrive

Branch to route the arriving transaction to the server

There are several important features to note about the above graphical representation. The label 5 has been assigned to the node. Node 5 is not a Q-node as it does not have a line or "hash" mark in the lower righthand corner that makes it look like the letter Q. Since node 5 is not a Q-node, the branches emanating from it cannot represent service activities. The branches leaving node 5 represent activities 1 and 2 as indicated by the numbers in the squares beneath the branches. For nonservice activities, transactions are always accepted and the number of parallel servers is not prescribed, hence, no circle under the branch is required. In fact, activity numbers for nonserver activities need not be assigned.

Any transaction arriving at a node that is not a Q-node can be processed immediately by routing the transaction along the branches leaving the node. The semicircle on the right hand side of node 5 specifies that all branches leaving node 5 are taken. This is referred to as *deterministic* branching or routing. The branch from node 5 back to node 5 is labeled as activity 1 and is used to schedule the next transaction to arrive to the system. This is an example of one transaction causing the generation of a new transaction. Activity 2, the branch leaving node 5 labeled with the words "branch to route the arriving transaction to the server", is the mechanism by which the arriving transaction begins its journey through the service process.

If node 5 is the starting point of the system, then it is referred to as a source node. As shown below, a special symbol is used to indicate source

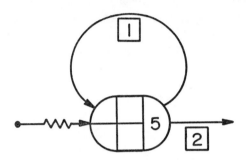

nodes in the network. Source nodes do not require incoming transactions to be activated or released the first time. The release of a node is the term used in Q-GERT to specify that an incoming transaction can pass through the node and be routed according to the characteristics of the node. The number of incoming transactions needed to release a node is specified by the Q-GERT modeler. After the first release of a node, it is possible to release the node again. This is accomplished by specifying the number of subsequent incoming transactions required to release the node. For this queueing example, we desire every incoming transaction to release the source node and, hence, a specification of 1 is given. The symbolism for specifying the number of incoming transactions required to release the node the first time and all subsequent times is shown below.

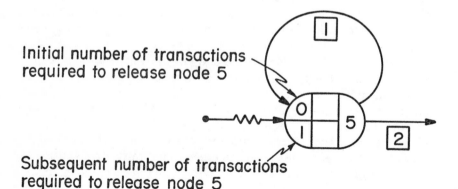

Modeling Departures of Transactions

We have now modeled the arrival pattern of transactions and the waiting and service operations. All that remains is the modeling of the departure process for the transaction. For our simple system, transactions leave the system following the completion of service. The modeling of the departure of a transaction is accomplished by a single node as shown below.

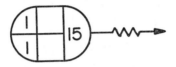

The number 15 has been assigned to the node. For both the first and subsequent releases of the node, a single incoming transaction is required and thus 1's are inserted in the upper and lower portions of the left hand side of the node. A squiggly line is used on the output side of node 15 to indicate that node 15 is a sink node. Sink nodes are used to specify the stopping procedure to be used when analyzing a Q-GERT network. For example, it could be specified that 100 releases of sink node 15 are desired. Sink nodes are described in detail in Chapter 3. As we shall see, a Q-GERT network is not required to have any sink nodes as the stopping condition could be based on a time period, for example, analyze the network for 1000 hours of operation.

Combining Modeling Concepts

We are now ready to combine the arrival, service and departure operations to obtain a complete network model of the one server, single queue process. This Q-GERT model is shown below.

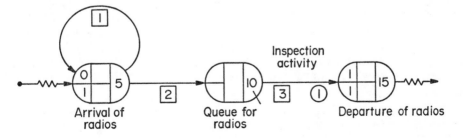

This network depicts the flow of a transaction and all the potential processing steps associated with the transaction. It models the processing of a transaction through a system. A transaction arrives to the system at node 5. Based on its time of arrival, the next transaction is scheduled to arrive. The current transaction is routed to the service activity by the branch from node 5 to Q-node 10. The branch represents the activity of traveling to the server. When the transaction arrives at the server, it will immediately go into service if the server is idle. If this occurs, the transaction flows from node 10 to node 15 and during the time the transaction is in this branch, server number 3 is busy.

If the server is busy when a transaction arrives at Q-node 10, the transaction remains at Q-node 10 and joins the queue of transactions waiting for server number 3. When a transaction joins a queue, a rule must be established that specifies the ranking of the transactions in the queue. If no ranking rule is specified, a first-in-first-out (FIFO) procedure is used, that is, transactions are taken from the queue in the order in which they arrived to the queue. After transactions are served by server number 3, they reach node 15. At node 15, the transaction is removed from the system as it has finished its routing through the process.

Collecting Statistical Information

As previously indicated, Q-GERT provides the capability for imbedding an information system within a network model. Suppose, for the inspection system discussed above, that we wish to record information on the amount of time a radio spends in the inspection system. This information is obtained by computing the difference between a radio's departure time and its arrival time.

The "marking" of the time at which a transaction passes through a node is accomplished in Q-GERT by *mark nodes*. The marking of a transaction at a node is indicated by an "M" in the lower center portion of the node symbol. The mark time assigned to a transaction is an attribute of the transaction. As the transaction is routed through the process, it carries its mark time attribute with it. A mark time allows statistics to be collected regarding the time required for a transaction to proceed through a portion of the network or through the entire network. The "mark" is simply a record of when a transaction last passed through a node that marked.

Whenever we wish to record this "travel" time for a transaction, we request the calculation of an *interval statistic*. An interval statistic is specified at a node by placing an "I" in the lower center portion of the node. This specification causes Q-GERT to collect statistics on the interval of time between the marking of a transaction and its arrival at the node where the statistical calculation is requested.

For the inspection system, we desire to calculate the time spent in the system by each radio and to accumulate statistical estimates of this time for all radios. The Q-GERT model that will accomplish this collection is given below.

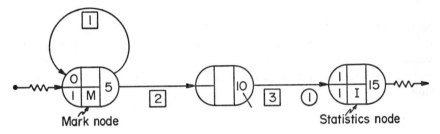

Each radio (transaction) is marked upon its arrival at node 5, and the time that each radio resides in the system is collected on its departure at node 15. Summary statistics associated with node 15 are then maintained and printed by the Q-GERT Analysis Program. *A source node automatically marks every transaction that passes through it.*

Queue Node Specification

At node 10, there is space for two additional pieces of information on the left hand side of the node. Inserted into these positions are the initial number of transactions at the Q-node and the maximum number of transactions allowed at the Q-node. A description of these items of information along with others discussed for Q-nodes is shown below.

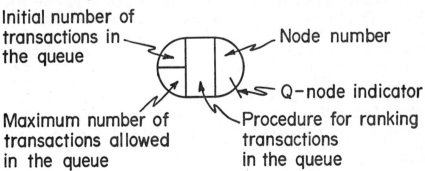

For this example, it will be assumed that there are no transactions at the Q-node initially, that an infinite queue is allowed to form before the server and that transactions will reside in the queue on a first-in, first-out basis. Filling in this information for Q-node 10 yields the symbol

Note that Q-nodes have different information specified on their input side than non-Q-nodes. The reason for this is that Q-nodes process transactions differently than non-Q-nodes. Note also that Q-nodes only provide storage space and do not cause explicit time delays for transactions.

Activity Durations

Let us now describe the activities of a network in more detail. Each activity in a Q-GERT network is assigned a time description. The time is specified by a *function type* and a *parameter identifier*. For function types that relate to random variables, the identifier is a parameter set number that points to where the values of the parameters for the function are maintained (specifically a row in an array). For example, a function type could be the normal distribution and the parameter set number could be given as 2. This would specify that the activity time should be a sample from a normal distribution with the parameters of the normal distribution maintained as the second set of parameters for the network. For constants, the parameter identifier is the value of the constant.

In Q-GERT, a shorthand notation is used in which the function type is abbreviated. On a branch, the function type and parameter identifier are prescribed within a set of parentheses separated by a comma. Thus, the specification of a normal distribution with parameters maintained in parameter set number 2 is made by writing (NO,2). For a constant activity duration of 100. time units, the code is (CO,100.). This shorthand is inserted directly on the network and is placed above the branch for which the specification is made. A list of the available function types and their codes is given in Table 2-1. A detailed discussion of random variables and the selection of a specific distribution to represent an activity is given in Chapter 6.

Table 2-1. Distribution and Function Type Codes and Parameter Identifiers for the Q-GERT Network Language.

Code	Description	Identifier
AT	The value of an ATtribute of a transaction is to be assigned as activity duration time	Attribute Number
BE	BEta distribution	Parameter Set Number
BP	Beta distribution fitted to three parameters as in Pert	Parameter Set Number
CO	COnstant	Value of Constant
ER	ERlang distribution	Parameter Set Number
EX	EXponential distribution	Parameter Set Number
GA	GAmma distribution	Parameter Set Number
IN	INcremental assignment	Initial Value
LO	LOgnormal distribution	Parameter Set Number
NO	NOrmal distribution	Parameter Set Number
PO	POisson distribution	Parameter Set Number
TR	TRiangular distribution	Parameter Set Number
UF	User Function	User Function Number
UN	UNiform distribution	Parameter Set Number
US	User Subroutine	User Subroutine Number

For the one server, single queue system, we will assume that: the time between arrivals is exponentially distributed having parameters maintained in parameter set number 1; the time to route the current transaction to the service area is a constant three time units; and the service time is normally distributed with parameters as maintained in parameter set number 2. The shorthand notation for these three activity descriptions are: (EX,1); (CO,3.); and (NO,2); respectively.

Inserting the activity description information on the Q-GERT network results in the graphical portrayal of the one server, single queue process shown below.

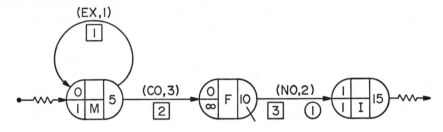

Q-GERT Model Execution

To analyze the system as represented by the Q-GERT network, it is only necessary to transform the data given on the network to a set of punched cards (or an equivalent input media). In general, one card is required to describe each node of the network and one card is required for each branch of the network. One card is also required for each parameter set specification. Thus, for the one server, single queue system, eight input data cards are required to describe the network: three to describe the nodes, three to describe the branches, and two for parameter set specification. In addition, a general information card is required on which the analyst's name, the project number, the date, and the analysis procedures are specified. Also, a card to indicate the end of Q-GERT data is required. With this 10 card input data description, a complete analysis of the Q-GERT network model can be performed.

In addition to obtaining estimates for the average time in the system for a transaction, the Q-GERT Analysis Program automatically obtains and provides statistical estimates of the average number of transactions in Q-node 10 and the fraction of time that server number 3 is busy. Also, the longest idle period and the longest busy period for server number 3 are estimated. Complete descriptions of the procedures for specifying the input and the types of outputs obtained from Q-GERT are given in Chapter 3. Suffice it to say that the translation of a network model to input data is direct and the generation of output statistics is automatic.

Basic Q-GERT Concepts Contained in the One Server, Single Queue Network Model

The small, three-node, three-branch model of a single server queueing system contains many fundamental concepts that are inherent to Q-

GERT network modeling. A summary of these basic characteristics is given below.

1. The time for a *transaction* to move through a network is specified on the *branches* of the network. Although a transaction can spend time waiting at a *Q-node,* this waiting time is in reality the sum of service times or a portion thereof of other transactions.

2. No explicit time delay is associated with a transaction passing through a node.

3. Decisions regarding the direction of flow for transactions are made at nodes. This decision process is called *branching,* and it can take on many forms. At node 5 in the example, a transaction was sent in two directions when leaving node 5. This is referred to as *deterministic branching.* A transaction was sent back to node 5 with an exponential time delay and a transaction was sent to node 10 with a constant time delay. Other types of branching will be discussed shortly.

4. When a transaction arrives at a node, it can *release* the node. Releasing a node causes branching to occur from that node. The number of incoming transactions required to release a node is a characteristic of the node. In Q-GERT, the modeler specifies the number of incoming transactions required to release a node the first time and the number required for all subsequent times. Every arriving transaction decrements the nodal release count requirement by one.

5. When a transaction arrives at a Q-node, it is either routed directly to the server or is placed in the queue until the server becomes free. The concept of nodal release does not apply to Q-nodes.

6. Transactions waiting at a Q-node are ordered in the waiting line in a specified manner. When a service activity associated with the branch emanating from the Q-node is completed, the transaction at the head of the waiting line is automatically put into service.

7. Transactions have *attributes* associated with them. In the example, the only attribute included was the time of arrival of the transaction to the system. This attribute was assigned through the *marking* operation at node 5. When deterministic branching occurs, new transactions are created with identical attributes for each additional branch. Thus, when the transaction returns to node 5, its arrival time is carried along with it. As the transaction proceeds through node 5, a new arrival time is assigned. When branching occurs from node 5, this new arrival time is assigned to all transactions leaving the node. Only one mark time is main-

tained per transaction, but marking or remarking can be specified at any regular node in the network. A source node automatically marks every transaction that leaves it.

8. In Q-GERT, statistics are automatically collected on Q-nodes and service activities. Statistics to be collected on nodal release times and transaction flow times are prescribed by the modeler through the specification of statistics collection operations at nodes of the network. Thus, in the example, node 15 was used to collect interval statistics.

9. In a network model, both service activities and regular activities are modeled using branches. In the example, the label 3 was used to identify the service activity represented by the branch between nodes 10 and 15, and the labels 1 and 2 were specified for the other branches. In general, any branch can be assigned an activity number. *However, only service activities can be assigned the number of concurrent transactions that can be processed by the service activity* (the value given in a circle below the service activity). *Non-service or regular activities always accept transactions.* Thus, in the example, there could be 8 transactions flowing along the branch from node 5 to node 10 at the same time. This would occur if node 5 was released every 2 minutes and the time delay as represented by the branch from node 5 to node 10 was 16 minutes long. Thus, for a regular branch, it is assumed that there is no limit to the number of transactions that can flow through it at a given time.

10. When multiple servers are prescribed for a service activity leaving a Q-node, the service provided to transactions is presumed to be identical. No distinction is made concerning the servers used to process the transactions. This would correspond to a model of a group of inspectors at the inspection station for which a single queue forms of all radios to be inspected by any one of the inspectors in the group. Output statistics for the inspectors would then consist of an estimate of the average number of busy inspectors.

11. From a modeling standpoint, the functional form prescribed for time delays is not significant with regard to the overall structural aspects of the network model. From a network modeling viewpoint, it is not important whether an exponentially or normally distributed time is assigned to the branch from node 5 to node 5 when building a model of the system. Changing from one specification to another is a simple matter. This allows the network modeling approach to be used as a means for specifying the data requirements to analyze a system. It also separates modeling and

structural characteristics of the system from the statistical descriptions of the system activities.

This list of fundamental concepts pertains to all Q-GERT models. As other examples are presented, we will point out other fundamental concepts.

EMBELLISHMENTS TO THE ONE SERVER, SINGLE QUEUE SYSTEM

In this section, the system previously described will be changed to illustrate other basic modeling features available in Q-GERT. By embellishing a small network, it is possible to highlight sequentially additional basic features of Q-GERT.

Single Queue, Parallel Server System

It is a simple matter to change a model of a one server system to a multiple server system if all the servers are assumed to be identical. With identical servers, no choice is made from among the available servers and, hence, the only decision required is whether all servers are busy or not. Consider the example of the radio inspection center. Suppose four inspectors were involved, instead of just one. For a four server model, the only change to the Q-GERT model is the specification of four servers associated with service activity number 3. This is accomplished by placing a 4 in the circle below the branch from node 10 to node 15. The Q-GERT model is shown below.

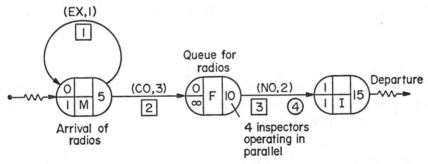

In this model, transactions arrive and are routed to node 10 in the same manner as previously described for the one server system. Now, however, a test is made at Q-node 10 to determine if less than 4 transactions are being processed by service activity 3. If this is the case, the arriving transaction at Q-node 10 is put into service and the number of busy servers is increased by one. If the number of transactions being served is 4, the arriving transaction is put in the queue and waits until one of the four servers completes the processing of a transaction. When the processing of a transaction is completed by one of the servers, the transaction is routed to node 15 and the disposition of the server is determined by examining the number of transactions currently residing in Q-node 10. If no transactions are waiting, the server becomes idle. If a transaction is waiting, it is removed from the queue and the service operation as represented by activity number 3 is performed. As can be seen from the above discussion, adding identical servers to a system does not change the Q-GERT model structure and is easily accomplished.

Initial Transactions at a Q-node

If it is desired to begin an analysis of a queueing situation with transactions initially in the queue, then this is specified directly at the Q-node as shown below.

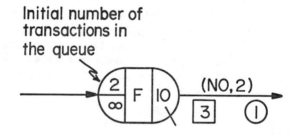

This specification implicitly assumes that all servers following Q-node 10 are busy initially and that 2 transactions are in Q-node 10 waiting for server 3 to complete service. Thus, a specification of 2 for the initial number in the queue places three transactions in the single server system.

Another possible use of the initial number in a Q-node is to generate a finite number of transactions for a system, that is, a Q-node can be used to provide a source of transactions. For example, if only four transactions are required, the following subnetwork could be employed to generate four transactions. The interarrival time of the transactions is given by the service time specification.

Using Q-node 2 in this fashion, the first arrival occurs at time 3, the second at time 6, the third at time 9, and the fourth and last at time 12. As will be seen in Chapter 4, the use of Q-nodes to generate transactions can be a convenience to the Q-GERT modeler.

Finite Queue Size

Suppose we are interested in studying a queueing system in which there is only a limited number of waiting spaces for transactions seeking service. This involves a capacity restriction on the number of transactions waiting at a Q-node. Situations in which this occurs include the following: a barber shop that has only 6 chairs for waiting customers; a waiting room for a doctor that can accommodate only 7 patients; and space for in-process inventory at a maintenance repair shop that is limited to 3. In our previous example suppose that there was room in front of the inspector to store only 6 radios. Specifying a limited capacity for a queue implicitly requires the modeling of a decision process regarding the disposition of a transaction that arrives at the queue when it is full. One possible disposition is that the transaction balks, that is, the transaction does not continue to seek service from the server whose queue is full. Two possibilities exist with regard to a balking transaction: the balking transaction can leave the system or the balking transaction can be routed to another node. It is the modeler's responsibility to specify the appropriate disposition for a balking transaction at each Q-node that has a limited capacity. Q-GERT automatically collects statistics on the number of transactions that balk from a Q-node.

A Q-GERT network model is given below for an inspection system in which a finite capacity of 6 radios is specified at Q-node 10 and balking transactions leave the system. The only difference in this network

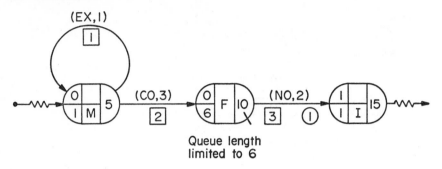

Queue length
limited to 6

model from the one given previously for the one server, single queue system is a change at Q-node 10 indicating that the infinite queue capacity is replaced by a capacity of six. Since the balking transactions are not routed to another node, no additional notation is required on the network model. This omission of a balking path presumes that balking transactions are lost to the system. That is, transactions that arrive at Q-node 10 when there are six transactions in the queue are destroyed in the same manner as transactions passing through node 15. Note that specifying a capacity of 6 at Q-node 10 allows seven transactions to be in the service-queue portion of the system: one transaction in service and six waiting for service.

Balking of Transactions

Suppose that balking transactions are modeled such that they return to Q-node 10 after one time unit. This time delay could represent the time to drive around the block for a drive-in bank situation or the time to get a cup of coffee in the doctor's office situation. In the radio inspection example, it could represent the time spent on a conveyor belt by the radio. A Q-GERT model for this situation is shown on the next page.

In Q-GERT, a dash-dot line is used to portray balking. Any non-solid line on a Q-GERT network is used to portray direct transfer of a transaction from one node to another. *In Q-GERT, non-solid branches do not represent activities.* The dash-dot branch specifies that transactions arriving when the queue is full are transferred from node 10 to node 20. The branch from node 20 back to node 10 models the one time-unit delay associated with the radio recirculating on a conveyor belt.

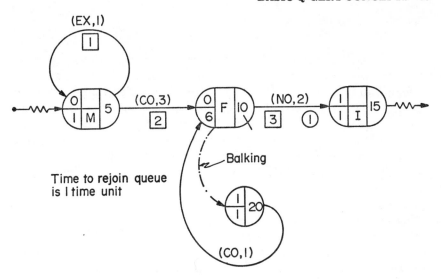

In Q-GERT, it is possible to balk to any other node in the network including other Q-nodes. In the above situation, the transaction could have balked from node 10 to node 15. The model of this latter situation is shown below.

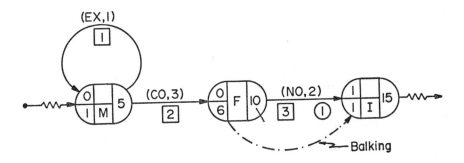

For this model, the transactions that balk from Q-node 10 are not served by activity 3. By modeling the transaction flow in this manner, the time spent in the system by transactions that balk is included in the statistics obtained at node 15.

Complex Arrival Process

In order to illustrate a different type of branching, two examples of a more complex arrival process will be presented. Consider first an arrival mechanism by which the next arrival time is sampled from an exponential distribution 30 percent of the time and is a constant value 70 percent of the time. This mixed distribution of the time between arrivals represents a random variable that would normally arise due to some complex physical characteristic of the system under study. Let us not be concerned with the physical processes but go directly to the modeling procedure.

The specification that one activity occurs 70% of the time and another 30% of the time requires the capability to route transactions to activities in a probabilistic manner. This is accomplished in Q-GERT by a *probabilistic branching* operation and is represented by a triangle on the right-hand side of a node. The Q-GERT model to portray this complex, mixed arrival distribution is shown below.

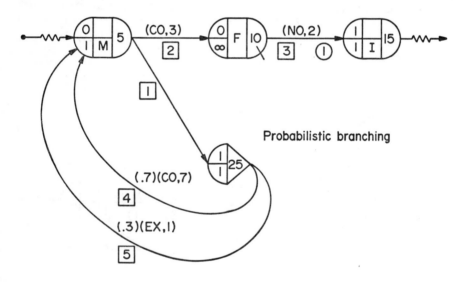

Probabilistic branching

In this network, node 25 has been added. Instead of routing the transaction directly back to node 5, the branch from node 5 to node 25 routes the transaction in such a manner that a probabilistic choice can be made between the constant interarrival time (activity 4) and the exponential interarrival time (activity 5). The time characteristic on the branch from node 5 to node 25 has been purposely omitted. Whenever the time specification is left off a branch, it is assumed that a zero time is associated with the branch, that is, (CO,0). Every transaction arriving at node 25 causes its release. The triangle on the output side of node 25 indicates that probabilistic routing (branching) of the transaction is to occur. The probabilities of selecting the branches emanating from node 25 are assigned to the branches as shown on the network. The sum of the probabilities of the branches emanating from a probabilistic node must be 1. With probability 0.7, the branch with a constant 7 time units (CO,7) is selected. With probability 0.3, the branch with the (EX,1) specification is selected. Since only one branch is selected when a probabilistic node is released, the complex arrival pattern of transactions is modeled by the above procedure. Note that in Q-GERT, parallel branches having the same start node and end node are allowed.

As another example of probabilistic branching, consider the situation in which two transactions arrive to the system simultaneously 40% of the time. Sixty percent of the arrivals are single transactions. The Q-GERT model cast in the terms of the radio inspection example, is shown below.

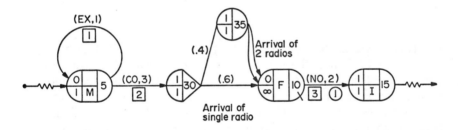

For this model, node 30 is inserted to model the decision as to whether one or two transactions (radios) should be routed to Q-node 10. If one transaction is to be routed, the branch from node 30 to node 10 is taken and this occurs with probability 0.6. With probability 0.4, the transaction is routed to node 35. Node 35 has deterministic branching with two branches emanating from it. This creates two transactions and routes them both to node 10. The delay times associated with the four branches between nodes 30 and 10 are all zero.

Accumulating Transactions

Suppose that it is desired to model a situation in which two transactions must arrive before service can be provided. A common situation where this occurs is in the construction industry. For example, a bulldozer must provide two loads to a loader before a loading operation can be initiated. In this situation, two transactions of one type must be accumulated before a single transaction of a new type can be routed to the service system. The accumulation of transactions can be accomplished in Q-GERT by requiring two incoming transactions at a node in order to release the node. Using our one server, single queue example and assuming that two arrivals are necessary before a transaction is sent to Q-node 10, we build the following model.

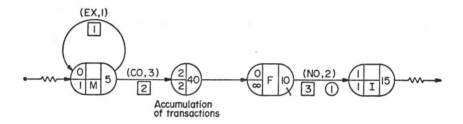

Accumulation
of transactions

For this network, the first transaction arriving to node 40 does not release node 40. When the second transaction arrives, the two requirements to release node 40 are satisfied, node 40 is released, and one transaction is sent to Q-node 10. The third transaction arriving at node 40 again does not release the node but the fourth one does. This continues with every even numbered transaction releasing node 40. Thus, the specification of more than one requirement for incoming transactions at a node provides the capability for accumulating transactions.

When accumulating transactions, a procedure must be provided for selecting the attributes to be given to the transaction that is routed from the node. In the current example, a choice must be made as to whether the mark time of the first arriving transaction or the mark time of the second arriving transaction is to be identified with the transaction routed to Q-node 10. The choice is problem dependent and must be made by the modeler. The modeler prescribes a choice by indicating his selection in the top middle portion of the node. Let us consider the choices the modeler can make. He can pass on the mark time of the first arriving transaction, in which case his *choice criterion* is to retain the attributes of the *first* arriving transaction. This criterion choice is specified by an F. Alternatively, the modeler can retain the attributes of the last arriving transaction, in which case the criterion choice is specified by an L. If the former choice is made, then statistics collected at node 15 will be the time in the system from when the first transaction arrived until the combined transaction left the system. If the latter choice is made, the statistics at node 15 would refer to the time interval from when the second transaction entered the system until the combined transactions left. (Other criterion choice mechanisms will be discussed in Chapter 5 in the section describing the assignment of attributes to transactions.) For the model presented here, we will assume that the attributes of the first arriving transaction are to be passed on to the combined transaction routed to Q-node 10. Since we are accumulating transactions at node 40, it might be of interest to compute the time between releases of node 40. This time would represent a sum of two exponential samples. In Q-GERT terminology, we specify that between statistics are to be calculated at node 40. This is indicated on the network by putting a "B" in the middle section of the node. The specification of the criterion choice mechanism and the between statistics collection for this network is shown below.

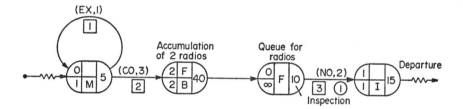

Several features of the above network require reiteration. No specification for the time for the branch from node 40 to node 10 is given. When no specification is made, a zero time is presumed. In the middle section of Q-node 10, an F is given. This F prescribes a first-in, first-out ordering of transactions in the queue. No criterion choice is ever associated with a Q-node because each transaction entering a Q-node is maintained as a separate entity and, hence, no selection of attributes is ever required. This is also the case for regular nodes when every incoming transaction causes the node to be released. Thus, for nodes 5 and 15, no choice mechanism is necessary. The specifying of marking or statistics collection at a node is made in the center portion of a node. Thus, marking occurs at node 5, and estimates of the time between releases of node 40 and the time in the system for transactions passing through node 15 are to be calculated. At node 40, the attributes of the first transaction of the set of transactions that causes the node to be released are saved.

Sequential Service Operations and Blocking

When two service activities are performed consecutively on a transaction in a prescribed order, a sequential queueing situation exists. The flow of the transaction through the system involves: its arrival; its routing into the first service operation where it either waits or is served; its routing to the second service operation where again it either waits or is served; and its departure from the system. Consider the radio inspection example where the inspection operation is followed by a cleaning operation that is performed by a separate operator. As shown below, sequential queueing systems are easily modeled in Q-GERT.

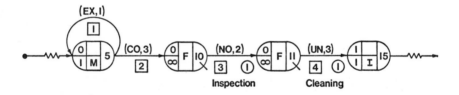

In this illustration, the second service activity, the cleaning operation, is prescribed as activity number 4. The 1 below activity 4 indicates that there is only one server associated with it. The service time is prescribed as being uniformly distributed with parameters as specified in parameter set number 3.

Transactions that complete service at activity number 3 are routed to Q-node 11 where they are either placed in the queue on a first-in, first-out basis or are directly put into service activity 4. The interval statistics collected at node 15 now pertain to the total time in the system including both service activities. This short description of the above network is an indication of the ease with which sequential servers can be modeled in Q-GERT.

A combination of series and parallel servers is easily obtained by changing the number of servers assigned to the service activities, that is, by changing the values within the circles below the service activities. Thus, the simple network presented above can, through specification changes, be made to represent a large queueing system.

As described earlier, transactions can balk from Q-nodes that have limited storage capacity. Thus, if node 11 has a limited storage capacity, transactions finishing service activity 3 when Q-node 11 is at its capacity could balk from Q-node 11. Alternatively, when one service activity routes transactions directly to a Q-node which has a limited capacity, it may be desired to model the blocking of the server until space in the subsequent queue becomes available. To provide this modeling capability, a symbol is required to keep the transaction at the first service operation and to stop processing by the server until space in the following Q-node becomes available. When this situation occurs, we say that the transaction and the first service activity are *blocked.*

The following Q-GERT network illustrates the blocking of the inspection operation by a limited queue capacity before the cleaning operation.

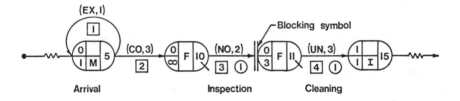

The double bar immediately to the left of Q-node 11 indicates the potential blocking of the preceding service activity. Blocking can only start when service activity 3 completes service on a transaction and Q-node 11 is full. When blocking occurs, service activity 3 cannot initiate another service activity, even though transactions are waiting in its queue. Under these conditions, the status of server activity 3 is termed "blocked". Service activity 3 becomes unblocked when service activity 4 completes the servicing of a transaction and a transaction is removed from Q-node 11. Since Q-node 11 will no longer be at its capacity at that time, the transaction residing in the blocked service activity 3 can enter Q-node 11. Also occurring at that time is the initiation of service activity 3 if a transaction is in Q-node 10. The Q-GERT Analysis Program performs all blocking, unblocking and associated functions automatically.

There are two basic concepts associated with this example. First, only service activities can be blocked, and only Q-nodes can cause blocking. *Thus, blocking only pertains to sequential queueing situations.* Second, blocking and balking are mutually exclusive concepts. A transaction, when encountering a Q-node that is at its capacity, can either be blocked or can balk. These two mechanisms provide the logic to determine the flow of transactions when a full queue is encountered.

With regard to blocking, *multiple servers represented by a single branch may not be blocked by a following Q-node.**

Alternative Service Activities and Probabilistic Routing from Servers

In some situations, a server can provide different types of service. For example, a bank teller can be involved in deposits, withdrawals and purchases of traveler's checks. Each of these operations can be performed by a single teller. One procedure for modeling different service activities performed by the same server is to employ *probabilistic branching from the Q-node* of the server. The branches emanating from the Q-node would represent the different types of service activities performed by the one server. Whenever any one of the activities is ongoing, the server is considered busy and none of the other activities may be started. The probabilities assigned to the service activities represent the proportion of time the server performs each of his distinct activities.

Consider an embellishment of the radio inspection example to include the inspection of AM radios and AM/FM radios. The percentage of AM radios is 80 and the inspection time for AM radios is normally distributed (parameter set 2). The percentage of AM/FM radios is 20 and the inspection time is exponentially distributed (parameter set 3). Only one inspector is involved in inspecting the two types of radios and a random selection is made of the next radio to be inspected. The Q-GERT network for this situation is shown below.

In this network, Q-node 10 has only one server that processes the transactions waiting in its queue. This server is service activity number 3. The two branches emanating from Q-node 10 represent this single server. Only one of the two activities as represented by the branches can be ongoing at a given time. When a transaction arrives at Q-node 10 and server 3 is idle, a selection is made from the two branches. The selection is made probabilistically. The branch indicating a normally distributed

---

* This is a technical restriction of the Q-GERT Analysis Program. Procedures for modeling around this restriction are discussed in Chapter 5 in the section on selector nodes.

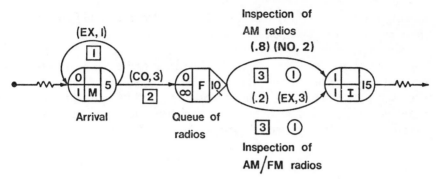

service time using parameters maintained in parameter set number 2, is selected with probability 0.8. The service operation which takes an exponentially distributed time with parameters as specified by parameter set number 3 is selected 20% of the time. When server number 3 completes the servicing of a transaction, the queue of transactions waiting at node 10 is examined and, if a transaction is waiting, a selection is again made of the type of service operation to be performed by server number 3. For this model, no matter which service operation is performed, transactions are routed to node 15.

In Q-GERT, it is not necessary to route transactions to the same node following a service operation. An example of this is given below.

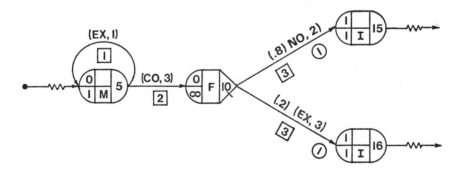

In this model, a segregation of transactions is made and statistics on the time spent in the system are collected for those transactions that required the normally distributed service time (at node 15) and those requiring the exponentially distributed service time (at node 16). In this manner, separate statistical estimates of the time spent in the system for each type of service are obtained.

If it is desired to collect separate statistical estimates and also joint statistical estimates on the time spent in the system for each transaction, the network model can be amended by adding one node and two branches as shown below. For this network, the time spent in the system for all transactions is collected at node 17.

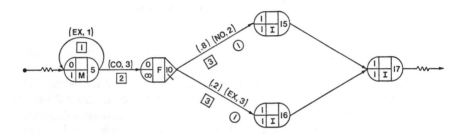

One last example for this chapter further demonstrates the power of Q-GERT by combining the probabilistic routing and the sequential service capabilities. For this example, assume that 90 percent of the radios inspected require no disassembly but that 10 percent require disassembly by the inspector. Two assistants are available to reassemble these inspected radios. The Q-GERT network model for this situation is given below.

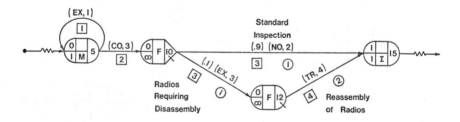

In this example, Q-node 12 and the service activity from node 12 to node 15 have been added. The service time associated with the branch from node 12 to node 15 is triangularly distributed (TR) with parameters as specified by parameter set number 4. The 2 in the circle below the branch indicates that two identical servers are available to perform this operation. The service activity number is 4 as indicated by a 4 in the square underneath the branch. Thus, two concurrent service operations of activity 4 can be performed, each of which takes an amount of time which is triangularly distributed.

Let us review the processing of transactions through this queueing network. At node 5, a transaction is routed to node 10 and arrives there 3 time units later. Also, a transaction is routed back to node 5 and will arrive at node 5 in a time that is a sample from an exponential distribution. When the transaction arrives at Q-node 10, it is routed probabilistically to one of the two activities following Q-node 10. If the branch from node 10 to node 15 is taken, the transaction arrives at node 15 after being served with a normally distributed service time. If a second transaction arrives at Q-node 10 while the first transaction is still being served, the transaction is put in the queue. The transaction cannot be routed from node 10 to node 12 because the server is busy, that is, he is performing the activity represented by the branch from node 10 to node 15. This statement is worth repeating. The servers associated with the branches from node 10 to node 15 and from node 10 to node 12 are the same.* The branches only represent different operations performed by the same server. After activity 3 is completed, service begins on the transaction waiting at Q-node 10. The type of service (and its associated routing) is done randomly.**

Now consider what happens if the branch from node 10 to node 12 is taken. Any arriving transaction to node 10 cannot proceed until the service activity from node 10 to node 12 is completed. When it is completed, the transaction is routed to the queue at node 12. The completion of service activity 3 permits any transaction waiting at node 10 to start service. The remainder of the network has been described previously.

SUMMARY OF BASIC Q-GERT CONCEPTS AND TERMINOLOGY

This section summarizes and integrates the basic Q-GERT concepts and terminology presented in Chapter 2. Also, the various alternative specifications relating to a concept are presented or referenced. A summary of basic Q-GERT symbols is given in Table 2–2.

* If multiple servers are assigned, the number of servers on each branch emanating from a Q-node with probabilistic branching must be the same.

** Randomly means a pseudorandom number is drawn and if it is less than 0.9, the branch from node 10 to node 15 is taken. If the random number is greater than 0.9, the branch from node 10 to node 12 is taken. A pseudorandom number has a value between 0 and 1 with every value being equally likely and successive values being independent.

Activity—An operation that could delay a transaction.

Activity Description—Information regarding the routing of transactions and an activity's duration and number.

Activity Time—The time delay incurred by transactions routed through an activity. The time could be a sample from a distribution or a value obtained from a function prescribed for the branch.

Balking—The routing of a transaction upon its arrival at a Q-node because the Q-node is at its capacity. Routing is indicated by a dash-dot line which does *not* represent an activity.

Basic Node Types—

Source Nodes—Nodes from which transactions are initially generated.

Statistics Nodes—Nodes at which statistics are maintained either on node realization times or on transaction flow times.

Sink Nodes—A sink node can be used to specify stopping conditions for the Q-GERT Analysis Program. The release of a sink node could end the processing of transactions, that is, complete the process as represented by the network. Multiple releases for a sink node can also be used to specify the stopping condition.

Regular Nodes—Nodes which do not have special functions other than the receiving and the routing of transactions.

Q-Nodes—Nodes at which transactions may wait for service activities. (In basic Q-GERT, a Q-node precedes service activities.) Statistics are automatically collected on Q-nodes.

Blocking—Enforced idleness on a service activity due to the inability to route a transaction to the Q-node following the service activity.

Branch (non-solid)—The network representation of the routing of transactions without their passing through an activity.

Branch (solid)—The network representation for an activity or service activity.

Branching—Routing.

Choice Criterion—Specification of the attribute value that should be retained when transactions are accumulated at a node. For basic Q-GERT, only F→ retain mark time of *first* arriving transaction or L→ retain mark time of *last* arriving transaction can be prescribed.

Decisions—The routing procedures for transactions.

Deterministic Branching—The selection of each branch emanating from a node. A duplicate transaction flows over each branch emanating from a node with the deterministic branching specification.

Events—Points in time at which the status of transactions and servers can change.

Network—A system of nodes and branches that models a process.

Network Symbols—The graphical portrayal of concepts to permit the construction of visual models. Table 2–2 gives a summary of the network symbols corresponding to the basic Q-GERT concepts.

Node—The network representation for decision points, end of activity events and routing.

Probabilistic Branching—Selection of one of a set of branches emanating from a node. The probability of selecting each branch is part of the activity description for the branch. The sum of the probabilities of branches emanating from a node with probabilistic branching must be 1.

Process—A sequence of activities, events and decisions that regulate the flow of transactions.

Queue Ranking Rules—Specification for ordering transactions in Q-nodes. For basic Q-GERT, the rules available are: F→ first-in, first-out (FIFO) or L→ last-in, first-out (LIFO).

Service Activity—An activity that can process only a prescribed number of transactions at one time. In basic Q-GERT, a service activity can only emanate from a Q-node.

Time Delay Specification—A distribution type or function type prescribed to a branch. Table 2–1 lists the alternative possibilities. For each branch, a parameter set number or constant value is also prescribed to provide the parameters to be used in conjunction with the distribution type or function type.

Transaction—An entity or item.

Table 2-2. Summary of Basic Q-GERT Symbols.

Symbol	Definition
	R_f is the number of incoming transactions required to release the node for the first time. R_s is the number of incoming transactions required to release the node for all subsequent times.
	C is the criterion for holding the attribute set at a node. S is the statistics collection type or marking. # is the node number.

 indicates deterministic branching from the node.

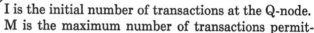 indicates probabilistic branching from the node.

I is the initial number of transactions at the Q-node.

M is the maximum number of transactions permitted at the Q-node.

R is the ranking procedure for ordering transactions at the Q-node.

is the Q-node number.

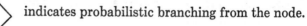 Pointer to a source node or from a sink node.

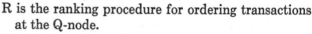

P is the probability of taking the activity (only used if probabilistic branching from the start node of the activity is specified).

D is the distribution or function type from which the activity time is to be determined.

PS is the parameter set number (or constant value) where the parameters for the activity time are specified.

⊞ is the activity number

Ⓝ is the number of parallel servers associated with the activity (only used if the start node of the activity is a Q-node).

— · — · — · → Routing of a transaction that balks from a Q-node. This symbol can not emanate from a regular node.

Blocking indicator (only used with Q-nodes that can force preceding *service* activities to hold transactions because the Q-node is at its maximum capacity).

EXERCISES

2-1. Describe a banking operation in terms of transactions, events, servers and activities.

2-2. For the Q-GERT network shown below, place the following variable labels in their appropriate locations.
a) N, number of parallel identical servers
b) C, maximum queue capacity
c) IN, initial number in the queue
d) QR, queue ranking rule
e) IA, interarrival time distribution
f) PIA, parameter set number for interarrival time distribution
g) D, delay time distribution until arrival at queue
h) PD, parameter set number for delay time
i) S, service time distribution
j) PS, parameter set number associated with service time distribution

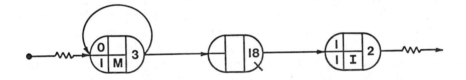

2-3. At a drive-in bank where there is only one teller, there is space for five waiting cars. If a customer arrives when the waiting line is full, the customer drives around the block and tries to join the waiting line again. The interarrival time between customer arrivals is exponentially distributed with parameter set 1. The time to drive around the block is normally distributed with parameter set 2. The teller service time is lognormally distributed with parameter set 3. When a customer arrives and can join the queue, it takes a negligible amount of time to join the queue which is organized on a first come, first served basis. Initially, no customers are waiting to be served and the teller is idle. Draw the Q-GERT network associated with this situation which collects statistics on the customer's time in the system.

2-4. For the banking situation described in Exercise 2-3, it has been found that the cars depart from the teller into a street and that the amount of time for a car to find a gap large enough to depart into the street is exponentially distributed with parameter set number 4. The design of the drive-in bank parking lot only allows three cars to be waiting to enter the street. Modify the network developed in Exercise 2-3 to include this new feature.

2-5. A barber has categorized his customers according to the length of their hair. He has determined that the time to cut the hair of a customer with short hair is uniformly distributed with parameter set 1, whereas the time for customers with long hair is exponentially distributed with parameter set 2. The barber has determined that 60 percent of his customers have long hair. Assuming that the time between customer arrivals is gamma distributed with parameter set 3 and that the barber serves customers on a FIFO basis, draw the Q-GERT network to represent this situation. Include in the network the collection of statistics on the time spent in the system by each type of customer and both types of customers collectively.

2-6. A server is stationed by a conveyor belt and the server can only take items off the conveyor belt if he is idle. Items arrive to the conveyor belt with the time between arrivals a constant 10 time units. Once the item is placed on the conveyor belt, it takes three time units for it to reach the service station. If the server is busy, the item continues on the conveyor belt and returns to the server in 9 time units. Service for the item is exponentially distributed with parameter set number 1. When the server finishes working on an item, he places it on a second conveyor belt to be processed by a second server. The item spends five time units on the second conveyor belt before arriving at the second server. If the second server is busy, the item stays on the second conveyor belt for 12 time units before it is returned to the second server. The service time of the second server is lognormally distributed with parameter set 2. After being served by the second server, the item departs the system. Draw a Q-GERT network of this situation that collects information on the amount of time an item spends in the system described by the two conveyor belts and two servers.

2-7. For the following network, fill in the entries in the following charts for 28 time units and compute the utilization of the server, the average number in the queue, and the average time spent in the system by a transaction. Assume that the initial transactions in the system arrived at time 0 and note that the first arrival occurs at time zero.

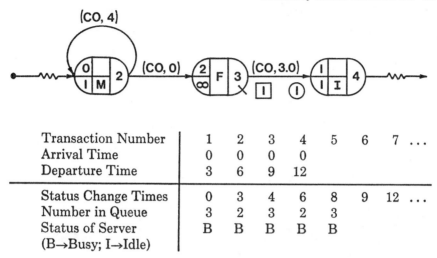

Transaction Number	1	2	3	4	5	6	7 ...
Arrival Time	0	0	0	0			
Departure Time	3	6	9	12			

Status Change Times	0	3	4	6	8	9	12 ...
Number in Queue	3	2	3	2	3		
Status of Server (B→Busy; I→Idle)	B	B	B	B	B		

2-8. Convert a PERT network with which you are familiar into a GERT network representation.

2-9. For the PERT network developed in the previous exercise, presume that there is a probability that some activities in the network will fail which would cause project failure. Redraw the Q-GERT network to represent this situation.

2-10. Describe how a regular node of a Q-GERT network can be used to represent the following logic operations: all preceding activities must be completed before successor activities can be started; any one of the preceding activities must be completed before the activity can be started; and three out of five of the preceding activities must be completed before the activity can be started (or, in general, a majority voting type of logic).

2-11. The thief of Baghdad has been placed in a dungeon with three doors (103). One door leads to freedom, one door leads to a long tunnel and a third door leads to a short tunnel. The tunnels return the thief to the dungeon. If the thief returns to the dungeon, he attempts to gain his freedom again but his past experiences do not help him in selecting the door that leads to freedom, that is, we assume a Markov thief. Let p_F, p_S, and p_L denote the thief's probabilities of selecting the doors to freedom, the short tunnel and the long tunnel, respectively. Let the time in the short tunnel be exponentially distributed with parameter set 1 and the time in the long tunnel be lognormally distributed with parameter set 2. Draw the Q-GERT network to obtain the time required for the thief to reach freedom.

Chapter 3

THE Q-GERT ANALYSIS PROGRAM

The analysis of a Q-GERT network is performed on a digital computer by the Q-GERT Analysis Program. The Q-GERT Analysis Program is written in ANSI FORTRAN IV (2) and has been run on a wide class of computers.

The Q-GERT Analysis Program employs simulation techniques to analyze the flow of transactions through the network in order to obtain statistical estimates of the quantities prescribed on the Q-GERT network. The estimates can be obtained from a single simulation run or over a specified number of runs. The completion of one simulation run of the network can be defined by specifying any of the following quantities: 1) the number of transactions reaching sink nodes; 2) the number of sink nodes to be released; and 3) a specified time period. These values and other information concerning the analysis procedure are specified on one data input card to the Q-GERT Analysis Program. One data card is used to indicate the end of data input. All other data cards for the Q-GERT Analysis Program are used to describe the Q-GERT network elements.

For the basic concepts presented in Chapter 2, a data card is required for each node, activity and parameter set included in the network. The initial emphasis of this chapter will be on the procedures for preparing the data cards that define the basic Q-GERT network elements. The procedures for obtaining statistical estimates of the quantities of interest will also be described, and examples of the outputs of the Q-GERT

Analysis Program will be given. Before discussing inputs and outputs, a brief description of the internal operation of the Q-GERT Analysis Program is given.

THE BASIC Q-GERT ANALYSIS PROGRAM

The Q-GERT Analysis Program employs discrete event procedures (105, 111) to simulate the flow of transactions through a network. Basically, only one event type is included in the program: the arrival of a transaction at a node. All the decision logic that can occur when a transaction arrives at a node are included in the program and the appropriate actions are taken based on the network model provided by the analyst. This includes the collection of statistical quantities.

To start the analysis program after the network has been described (inputted), each source node for the network is evaluated. This could be considered as a special start of simulation event. However, we consider the start of simulation to be equivalent to an arrival of a transaction at the source node which causes the source node to be released. At each source node, transactions are generated and marked and then are routed according to the branching characteristics prescribed for the source node. The performance of activities associated with each branch selected from the source nodes are simulated by selecting a time for the activity in accordance with the distribution type and parameter values prescribed for the activity. An event corresponding to the arrival of the transaction at the end node of the activity is scheduled and placed on an event calendar.

When all source nodes have been considered in this fashion, time is advanced to the time of the next (first) event which is removed from the event calendar. The type of node to which the transaction is arriving is first examined. If it is not a Q-node, the number of incoming transactions to release the node is decreased by 1. If the node is not released, that is, it requires more incoming transactions, no further action is taken and time can be advanced to the next event time. If the node is released, statistics are collected if necessary, marking is performed if necessary, and the transaction is routed along the branches emanating from the node just released. If the node has deterministic branching, identical transactions are routed along each branch emanating from the node. If the node has probabilistic branching, a selection of one branch is made using a pseudo-random number generator. For each branch selected, an activity time is obtained and the transaction is scheduled to arrive at the end node at the current time plus the activity time. This arrival-of-transaction event is placed on the event calendar. After all branches have been selected and their associated events scheduled, the next event is removed from the event calendar and the above process is repeated.

When a transaction arrives at a sink node, a check is made to see if the simulation run is completed. If not, the process continues. If the run is completed, summary statistics for one run of the simulation are stored. In addition, each time an event is taken from the event calendar, the time of the event is compared to a total time allocated for the simulation. If all time has expired, then the simulation run of the network is also considered to be completed, and statistics on the run are stored.

When a transaction arrives at a Q-node, a slightly more complex decision process is involved. First, a check is made to see if the queue is full. If it is, the transaction either balks from the Q-node or blocks its current service activity. If it balks and there is no balking node prescribed, the transaction is deleted from the system. If a balking node was prescribed, the transaction is routed directly to the balking node. If blocking occurs, the service activity which just completed processing the transaction is not made available for processing another transaction.

If the queue is not full but the servers following the queue are all busy, the transaction is placed in the queue in its proper position. If a server is available, the transaction is scheduled to arrive at the node following the service activity at the current time plus the service time. Statistics are maintained on the number of transactions in the queue and the busy time for servers.

When a transaction completes a service activity, additional processing must be performed. Not only must the transaction be routed to the end node of the service activity, but the disposition of the service activity must be considered. The logic involved in determining the disposition of the service activity involves examining the Q-node associated with the service activity. If no transactions are in the Q-node, the service activity is made idle. If a transaction is waiting at the Q-node, it is removed from the Q-node and the transaction is routed along the service activity, that is, the transaction is scheduled to arrive at the end node of the service activity. If, before removing the transaction from the Q-node, the Q-node was at its maximum capacity, a check is also made to unblock any service activities preceding the Q-node.

When two events have the same time of occurrence, a complex tie-breaking procedure is used. For an event that is to occur immediately, that is, the activity associated with the event involves no delay time, a last-in, first out (LIFO) rule is employed. For events that are scheduled to occur at a future time, the tie-breaking rule is first-in, first-out (FIFO).

This brief description of the Q-GERT Analysis Program illustrates the initiation and routing of transactions through the network. In the next section, the procedures for describing a Q-GERT network to the analysis program are given.

BASIC Q-GERT DATA INPUT CARDS

In this section, the data input requirements to analyze models containing only the basic concepts are detailed. Appendix 1 contains a complete description of all Q-GERT data input cards. The duplication of subnetworks is described in Chapter 10 along with input editing capabilities.

The data cards required by the Q-GERT Analysis Program are uniquely identified with a 3 character alphanumeric identification (ID) specified in the first field of the card. More characters can be used as the card identifier, but only the first three characters are significant. Valid card types for the basic concepts are:

1. GEN — *gen*eral project information
2. REG — *reg*ular node description
3. SOU — *sou*rce node description
4. SIN — *sin*k node description
5. STA — *sta*tistics node description
6. QUE — *que*ue node description
7. PAR — *par*ameter set values
8. ACT — *act*ivity description
9. BEG — signals *beg*inning of a new network (used only when multiple networks are to be analyzed)
10. FIN — signals end (*fin*ish) of all Q-GERT input cards

The order in which data cards are submitted for processing is very flexible. The first card of a deck describing a network must be a GEN card. The last card for a network must be a BEG card or a FIN card. BEG cards indicate the end of one network description and the beginning of the cards that describe a new network. A FIN card indicates the end of the last network description. The only other requirement regarding card order is that the start node referenced on an ACT (activity) card must be defined prior to the ACT card. Node definitions are given by REG, SOU, SIN, STA and QUE cards.

The definitions of the fields for each data card are presented in Figure 3-1. The options for fields containing alphanumeric data are given in parentheses in Figure 3-1. Default values are indicated in brackets in Figure 3-1. Note that the REG and SOU cards and the SIN and STA cards have the same field definitions. The BEG and FIN cards have no field specifications and, hence, are not listed in Figure 3-1. For complete definitions of each card type, default values, and editing features, see Appendix 1. As an illustration of the data card specification contained in Appendix 1, the data description form for the PAR card is given in Figure 3-2. The information in Figure 3-2 is required to define the parameter values for each distribution specification that can be associated with time delays for transactions as they flow through activities. A discussion of distribution types and their properties is included in Chapter 6.

The input to the Q-GERT program is in a *free form*. Free form input permits information to be punched without card column restrictions. The features of the free form input are given in the next section.

FREE FORM INPUT FEATURES

1. *Blanks*—Blanks are ignored except in the analyst and project name fields. Hence, information may be punched in any column of the input card.
2. *Field Termination*—All fields on a card except the last are terminated by commas.
3. *Multiple Values in a Field*—Selected fields may require two inputs. These inputs are separated by a slash (/). In basic Q-GERT, multiple values are used to assign labels to nodes and activities.
4. *Continuation Cards*—Continuation cards are permitted. If the last nonblank character of a card is a comma, it is assumed that additional fields of the input record are contained on the card which follows. Fields may *not* be split between cards. A continuation card contains no card ID and the additional fields may be punched anywhere on the card. Continuation cards may themselves be continued. However, an input record may not exceed 50 fields.
5. *Record Termination*—An asterisk should be punched after the last field of an input card. If no asterisk is present and the last nonblank character on the card is *not* a comma, then an end of input record is assumed. The use of an asterisk is preferred since

it reduces scanning time. Also, comments can be placed on the data card following the asterisk even if placed in column 1.

6. Characters not significant will be ignored. Accordingly, for added clarity and for documentation purposes, the user may specify additional characters if desired (parentheses, asterisks, slashes, periods and commas are not permitted). Alphanumeric fields may be of any length that will fit on a single card.

7. *Numeric Information*—Any numeric information may be input as an integer or as a real number.

   a. If an integer is input for a field specified as real, the real equivalent of the integer value is used.

   b. If a real is input for a field specified as integer, the decimal portion of the real field is truncated and the integer equivalent of the truncated result is used.

8. *Default Values*—Default values are defined for all nonessential input fields. To indicate that the default value is to be used for a certain field (or that a field is not applicable in a given context), the user should do one of the following:

   a. *Omit the field*—Omission of a field is indicated by a comma or by blanks followed by a comma.

   b. *Skip to the next user specified input field*—If the user lists the number (enclosed in parentheses) of the next field for which he wishes to specify information, all intermediate fields will be bypassed and will assume default values.

   For example, if the following card is input
   QUE, 3/CUSTQ, (8)1.*
   these assumptions will be made
   Field 1 = QUE
   Field 2 = 3 with label CUSTQ
   Field 3 through 7 will assume default values
   Field 8 = 1.

   c. *Terminate the card* before giving a value for the field. For instance, in the preceding example, Field 9 assumes a default value since nine fields are associated with card type QUE and no values were specified after Field 8.

   Note: A field left blank is not automatically assumed to contain the value zero (unless zero is the established dafault value for the field); therefore, when a zero value is intended, it should actually be specified.

9. *Error Checking*—Each input card will be read, listed, and scanned for errors. Default values will be assumed for fields containing errors. Nonfatal errors will be flagged as warnings and *will not*

Fields*

1	2	3	4	5	6	7	8	9	10	11
GEN	Name [Blank]	Project number [Blank]	Month [1]	Day [1]	Year [2001]	Number of statistics nodes [0]	Number of sink nodes [0]	Number of sink node releases to end one run [value in field 8]	Time to end one run of network [10^{20}]	Number of runs of network [1]
REG or SOU	Node number	Initial number to release node [1]	Subsequent number to release node [∞]	Branching (D, P) [D]	Marking (M) [M if SOU, no M if REG]	Choice criterion (F,L) [L]				
SIN or STA	Node number/label	Initial number to release node [1]	Subsequent number to release node [∞]	Branching (D,P) [D]	Statistics desired (F,A,B,I,D,) [F]	Upper limit of first cell [N]	Width of histogram cell [N]	Choice of criterion (F,L) [L]		

Fields*

1	2	3	4	5	6	7	8	9	10	11
QUE	Node number/label	Initial number in queue [0]	Capacity of queue [∞]	Branching (D,P) [D]	Ranking (F,L) [F]	Block or node number for balkers (B) [balkers are destroyed]	Upper limit of first cell [N]	Width of histogram cell [N]	†	
PAR	Parameter set number	Parameter 1 [0.]	Parameter 2 $[-10^{20}]$	Parameter 3 $[10^{20}]$	Parameter 4 [0.]	†				
ACT	Start node	End node	Distribution or function type [CO]	Parameter set or constant [0.]	Activity number/label	Number of parallel servers [1]	Probability of selecting activity [0.5]	†		

*Default values are given in brackets [ ]. If no default value is indicated, data for the field is required. Options for a field are given in parentheses ( ). A slash(/) indicates the field may contain two entries where the slash and second entry are optional.

† These fields are used to input values associated with intermediate concepts.

Figure 3-1 Input description for basic Q-GERT concepts.

59

PAR - parameter set description

Field Number	Description	Value	Default	Editing	Associated Errors
1	Card type	PAR	(Required)	= 'PAR'	8000
2	Parameter set number	Integer	(Required)	Integer between 1 and maximum number of parameter sets	8902
3	Parameter 1	Real	0.	Real	903
4	Parameter 2	Real	-10^{20}	Real	903
5	Parameter 3	Real	$+10^{20}$	Real	903
6	Parameter 4	Real	0.	Real	903
7	Random Number Stream	Integer	MXSTR=10	Integer	903

Figure 3-2. Parameter value specifications for PAR cards by distribution type.

A sample is obtained from a distribution such that if a sample is less than the minimum value, the sample value is given the minimum value. Similarly, if the sample is greater than the maximum value, the sample value is assigned the maximum value. This is not sampling from a truncated distribution but sampling from a distribution with a given probability of obtaining the minimum and maximum values.

The parameters required to sample from the distributions are described below. The parameter values for the lognormal (LO), triangular (TR), beta (BE), gamma (GA), and beta PERT (BP) are modified to simplify random sampling. Thus, parameter sets for these distributions must not be used for any other distributions, i.e., a parameter set for a lognormal distribution must only be used for sampling from a lognormal distribution.

For COnstants, no PAR card is used. The value of the constant is taken as the value given to parameter set specification.

For NOrmal, LOgnormal, BEta, and GAma distributions

Parameter 1	The mean value
Parameter 2	The minimum value
Parameter 3	The maximum value
Parameter 4	The standard deviation

For UNiform distribution

Parameter 1	Not used
Parameter 2	The minimum value
Parameter 3	The maximum value
Parameter 4	Not used

For EXponential distribution

Parameter 1	The mean value
Parameter 2	The minimum value
Parameter 3	The maximum value
Parameter 4	Not used

For ERlang distribution

Parameter 1	The mean time for the Erlang variable divided by the value given to Parameter 4
Parameter 2	The minimum value
Parameter 3	The maximum value
Parameter 4	The number of expotential deviates to be included in the sample obtained from the Erlang distribution

For POisson distribution

Parameter 1	The mean minus the minimum value
Parameter 2	The minimum value
Parameter 3	The maximum value
Parameter 4	Not used

Care is required when using the POisson since it is not usually used to represent an interval of time. The interpretation of the mean should be the mean number of time units per time period.

For BP and TRiangular distributions

Parameter 1	The most likely value, m
Parameter 2	The optimistic value, a
Parameter 3	The pessimistic value, b
Parameter 4	Not used

Figure 3-2. Parameter value specifications for PAR cards by distribution type. (Continued)

prevent execution. Errors flagged as fatal *will* cancel execution. Error messages associated with a given card are listed for each card by field number in Appendix 1. A complete list of error messages is given in Appendix 2.

EXAMPLES OF DATA INPUT

In this section, examples of the data input for models presented in Chapter 2 are given. Each example is presented in a figure where the network is illustrated and the corresponding data input is listed. Since an asterisk indicates the end of the specified data fields, comments and card numbers can be put directly on the data cards.

The graphical portrayal of the one server, single queue system and the corresponding data cards for the Q-GERT Analysis Program are shown in Figure 3–3. Reference to the data cards will be made by a card number shown on the right and by card type. The GEN card contains the analyst's name, the project number and the date. Other pertinent information on the GEN card are the number of statistics nodes (0), the number of sink nodes (1), the number of releases of sink nodes to realize the network (100), and the number of runs to be completed for the network (10). A default value is prescribed for the time to end one run of the network. The run definition of 100 sink node releases is equivalent to requiring 100 transactions to arrive at sink node 15. When 100 transactions have arrived at node 15, one run is completed. The network is then reinitialized and another run is made. This is continued until the 10 runs specified by the data input have been completed. Data cards 20 through 90 provide the detailed information concerning the nodes, activities and parameter sets for the network. Data card 100, the FIN card, is used to indicate the end of Q-GERT data cards.

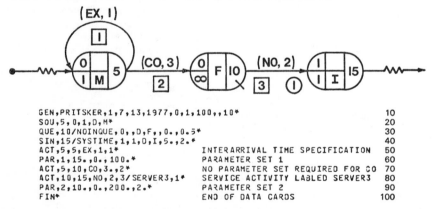

```
GEN,PRITSKER,1,7,13,1977,0,1,100,,10*                              10
SOU,5,0,1,D,M*                                                     20
QUE,10/NOINQUE,0,,D,F,,0.,0.5*                                     30
SIN,15/SYSTIME,1,1,D,I,5.,2.*                                      40
ACT,5,5,EX,1,1*            INTERARRIVAL TIME SPECIFICATION         50
PAR,1,15.,0.,100.*         PARAMETER SET 1                         60
ACT,5,10,CO,3.,2*          NO PARAMETER SET REQUIRED FOR CO        70
ACT,10,15,NO,2,3/SERVER3,1*  SERVICE ACTIVITY LABLED SERVER3       80
PAR,2,10.,0.,200.,2.*      PARAMETER SET 2                         90
FIN*                       END OF DATA CARDS                      100
```

Figure 3-3   Network and data cards for a one-server, single queue process.

On the QUE card, card 30, the second field has the Q-node number and a label for the Q-node. The fourth field is left blank to allow the Q-GERT program to supply the default value for the capacity of the queue. In Figure 3-1, the default value for this field is shown as infinite. A histogram on the average number of transactions in the queue will be provided. The data specifies an upper limit of the first cell of 0. and a cell width of 0.5. The histogram will contain 10 values of the average number in queue, one for each simulation run of the network.

On the SIN card (card 40), the first eight fields are specified but the ninth field is not. Thus, the ninth field will take on the default value. For the SIN card, the ninth field corresponds to the choice criterion which, since each incoming transaction releases node 15, does not matter. The interarrival time distribution is specified by an ACT card (card 50) showing an activity from node 5 back to node 5 whose delay is exponentially distributed with parameters from parameter set 1. On card 60, parameter set number 1 is specified where the parameters indicate a mean of 15. time units and a minimum of 0. and a maximum of 100. time units. Figure 3-2 provides the definitions of parameter values for the exponential distribution.

The delay time between the arrival of transactions to the system and their arrival at the queue is indicated by card number 70. A constant (CO) of 3. is specified for this activity time. No PAR card is necessary for this activity. Card numbers 80 and 90 specify that the time for service activity 3 is to be normally distributed with the parameters as given by parameter set number 2. For this example, the mean service time is 10. time units and the standard deviation is 2. time units as defined by card 90.

To convert the single server system to a parallel server system consisting of 4 servers, the description of activity 3 on card 80 would be changed. The value in Field 7 would be changed from a 1 to a 4 as shown below.

ACT,10,15,NO,2,3/SERVER3,4*   4 PARALLEL SERVERS   80

This change in one data field accomplishes the desired conversion.

To specify a finite queue capacity, data card 30 would be altered by placing a 6 in Field 4 of the QUE card. Thus, to define the capacity of the queue to be six transactions, the following QUE card would be used:

QUE,10/NOINQUE,0,6,D,F,,0,0.5*   QUEUE NODE WITH FINITE CAPACITY   30

Since no balking node is specified, transactions that arrive to Q-node 10 when it contains six transactions will be deleted from the system. To allow transactions to balk from Q-node 10 to node 20 and to have the transactions return to Q-node 10 in one time unit, the following data cards would be inserted in place of card 30:

QUE, 10/NOINQUE,0,6,D,F,20,0,0.5*		30
REG,20,1,1*	NODE FOR BALKERS	32
ACT,20,10,CO,1*	TIME TO RETURN BALKERS TO QUEUE	34

Figures 3-4 through 3-6 present other networks described in Chapter 2 and the data cards required to translate the networks to input data for the Q-GERT Analysis Program. Note the use of the field skip option on card 92 of Figure 3-4. For this card, Fields 4 and 5 will take default values as will Fields 7 and 8.

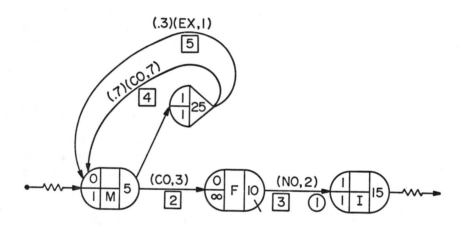

```
GEN,PRITSKER,1,7,13,1977,0,1,100,,10*    RUN = 100 RELEASES N15    10
SOU,5,0,1,D,M*                                                     20
QUE,10,0,,D,F,,0.,0.5*                                             30
SIN,15,1,1,D,I,5.,2.*                                              40
PAR,1,15.,0.,100.*                                                 60
ACT,5,10,CO,3.,2*                                                  70
ACT,10,15,NO,2,3,1*                                                80
PAR,2,10.,0.,200.,2.*                                             90
REG,25,1,1,P*                                                      91
ACT,5,25,(6)1*                                                     92
ACT,25,5,CO,7.,,4,,0.7*                                            93
ACT,25,5,EX,1,5,,0.3*                                              94
FIN*                                                             100
```

Figure 3-4 Network and data cards for one server, single queue process with complex arrivals.

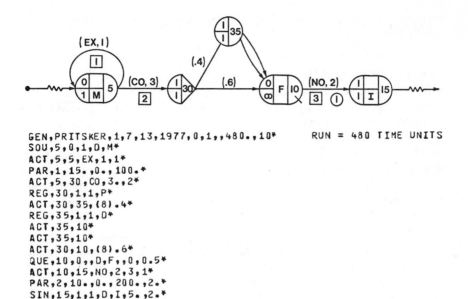

```
GEN,PRITSKER,1,7,13,1977,0,1,,480.,10*      RUN = 480 TIME UNITS
SOU,5,0,1,D,M*
ACT,5,5,EX,1,1*
PAR,1,15.,,0.,,100.*
ACT,5,30,CO,3.,2*
REG,30,1,1,P*
ACT,30,35,(8).4*
REG,35,1,1,D*
ACT,35,10*
ACT,35,10*
ACT,30,10,(8).6*
QUE,10,0,,D,F,,0,0.5*
ACT,10,15,NO,2,3,1*
PAR,2,10.,,0.,,200.,,2.*
SIN,15,1,1,D,I,5.,,2.*
FIN*
```

Figure 3-5 Network and data cards for one server, single queue process with single and multiple arrivals.

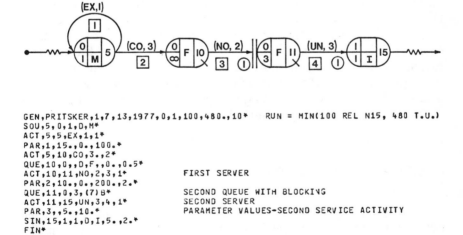

```
GEN,PRITSKER,1,7,13,1977,0,1,100,480.,10*   RUN = MIN(100 REL N15, 480 T.U.)
SOU,5,0,1,D,M*
ACT,5,5,EX,1,1*
PAR,1,15.,,0.,,100.*
ACT,5,10,CO,3.,2*
QUE,10,0,,D,F,,0.,0.5*
ACT,10,11,NO,2,3,1*              FIRST SERVER
PAR,2,10.,,0.,,200.,,2.*
QUE,11,0,3,(7)B*                 SECOND QUEUE WITH BLOCKING
ACT,11,15,UN,3,4,1*              SECOND SERVER
PAR,3,,5.,,10.*                  PARAMETER VALUES-SECOND SERVICE ACTIVITY
SIN,15,1,1,D,I,5.,,2.*
FIN*
```

Figure 3-6 Network and data cards for sequential server system with blocking.

RUN DEFINITION, STOPPING A RUN AND MULTIPLE RUN ANALYSIS

Before proceeding with the discussion of data collection and output, another discussion on the definition of a run seems appropriate. A run corresponds to one complete independent simulation of a Q-GERT network. A run is terminated when either of the following conditions occurs: 1) a specified number of sink nodes is released; or 2) the time of arrival of a transaction at a node equals or exceeds a specified run time. The conditions for ending a run are included in the data input for the GEN card. In addition, a run will be terminated when no activities are being performed, that is, no end of activity event is scheduled on the event calendar (see Example 8).

In the previous examples, the various options for defining a run are used. In Figure 3-4, 100 releases of sink node 15 are specified. In Figure 3-5, each run is specified to take 480 time units. In Figure 3-6, a run is specified to be completed either when 100 releases of node 15 have occurred or when time reaches 480 time units. In this case, the condition that occurs first causes the run to be completed.

The Q-GERT Analysis Program has been designed to collect statistics over a set of runs. The outputs for many of the variables relate to averages which are estimates of a mean value. Multiple runs (replications) are used to obtain the variability of the estimates of the mean values. For example, on a given run, the average number of transactions residing in a Q-node would be calculated. This average is an estimate of the mean number of transactions in the queue represented by the Q-node. On a second run, another average number of transactions at the Q-node would be obtained. By looking at the variability of these average values over multiple runs, estimates of the standard deviation of the averages can be obtained. The procedure involved is to obtain an average value for a given run and then to obtain an average of these average values over multiple runs. A variance estimator is then obtained by examining the variation of the average values obtained from each run.

STATISTICAL COLLECTION AND OUTPUT

In developing a Q-GERT network, a modeler includes, directly on the network, nodes for collecting data. Such nodes are referred to as statistics or STA nodes. The Q-GERT Analysis Program maintains information on statistics nodes, sink nodes, Q-nodes, and servers. All the data collected is presented in the Q-GERT summary report. In this section, the details regarding how the Q-GERT Analysis Program collects and maintains data to estimate the quantities indicated above are described. Examples of the Q-GERT summary report will be presented where appropriate.

Data Collected on Nodes

Five types of variables can be associated with statistics and sink nodes. Each of the variables refers to a time that a specified node is released. The five types of variables are:

1. Time of *first* release (F).
2. Time of *all* releases (A).
3. Time between releases (B). The time of first release is used only as a reference point for the first value of the time between releases.
4. *Interval* statistics (I). This statistic relates to the transaction that releases the node. It records the interval of time from the marking of the transaction to the release time of the statistics node. Recall that all source nodes are mark nodes. If a transaction passes through two or more mark nodes before reaching a node at which interval statistics are collected, it is the time of last marking that is referenced when the time interval is computed.
5. Delay statistics (D). This statistic relates to nodes at which transactions are accumulated, that is, nodes for which the number of incoming transaction requirement is greater than one. The delay time is the time interval from the first arrival of a transaction at the node until the node is released. A delay time is computed each time the node is released. Thus, if a node requires three incoming transactions for each release, a D specification for statistics would compute the time from the first transaction arrival until the arrival time of the third transaction. If the node was released twice, then the second delay time would be the time between the arrival of the fourth transaction and the time of arrival of the sixth transaction.

For each of the above five types of variables, the Q-GERT Analysis Program obtains estimates for the mean and standard deviation of the variables. The estimate for the mean is obtained by summing up the average for each run and dividing by the number of runs. The estimate for the standard deviation assumes all runs have equal weight. Also printed on the Q-GERT summary report are estimates of the standard deviation of the mean assuming independent runs. This calculation involves dividing the standard deviation estimate by the square root of the number of runs. The number of runs associated with each variable and the minimum and maximum average value observed over all simulation runs of the network are included on the summary report. In networks in which probabilistic branching is involved, there is the possibility that a statistics node is not released. On the output report, an estimate of the probability that a node is released on a run of the network is provided. This value is obtained by dividing the total number of runs into the number of runs on which the node was released at least once. A sample of the output for statistics and sink nodes is shown in Figure 3-7. Discussion of the report is deferred until the last section of this chapter.

On the first run, an option is available to obtain estimates of the average, standard deviation, minimum and maximum that are based on each observation associated with a node. Also, a histogram of the observed values for the first run can be obtained.

Data Collected on Q-nodes

The variables of interest associated with a Q-node are the average number in the Q-node and the average number of transactions balking from the Q-node. The number of transactions in a Q-node is a time persistent variable, an example of which is shown in Figure 3-8. The average number of transactions in the Q-node is obtained by averaging the number of transactions in the queue over time. An example calculation for a simple case is shown in Figure 3-8. Thus, for each run of the network, one sample value of the average number in a Q-node is obtained. Multiple runs are made to obtain estimates of the standard deviation of these average values. The Q-GERT Analysis Program records and outputs the average of the average values obtained over a set of runs and the standard deviation of these averages. Also printed are the minimum average and maximum average obtained over a set of runs.

Another output provided for Q-nodes is the minimum and maximum number of transactions ever in the Q-node. Care should be taken in using these values as longer or more simulation runs could provide more extreme values for the minimums and maximums, that is, the chances of getting a larger number in the queue increase as the Q-node is observed for a longer period of time. An example of the outputs for Q-nodes is presented in Figure 3-9. Since ten runs were made of the network, ten average queue lengths were calculated for each queue. For Q-node 10,

GERT SIMULATION PROJECT MAINT-FAC-5   BY PRITSKER
DATE 6/ 30/ 1977

FINAL RESULTS FOR   10 SIMULATIONS

AVERAGE NODE STATISTICS

NODE	LABEL	PROBABILITY	AVE.	STD.DEV.	SD OF AVE	NO OF OBS.	MIN.	MAX.	STAT TYPE
20	REP-TIME	1.0000	2.9096	.1963	.0621	10.	2.5636	3.2138	I
12	SUB-UNIT	1.0000	1.5675	.2056	.0650	10.	1.3195	1.9313	B

Figure 3-7 Q-GERT Analysis Program output for statistics and sink nodes.

		AVERAGE NUMBER IN Q-NODE					**AVERAGE WAITING TIME**			**NUMBER IN Q-NODE**
NODE	LABEL	AVE.	STD.DEV.	SD OF AVE	MIN.	MAX.	AVE.	STD.DEV.	SD OF AVE	MAX.
10	WS1-QUE	2.1062	.1438	.0455	1.8828	2.3279	1.1261	.1063	.0336	4.0000
15	WS2-QUE	1.5060	.0557	.0176	1.3919	1.5622	.8089	.0518	.0164	2.0000

Figure 3-9 Sample Q-GERT output relating to number of transactions in Q-nodes.

AVERAGE NO. BALKING PER UNIT TIME

NODE	LABEL	AVE.	STD.DEV.	SD OF AVE	NO. OF OBS.	MIN.	MAX.
10	WS1-QUE	.6217	.0826	.0261	10.	.4967	.7500

Figure 3-10 Sample Q-GERT output relating to number of transactions balking from Q-nodes.

69

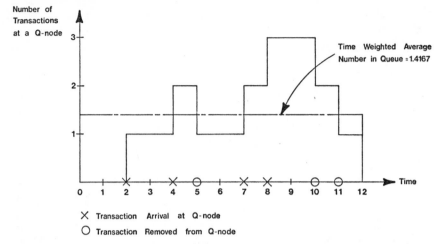

Figure 3-8   Graphical portrayal of number of transactions at a Q-node and calculation of average number in queue.

the average of these averages was 2.1062. The standard deviation was 0.1438, the minimum of the averages was 1.8828 and the maximum was 2.3279. By the central limit theorem, the standard deviation of the grand average is $0.1438/\sqrt{10}=0.0455$. The smallest number ever in Q-node 10 over all runs was 0. The largest number ever in Q-node 10 was 4.

The number of balkers from a Q-node is maintained for each run of a network. Clearly, the number of balkers is dependent on the length of the run. To normalize the outputs, the number of balkers per unit time is used as a measure of balking from a Q-node. That is, the number of balkers from each queue is divided by the length of the simulation run to obtain a balking rate for the run. An average and standard deviation over all runs of the balking rate is then computed along with the minimum and maximum balking rate observed on a run. An example of the outputs for the number of balkers per unit time averaged over 10 runs is shown in Figure 3-10.

Data Collected on Servers

The status of a single server is either busy or idle. Average server utilization is defined as the fraction of time that the server is busy and is computed as the total amount of time the server is busy divided by the total time period for a run. Thus, each run yields one value of average server utilization. As with the average number in a Q-node, multiple runs are made to obtain estimates of the variation of the average server utilization. The Q-GERT summary report records and prints the minimum and maximum values of average server utilization obtained over multiple runs. Also obtained for a single server are the longest consecutive period of time that he is idle or busy. These values provide information as to whether the server can be assigned secondary tasks and whether the server requires breaks. Care is required in using these outputs since the longest period idle and the longest period busy depend on the length of a run and on the number of runs made. Larger values should be expected from longer runs or more runs since extreme values are being collected.

If one activity is used to represent multiple servers (as specified by the value in a circle under a branch being greater than 1), then the average server utilization refers to the average number of busy servers. In this case, at the end of each run the average is computed as the time weighted average of the number of busy servers. As with queue length, the program prints the average of these averages, the minimum average, maximum average and standard deviation of these averages. When multiple servers are associated with an activity, the longest period idle and longest period busy quantities are not meaningful. For this situation, the maximum number of idle servers and the maximum number of busy servers is printed.

Another quantity of interest with regard to servers is the fraction of time the server is blocked. For a run, this value is obtained by summing up the times at which the server is blocked and dividing by the total time for the run. This provides one value of the blocked time per unit time. Again, the variability for this quantity is obtained by making multiple runs. Also printed on the output is the longest period of time the server is blocked.

In the next section, an example is provided to illustrate the computations and outputs of the Q-GERT Analysis Program relating to server utilization and blocking.

ILLUSTRATION OF QUEUE, SERVER UTILIZATION, BLOCKING AND BALKING STATISTICS

Consider the Q-GERT model presented in Figure 3-11. For illustrative purposes all activity times have been given as constants. An arrival occurs at time zero and every four time units thereafter. Initially three transactions are in Q-node 3 which means that server 1 is busy with a transaction at the start of a run. Q-node 4 initially has two transactions in it and has a capacity of 2. Q-node 4 also blocks server number 1. Server number 2 is busy initially since transactions are waiting at Q-node 4. This network will be examined for 28 time units. A graph of the

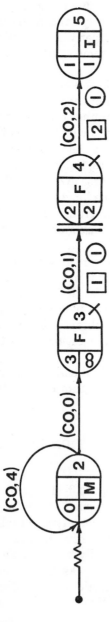

Figure 3-11 Q-GERT network to illustrate statistical collections.

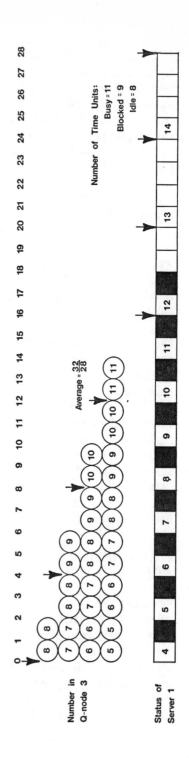

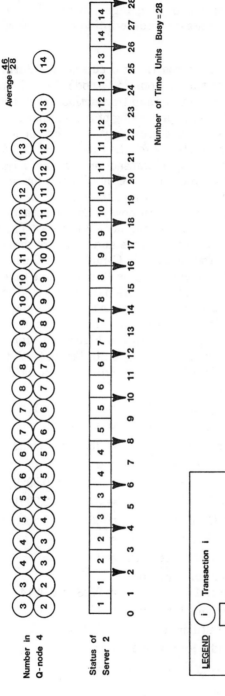

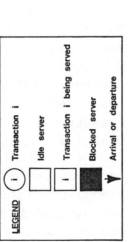

Figure 3-12 Graph of system status for Q-GERT network of Figure 3-11.

73

status of system variables is shown in Figure 3-12. The transactions have been numbered to facilitate the description of their flow through the system.

At time zero, the arrival of transaction 8 occurs so that during the period 0 to 1, there are four transactions in Q-node 3 consisting of the three prescribed by initial conditions and transaction 8 that just arrived. At time 1, server 1 completes the processing of transaction 4 but cannot route the transaction to Q-node 4 because it is at its capacity. Thus, server 1 is blocked with transaction 4 for the time period 1-2. At time 2, server 2 completes the processing of transaction 1, removes transaction 2 from Q-node 4 and begins processing it. Q-node 4 now has space to receive the transaction blocking server 1 and the number of transactions in Q-node 4 remains at 2. Server 1 can now remove transaction 5 from Q-node 3 which reduces the number in Q-node 3 to three. Thus, for the time interval 2-3, both servers are working and there are three transactions in Q-node 3 and two transactions in Q-node 4. At time 3, server 1 again becomes blocked and remains in this status for one time unit. At time 4, server 2 completes service, transaction 3 is removed from Q-node 4, server 1 is unblocked, transaction 6 is removed from Q-node 3 and an arrival (transaction 9) is placed in Q-node 3. The changes in status variables for all the above changes are shown in Figure 3-12 for each time interval up to time 28. From the values given in Figure 3-12, the statistics computed by the Q-GERT Analysis Program can be illustrated. These values are listed below.

Average number in Q-node 3	$= 32/28 = 1.1429$
Maximum number in Q-node 3	$= 4$
Average number in Q-node 4	$= 46/28 = 1.6429$
Maximum number in Q-node 4	$= 2$
Average server 1 utilization	$= 11/28 = 0.3929$
Average time in Q-node 3	$= 32/11 = 2.9091$
Average time in Q-node 4	$= 46/13 = 3.5385$
Longest period idle for server 1	$= 3$
Longest period busy for server 1	$= 1$
Blocked time per unit time for server 1	$= 9/28 = 0.3214$
Longest blocked time for server 1	$= 1$
Average server 2 utilization	$= 28/28 = 1$
Longest period idle for server 2	$= 0$
Longest period busy for server 2	$= 28$

The report for the first simulation run performed by the Q-GERT Analysis Program is shown in Figure 3-13.

```
GERT SIMULATION PROJECT BLOCKTEST      BY PRITSKER
               DATE   2/  8/ 1977


        **FINAL RESULTS FOR FIRST SIMULATION**


        TOTAL ELAPSED TIME =     28.0000



           **NODE STATISTICS**

 NODE     LABEL        AVE.       STD.DEV.    NO OF   STAT
                                             OBS.    TYPE

  5     SYSTIME       9.0000      4.2787     14.     I




         **NUMBER IN Q-NODE**                  ** WAITING TIME **
                                                   IN QUEUE


 NODE    LABEL        AVE.     MIN.  MAX.    CURRENT      AVERAGE
                                            NUMBER

  4     QOFSERV2     1.6429     0    2.        0          3.5385
  3     QOFSERV1     1.1429     0    4.        0          2.9091




           **SERVER UTILIZATION**


 SERVER   LABEL      NO. PARALLEL  AVE.      MAX. IDLE          MAX. BUSY
                     SERVERS             (TIME OR SERVERS) (TIME OR SERVERS)

   2     SERVER2         1       1.0000          0              28.0000
   1     SERVER1         1        .3929       3.0000             1.0000




           **BLOCKED TIME PER UNIT TIME**


 SERVER   LABEL        AVE.       LONGEST
                              PERIOD BLOCKED

   1     SERVER1       .3214      1.0000
```

Figure 3-13   Q-GERT report of first run for network of Figure 3-11.

The values on the report correspond exactly to those given above. Also shown in Figure 3-13 is the average time for a transaction to flow through the network. This is provided by the interval statistics collected at node 5 of the network. It is seen that the average time per transaction is 9 for 14 transactions. The minimum time through the network was 2 time units and the maximum time was 16.

Table 3-1 presents the time of arrival, the time of departure and the time in the system for each transaction. This table is easily derived from Figure 3-12. Note that seven transactions were initially in the system (three in Q-node 3, one being served by server 1, two in Q-node 4 and one being served by server number 2) and that one transaction arrived at time 0. The arrival times of the remaining six transactions for which processing was completed within the 28 time units for the run were 4, 8, 12, 16, 20 and 24. As shown in Table 3-1, the total time in the system for the fourteen transactions was 126 time units which yields an average time per transaction of 9. The minimum and maximum time for a transaction also agree with the results presented in Figure 3-13. A histogram* of the time in the system for transactions is shown in Figure 3-14. The histogram specifies that the time in the system for one of the transactions was between 0 and 2 time units. This histogram illustrates that one transaction took 2 time units, two took 4 time units, two took 6 time units, etc. The histogram output for individual node or transaction times is obtained from *the output of the first* run.

Table 3-1. Time in System for Transactions.

Transaction Number	Time of Arrival	Time of Departure	Time in System
1	0	2	2
2	0	4	4
3	0	6	6
4	0	8	8
5	0	10	10
6	0	12	12
7	0	14	14
8	0	16	16
9	4	18	14
10	8	20	12
11	12	22	10
12	16	24	8
13	20	26	6
14	24	28	4
Totals	84	210	126

* Cells of the histogram are closed at the upper bound. The second cell in the histogram of Figure 3-14 is the interval (0.0,2.0]. Each * on the plot represents 2 percent. Values are rounded to the nearest 2 percent. Thus, 7.1 percent yields 4 *'s and 14.3 percent gives 7 *'s. The C plotted on the histogram provides a graphical display of the cumulative distribution function.

```
I  STAT HISTOGRAM FOR NODE

              SYSTIME


   OBSV    RELA     CUML      UPPER      0        20       40       60       80      100
   FREQ    FREQ     FREQ    BOUND OF CELL  I....I....I....I....I....I....I....I....I....I....I
    0       0        0         0         I                                                   I
    1     .071     .071      2.00        I****                                               I
    2     .143     .214      4.00        I*******  C                                         I
    2     .143     .357      6.00        I*******          C                                 I
    2     .143     .500      8.00        I*******                   C                        I
    2     .143     .643     10.00        I*******                            C               I
    2     .143     .786     12.00        I*******                                     C       I
    2     .143     .929     14.00        I*******                                          C  I
    1     .071    1.000     15.00        I****                                               C
    0       0     1.000     18.00        I                                                   C
    0       0     1.000     20.00        I                                                   C
    0       0     1.000     22.00        I                                                   C
    0       0     1.000     24.00        I                                                   C
    0       0     1.000     26.00        I                                                   C
    0       0     1.000     28.00        I                                                   C
    0       0     1.000     30.00        I                                                   C
    0       0     1.000     32.00        I                                                   C
    0       0     1.000     34.00        I                                                   C
    0       0     1.000     36.00        I                                                   C
    0       0     1.000     +INF         I                                                   C
                                         I....I....I....I....I....I....I....I....I....I....I
              ---
TOTAL         14
```

Figure 3-14   Histogram of time in the network for a transaction.

The network presented in Figure 3-11 was reanalyzed with the blocking at node 4 replaced by balking from Q-node 4. Figure 3-15 presents the Q-GERT report of the first run for this situation. As can be seen from Figure 3-15, balking statistics are now included in the summary report in place of blocking statistics. Since constant times are used, a diagram similar to Figure 3-12 for the balking case can be constructed to illustrate the statistics obtained in Figure 3-15.

Figure 3-16 presents the Q-GERT summary report for the first run of the network presented in Figure 3-11 when all the constant times are replaced by exponentially distributed times using the constant times as the average values. In this situation, random variation will occur from run to run. Figure 3-17 illustrates the outputs from 10 runs and shows the variability associated with using the exponential distribution. In the next section, a definition and a description of each output line on the Q-GERT summary report is given.

DESCRIPTION OF Q-GERT ANALYSIS PROGRAM OUTPUT REPORTS

The purpose of this section is to provide a single location in this book where definitions can be found for all outputs. Examples of outputs will not be presented in this section as they are presented throughout the book.

```
GERT SIMULATION PROJECT BLOCKTEST     BY PRITSKER
              DATE  2/  8/ 1977


       **FINAL RESULTS FOR FIRST SIMULATION**


          TOTAL ELAPSED TIME =     28.0000



           **NODE STATISTICS**

  NODE      LABEL       AVE.      STD.DEV.    NO OF   STAT
                                             OBS.    TYPE

   5      SYSTIME      5.1818      2.6007     11.     I



          **NUMBER IN Q-NODE**                    ** WAITING TIME **
                                                       IN QUEUE


  NODE     LABEL       AVE.    MIN.  MAX.   CURRENT      AVERAGE
                                           NUMBER

   4     QOFSERV2      .7857     0    2.       0         2.2000
   3     QOFSERV1      .3929     0    4.       0         1.0000



          **SERVER UTILIZATION**

 SERVER    LABEL    NO. PARALLEL   AVE.      MAX. IDLE          MAX. BUSY
                      SERVERS            (TIME OR SERVERS) (TIME OR SERVERS)

   2     SERVER2        1        .7857      2.0000            16.0000
   1     SERVER1        1        .3929      3.0000             6.0000



          **NO. BALKING PER UNIT TIME**

  NODE     LABEL       AVE.

   4     QOFSERV2      .1071
```

Figure 3-15 Q-GERT report of first run for the network of Figure 3-11 with balking replacing blocking.

```
GERT SIMULATION PROJECT BLOCKTEST     BY PRITSKER
            DATE  2/  8/ 1977


      **FINAL RESULTS FOR FIRST SIMULATION**


        TOTAL ELAPSED TIME =     28.0000



            **NODE STATISTICS**

NODE     LABEL        AVE.      STD.DEV.    NO OF   STAT
                                           OBS.    TYPE

 5      SYSTIME      11.2248     6.4335      7.     I



        **NUMBER IN Q-NODE**                    ** WAITING TIME **
                                                    IN QUEUE


NODE    LABEL        AVE.    MIN.  MAX.    CURRENT     AVERAGE
                                          NUMBER

 4     QOFSERV2     1.8138    0     2.        2        5.6428
 3     QOFSERV1     2.3393    1.    4.        3        6.5501



          **SERVER UTILIZATION**


SERVER   LABEL    NO. PARALLEL    AVE.      MAX. IDLE         MAX. BUSY
                   SERVERS              (TIME OR SERVERS) (TIME OR SERVERS)

 2      SERVER2       1         1.0000          0            28.0000
 1      SERVER1       1          .4899          0             6.7280



        **BLOCKED TIME PER UNIT TIME**

SERVER   LABEL        AVE.       LONGEST
                             PERIOD BLOCKED

 1      SERVER1       .5101      8.4451
```

Figure 3-16 Q-GERT results for first run for network of Figure 3-11 with exponential samples replacing the constant times.

GERT SIMULATION PROJECT BLOCKTEST   BY PRITSKER
DATE 2/ 8/ 1977

FINAL RESULTS FOR   10 SIMULATIONS

AVERAGE NODE STATISTICS

NODE	LABEL	PROBABILITY	AVE.	STD.DEV.	SD OF AVE	NO OF OBS.	MIN.	MAX.	STAT TYPE
5	SYSTIME	1.0000	8.9217	4.0218	1.2718	10.	4.0705	14.7603	I

AVERAGE NUMBER IN Q-NODE

NODE	LABEL	AVE.	STD.DEV.	SD OF AVE	MIN.	MAX.	**NUMBER IN Q-NODE** MAX.
4	QOFSERV2	1.3516	.5467	.1729	.5908	1.9988	2.0000
3	QOFSERV1	1.6512	1.1938	.3775	.3652	3.0969	7.0000

AVERAGE SERVER UTILIZATION

SERVER	LABEL	NO. PARALLEL SERVERS	STD.DEV.	SD OF AVE	NO. OF OBS.	MIN.	MAX.	**EXTREME VALUES** MAX. IDLE (TIME OR SERVERS)	MAX. BUS
2	SERVER2	1	.1689	.0534	10.	.5986	1.0000	6.6469	28.0000
1	SERVER1	1	.1246	.0394	10.	.1762	.5415	8.6965	9.0771

AVERAGE BLOCKED TIME PER UNIT TIME

SERVER	LABEL	AVE.	STD.DEV.	SD OF AVE	NO. OF OBS.	MIN.	MAX.	**BLOCKED TIME OF SERVER** LONGEST PERIOD BLOCKED
1	SERVER1	.3762	.2779	.0879	10.	.0738	.8238	11.4265

Figure 3-17 Q-GERT summary report for ten runs with exponential times.

FINAL RESULTS FOR FIRST SIMULATION
TOTAL ELAPSED TIME—total time for the first simulation run
NODE STATISTICS—Headings for node statistics
NODE—sink or statistics node number
LABEL—eight character name associated with node
AVE.—the estimate of the mean time. The time could be a release
time, a delay time or an interval of time
STD.DEV.—the standard deviation of the time
NO OF OBS.—number of observations obtained during the first
simulation run for the statistical variable of interest
STAT TYPE—statistics type specified for the node by the user, that
is: F,A,B,I or D.
NUMBER IN Q-NODE—section of the report which provides in-
formation on Q-node statistics
NODE—the Q-node number for which statistics are to be printed
LABEL—a user supplied name associated with the Q-node
AVE.—the time weighted average number of transactions in the Q-
node for the first simulation run
MIN.—the minimum number of transactions in the Q-node for the
first simulation run
MAX.—the maximum number of transactions in the Q-node for the
first simulation run
CURRENT NUMBER—the number of transactions in the Q-node at
the end of the first simulation run
WAITING TIME IN QUEUE—section of the report which
provides information on Q-node waiting time statistics
AVERAGE—the time integrated number in the queue divided by the
rate of transaction arrivals to the queue. This represents the average waiting time for a transaction in the Q-node
SERVER UTILIZATION—heading to indicate server utilization
section of the report
SERVER—the activity number associated with the branch representing the service activity
LABEL—a user supplied name associated with the service activity
NO. PARALLEL SERVERS—the number of parallel servers represented by the activity
AVE.—For single servers, that is, the number of parallel servers is 1,
this quantity is the fraction of time the server is busy. For multiple servers, the average number of busy servers during the first
simulation run.

MAX. IDLE (TIME OR SERVERS)—for a single server activity, the largest time period for which the single server was idle. For a multiple server activity, the largest number of servers who are idle simultaneously.

MAX. BUSY (TIME OR SERVERS)—for a single server activity, the largest time period that the single server was busy. For a multiple server activity, the largest number of servers that were simultaneously busy.

BLOCKED TIME PER UNIT TIME—section of report where statistics on the time a server is blocked per unit time is reported

SERVER—the server number for which blocking statistics are being reported

LABEL—a user supplied name associated with the service activity

AVE.—the total time the server was blocked divided by the total elapsed time. This represents the fraction of time the server was blocked.

LONGEST PERIOD BLOCKED—the longest consecutive time that the server was in a blocked status

NUMBER BALKING PER UNIT TIME—a heading to indicate the balking section of this report

NODE—the number of the node from which balking is occurring

LABEL—the user supplied name that describes the Q-node from which balking is occurring

AVE.—the total number of transactions balking from the Q-node divided by the total elapsed time for this run. This represents the balking rate.

RESOURCE UTILIZATION—heading to indicate resource utilization section of the report

RESOURCE—the resource number

LABEL—the user supplied name associated with the resource type

NOW IN USE—the number of resource units in use at the end of the first simulation run

AVE. IN USE—the time weighted average number of resource units in use for the first simulation run

MAX. IN USE—the maximum number of resource units in use during the first simulation run

NOW AVAILABLE—the number of resource units available for use at the end of the first simulation run

AVE. AVAILABLE—the time weight average number of resource units available for use for the first simulation run

MAX. AVAILABLE—the maximum number of resource units available during the first simulation run

RESULTS FOR RUN i—this report provides a summary of statistics obtained on run i. The values printed on this report have the same definitions as those given for the report on "FINAL RESULTS FOR FIRST SIMULATION".

TRANSACTION PASSAGES THROUGH NODES:

NODE—the node number

TRANSACTION PASSAGES—the number of times a transaction released or passed through the node during the simulation run

PRINTOUT OF ONGOING ACTIVITIES—heading for the section of the report where ongoing activities at the end of the simulation run are listed

ACTIVITY END TIME—time at which the ongoing activity will be completed

END NODE—node which transaction will reach upon completion of present activity

ACTIVITY NUMBER—number of the ongoing activity

FINAL RESULTS FOR n SIMULATIONS—heading for defining n, the number of runs for which this report is a summary

AVERAGE NODE STATISTICS—heading for node statistics

NODE—sink or statistics node number

LABEL—the user supplied name that describes the node

PROBABILITY—an estimate of the probability that the node is released during a run and is computed as the total number of runs on which this node was released at least once divided by the total number of runs

AVERAGE—an estimate of the mean time requested for the node. This is an average of all values collected over all runs

STD.DEV.—the standard deviation of the time requested for the node

SD OF AVE—the standard deviation divided by the square root of the number of observations

NO. OF OBS.—the number of observations for the node on all runs

MIN.—the minimum value observed for the node over all runs

MAX.—the maximum value observed for the node over all runs

STAT TYPE—statistics type specified for the node by the user

AVERAGE NUMBER IN Q-NODE—heading to indicate the section of report dealing with statistics on the average number in Q-nodes. The variable of interest in this section of the report is the average number in a Q-node as recorded during one complete run.

NODE—the Q-node number for which statistics are to be printed

LABEL—a user supplied name associated with the Q-node

AVE.—the average over multiple runs of the one run time weighted average number of transactions in a Q-node

STD.DEV.—the standard deviation of the average number of transactions in a Q-node

SD OF AVE—the standard deviation divided by the square root of the number of observations

MIN.—the smallest average number of transactions in a Q-node obtained from one run

MAX.—the largest average number of transactions in a Q-node obtained from one run

AVERAGE WAIT TIME—heading to indicate the section of the report dealing with statistics on the average waiting time in the Q-node

AVE.—the average over multiple runs of the average waiting time of a transaction in the Q-node obtained on a single run

STD. DEV.—the standard deviation of the average waiting time of a transaction in the Q-node obtained from one run

SD OF AVE.—the standard deviation divided by the square root of the number of observations

NUMBER IN Q-NODE—heading to indicate values are obtained regarding the number of transactions in a Q-node (as opposed to the average number of transactions in a Q-node)

MAX.—the largest number of transactions in the Q-node in any simulation run

AVERAGE SERVER UTILIZATION—heading to indicate the section of the report dealing with statistics on the average server utilization

SERVER—the activity number associated with the branch representing the service activity

LABEL—a user supplied name associated with the service activity

NO. PARALLEL SERVERS—the number of parallel servers represented by the activity

AVE.—the average over multiple runs of the average server utilization obtained on a single run

STD.DEV.—the standard deviation of the average server utilization obtained on a single run

SD OF AVE—the standard deviation divided by the square root of the number of observations

NO. OF OBS.—number of runs

MIN.—the smallest average server utilization obtained from one run

MAX.—the largest average server utilization obtained from one run

EXTREME VALUES—section of the report which deals with extreme values for server utilization which may have occurred on any run

MAX. IDLE (TIME OR SERVERS)—if the number of parallel servers is 1, this value is the longest consecutive period of time that the server was idle on any of the runs. If the number of parallel servers is greater than 1, this value is the maximum number of servers that were simultaneously idle on any one of the runs.

MAX. BUSY (TIME OR SERVERS)—if the number of parallel servers is 1, this value is the longest consecutive period of time that the server was busy on any of the runs. If the number of parallel servers is greater than 1, this value is the largest number of simultaneously busy servers on any run.

AVERAGE BLOCKED TIME PER UNIT TIME—heading to indicate the section of the report in which average blocking statistics are reported

SERVER—the server number for which blocking statistics are being reported

LABEL—a user supplied name associated with the service activity

AVE.—the average of the fraction of time the server was blocked on a single run

STD.DEV.—the standard deviation of the fraction of time the server was blocked on a single run

SD OF AVE—the standard deviation divided by the square root of the number of observations

NO. OF OBS.—number of runs

MIN.—the smallest fraction of time the server was blocked on any of the runs

MAX.—the largest fraction of time the server was blocked on any of the runs

BLOCKED TIME OF SERVER—heading to indicate the section of the report dealing with data on blocked time of servers

LONGEST PERIOD BLOCKED—longest consecutive period of time that the server was blocked on any of the runs.

AVERAGE NUMBER BALKING PER UNIT TIME—heading to indicate the section of the report in which average balking statistics are reported

NODE—the node number for which balking statistics are being reported

LABEL—a user supplied name associated with the node from which balking occurs

AVE.—the average of the balking rates obtained from each run

STD.DEV.—the standard deviation of the balking rates obtained from each run

SD OF AVE—the standard deviation divided by the square root of the number of observations

NO. OF OBS.—number of runs

MIN.—the smallest balking rate obtained from any of the runs

MAX.—the largest balking rate obtained from any of the runs

AVERAGE RESOURCE UTILIZATION—heading to indicate the section of the report dealing with statistics on the average resource utilization

RESOURCE—the resource number

LABEL—the user supplied name associated with the resource type

AVE.—the average over multiple runs of the time weighted average number of resource units in use obtained on a single run

STD. DEV.—the standard deviation of the average number of resource units in use obtained on a single run

SD OF AVE.—the standard deviation divided by the square root of the number of observations

NO. OF OBS.—the number of runs completed

MIN.—the smallest average number of resources utilized in any one simulation run

MAX.—the largest average number of resources utilized in any one simulation run

NUMBER OF RESOURCES—section of the report which deals with the number of resource units utilized

MAX.—maximum number of resource units utilized over all runs

AVERAGE RESOURCE AVAILABILITY—heading to indicate the section of the report dealing with statistics on the average resource availability

RESOURCE—the resource number

LABEL—the user supplied name associated with the resource type

AVE.—the average over multiple runs of the time weighted average number of resource units available for use obtained on a single run

STD. DEV.—the standard deviation of the average number of resource units available for use obtained on a single run

SD OF AVE.—the standard deviation divided by square root of the number of observations

NO. OF OBS.—the number of runs completed

MIN.—the smallest average number of resources available in any one simulation run

MAX.—the largest average number of resources available in any one simulation run

NUMBER OF RESOURCES—section of the report which deals with the number of resource units available

MAX.—maximum number of resource units available during any run

HISTOGRAM OUTPUTS

Histograms are produced on request for each Q-node and each statistics node. Four columns of data and a graph are contained on each histogram. The four columns of information are:

OBSV FREQ—the observed frequency with which the variable of interest was within a specified range, that is, the number of times that the variable of interest was in a specified range.

RELA FREQ—the relative frequency that a variable had a value in a specified range. The relative frequency is equal to the observed frequency divided by the total number of observations.

CUML FREQ—the cumulative frequency, that is, the number of values for the variable that were less than or equal to the value of the upper bound of the cell divided by the number of observations

UPPER BOUND OF CELL—the value that defines the topmost point of the cell. All cells are closed at the high end, that is, if a value of the variable equals the upper bound of cell I, the observed frequency for cell I is increased by 1. The first cell of each histogram has a range from minus infinity to the upper bound of the first cell. The last cell of a histogram has a range from the upper bound of the next-to-last cell to plus infinity.

Histogram outputs can be requested for the following two situations: 1) at statistics and sink nodes on the first run if multiple values are observed; and 2) at statistics nodes, sink nodes, and Q-nodes for histograms of average values over all runs. The user has the option of specifying the width of each histogram cell. If no cell width is specified, a histogram is not printed. If a zero cell width is specified, then Q-GERT sets the upper limit for the first cell to zero and the width of a cell to one for a first run histogram and computes appropriate values for the histogram of averages based on the values obtained from the first run. If a positive width is prescribed then Q-GERT assumes that values for the first run have been prescribed unless no first run report is requested. To prescribe the upper limit and width for a histogram over all runs, a negative value is specified for the cell width which Q-GERT interprets as the negative of the cell width for the average values obtained over all runs.

EXERCISES

3-1   Prepare the Q-GERT input for the following networks using default conditions for the upper limit of the first cell and width of a cell for histograms.

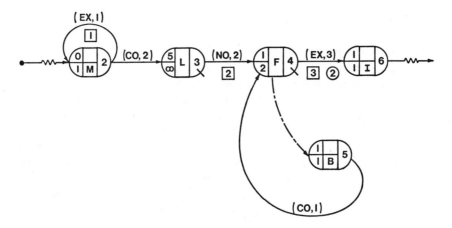

Set up the input data to make 10 runs with each run processing 500 transactions with the following PAR cards: PAR,1,5.0*
                 PAR,2,4.0,,,1.0*
                 PAR,3,4.0*

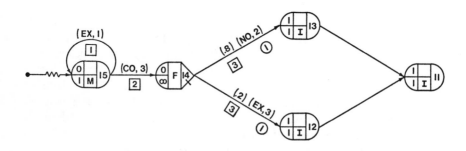

Set up the input data to make 5 runs with each run lasting for 1000 time units with the following PAR cards: PAR,1,5.*
                 PAR,2,4.0,0.0,8.0,1.0*
                 PAR,3,4.0*

3-2   Given the following input data cards, draw the equivalent Q-GERT network.

    GEN,INVERT,32,9,29,1976,1,0,0,1000,5*
    SOU,2,0,1,D,M*
    ACT,2,2,EX,1,1*
    PAR,1,10.*
    ACT,2,3,CO,0,2*
    QUE,3,1,5,D,L*
    ACT,3,4,NO,2,3,2*
    PAR,2,4.0,0.0,8.0,1.0*
    PAR,3,,0.0,20.0*
    REG,4,1,1,P*
    ACT,4,3,UN,3,5,,0.2*
    ACT,4,5,CO,0,4,,0.8*
    STA,5,1,1,,I*
    FIN*

3-3   In the following data input cards, detect at least nine errors.

    GEN,777,(7)3,,1,10,1000.*
    SOU*
    SIN,5,3*
    SIN,4,1*
    ACT,2,3,NO,1,1*
    ACT,2,4,CS,2.,2*
    ACT,2,5,EX,3,3*
    PAR,1,10.,,,SIGMA*
    PAR,3,4.*
    END*

3-4   Redo the input data çards for the one server, single queue process given in Figure 3-3 so that three consecutive runs are made. On the second run, the interarrival distribution should be exponential with a mean of 20. No other changes are required. On the third run, the interarrival time is exponentially distributed with a mean of 15 and a last-in, first-out queue discipline is to be used.

3-5   For the thief of Baghdad problem given in Exercise 2-11, prepare the data input for 1000 runs of the network using the following information: $p_F = 0.3$, $p_S = 0.2$, $p_L = 0.5$ and the mean time in short tunnel is 3 and for the long tunnel the mean equals 6 and the standard deviation is 2.

    Suppose the thief's remaining time to live is normally distributed with a mean of 10 and standard deviation of 2. Redraw the network and redo the data input in order to ascertain the probability that the thief reaches freedom before he dies based on 1000 simulations of the network.

3-6 Redo the network of Figure 3-3 and the data input cards in order to collect statistics on the time between arrivals and on the time between end of services.

3-7 Prepare a figure from which statistics on queues and servers can be obtained for the situation involving two sequential servers where the queue of the second server causes transactions to balk from the system, that is, prepare a table similar to Figure 3-12 which verifies the output statistics presented in Figure 3-15.

3-8 Perform a simulation of a queueing situation using the Q-GERT Analysis Program and discuss the meaning of each output statistic on the Q-GERT summary report.

Chapter 4

EXAMPLES OF THE USE OF BASIC Q-GERT CONCEPTS

In this chapter, six examples of the use of the basic Q-GERT concepts are given. For each example, a statement of the problem is provided including the objective of the analysis. A description of the Q-GERT model is then given that outlines any special features associated with the problem. A brief discussion of the inputs for and outputs from the Q-GERT Analysis Program is then provided. The emphasis in the examples is on the construction of Q-GERT models rather than on the solving of specific problems.

EXAMPLE 1. INSPECTION AND ADJUSTMENT STATIONS ON A PRODUCTION LINE

Problem Statement

The problem statement for this example is taken from Schriber (121). Assembled television sets move through a series of testing stations in the final stage of their production. At the last of these stations, the vertical control setting on the TV sets is tested. If the setting is found to be functioning improperly, the offending set is routed to an adjustment station where the setting is adjusted. After adjustment, the television set is sent back to the last inspection station where the setting is again inspected. Television sets passing the final inspection phase, whether for the first time or after one or more routings through the adjustment station, pass on to a packing area.

The situation described is pictured in Figure 4-1 where "circles" represent television sets. "Open circles" are sets waiting for final inspection, whereas "circled x's" are sets whose vertical control settings are improper, and which are either being serviced at the adjustment station or are waiting for service there.

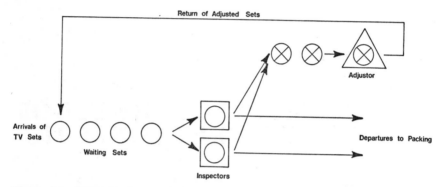

Figure 4-1   Schematic diagram of inspection and adjustment stations, Example 1.

The time between arrivals of television sets to the final inspection station is uniformly distributed between 3.5 and 7.5 minutes. Two inspectors work side-by-side at the final inspection station. The time required to inspect a set is uniformly distributed between 6 and 12 minutes. On the average, 85 percent of the sets pass inspection and continue on to the packing department. The other 15 percent are routed to the adjustment station which is manned by a single worker. Adjustment of the vertical control setting requires between 20 and 40 minutes uniformly distributed.

The inspection station and adjustor are to be simulated for 480 minutes to estimate the time to process television sets through this final production stage and to determine the utilization of the inspectors and the adjustor.

Q-GERT Model

In constructing a Q-GERT Model, a good starting point is the identification of the entities to be modeled by the transactions flowing through the network. For this example, the transactions will represent television sets. The television sets arrive and are routed to the inspection station. The two inspectors at the inspection station are represented as servers. If both inspectors are busy, a queue would form of television sets waiting for service by either inspector. Thus, the arriving transaction representing the television set is routed to a Q-node that precedes a service activity that represents two servers. Following the service activity representing inspection, 85 percent of the television sets are accepted and routed to packing. Since television sets routed to packing are no longer of interest, the transactions representing the television sets are routed to a node from which no branching occurs and, hence, the transactions are removed from the system.

Fifteen percent of the television sets are rejected and require adjustment. Thus, routing after inspection must be done probabilistically so that 15 percent of the transactions are routed to a Q-node representing the queue of rejected television sets waiting for the adjustor. Of course, if the adjustor is idle, the rejected television set is immediately served upon its arrival at the adjustment station. Following the adjustment operation, the transaction is routed back to the queue of the inspectors.

The above describes the complete processing and routing of television sets through the inspection and adjustment stations. The Q-GERT model can be built directly from this discussion and is shown in Figure 4-2. At node 1, arrivals of transactions are generated. The current arrival is routed directly to the queue for inspectors represented by Q-node 2. The next arrival is scheduled to occur by the branch from node 1 back to node 1. This branch has an activity time that is uniformly distributed using parameter set 1. When the transaction arrives at Q-node 2, it will proceed directly into service if either or both of the inspectors are free. Otherwise, it will remain at Q-node 2 until an inspector is free. The activity from Q-node 2 to node 3 represents the two inspectors. Note the 2 in the circle under the branch. Following inspection, the transaction is routed probabilistically to node 4 fifteen percent of the time, and to node 5, eighty-five percent of the time. These percentages represent the outcome of the inspection process. Of course, a single transaction will be routed either to node 4 or node 5, depending upon the draw of a random number. (If the random number is less than 0.85, the transaction is routed to node 5, otherwise the transaction is routed to node 4.) If the transaction is routed to node 5, it has been sent to packing and no further processing for the transaction is required. At node 5, the time that a television set spends in the inspection/adjustment system is computed. This time is obtained as an interval statistic where the mark node was source node 1. Note that the branches from node 3 to node 4 and from node 3 to node 5 do not have time descriptors as the time for the transaction to traverse either of these branches is zero.

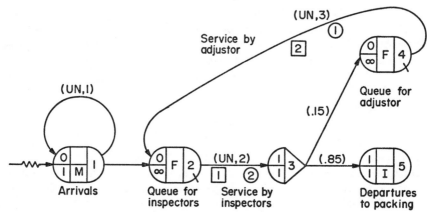

Figure 4-2   Q-GERT model of inspection and adjustment stations, Example 1.

When a transaction representing a rejected television set arrives at Q-node 4, it will be served by activity 2 if activity 2 is not busy. Activity 2 represents service by the adjustor. If the adjustor is busy, the arriving transaction waits at Q-node 4. As shown on the network, only one adjustor is employed for this example. Following the completion of activity 2, the transaction is routed back to Q-node 2. This completes the description of the Q-GERT model for the processing and routing of transactions representing television sets through two inspectors and one adjustor.

Data input for the Q-GERT analysis program for the network shown in Figure 4-2 is given in Figure 4-3. In addition to the GEN and FIN input lines, there is one line for each node of the network, one line for each branch of the network, and one line for each parameter set associated with the distributions describing the time to perform activities in the network. Note that node 5 is defined as a statistics node and not a sink node. For this example, the analysis is to be performed for 480 minutes (Field 10 on the GEN card) and no sink node is included in the network (Field 8 on the GEN card). Transactions are still destroyed at node 5 since no routing is prescribed. Since the analysis is not stopped in accordance with the number of releases of node 5, node 5 is not considered a sink node.

```
GEN,PRITSKER,TV-INS-ADJ-1,2,,1977,1,0,0,480.,,10*
SOU,1,0,1*
ACT,1,1,UN,1*                         INTERARRIVAL ACTIVITY
PAR,1,,3.5,7.5*                       INTERARRIVAL TIME PARAMETERS
ACT,1,2*                              TRANSFER TO INSPECTION
QUE,2/INSP-QUE*                       QUEUE FOR INSPECTION STATION
ACT,2,3,UN,2,1/INSPECT,2*             INSPECTION ACTIVITY
PAR,2,,6,12*                          INSPECTION TIME PARAMETERS
REG,3,1,1,P*                          NODE FOR ROUTING OF INSPECTED T V SETS
ACT,3,4,(8)0.15*                      ROUTING REJECTED T V SETS
ACT,3,5,(8)0.85*                      ROUTING ACCEPTED T V SETS
QUE,4/ADJ-QUE*                        QUEUE FOR ADJUSTOR
ACT,4,2,UN,3,2/ADJUST,1*              ADJUSTMENT ACTIVITY AND RECYCLING
PAR,3,,20,40*                         ADJUSTMENT TIME PARAMETERS
STA,5/SYS-TIME,1,1,,I,5.,5.*          STATISTICS COLLECTION ON THROUGHPUT TIME
FIN*
```

Figure 4-3   Data input for Q-GERT model of inspection and adjustment stations, Example 1.

Summary of Results

The outputs from the first run of the Q-GERT Analysis Program are shown in Figure 4-4.

```
GERT SIMULATION PROJECT TV-INS-ADJ-1 BY PRITSKER
         DATE   2/   1/ 1977


     **FINAL RESULTS FOR FIRST SIMULATION**


        TOTAL ELAPSED TIME =    480.0000



          **NODE STATISTICS**

  NODE     LABEL        AVE.      STD.DEV.   NO OF   STAT
                                            OBS.    TYPE

   5      SYS-TIME     21.7656    33.1351    81.    I



        **NUMBER IN Q-NODE**                 ** WAITING TIME **
                                                 IN QUEUE


  NODE     LABEL       AVE.    MIN.  MAX.    CURRENT    AVERAGE
                                            NUMBER

   2      INSP-QUE     .2744    0    2.        1        1.3721
   4      ADJ-QUE     1.1545    0    4.        0       46.1797



        **SERVER UTILIZATION**


 SERVER    LABEL    NO. PARALLEL   AVE.      MAX. IDLE           MAX. BUSY
                     SERVERS              (TIME OR SERVERS)  (TIME OR SERVERS)

   1      INSPECT       2        1.7797       2.0000             2.0000
   2      ADJUST        1         .7238      86.1116           301.2437
```

Figure 4-4   Results from first run of Q-GERT analysis program, Example 1.

This output illustrates that the time for a television set to be processed by the inspection and adjustment stations is 21.76 minutes on the average. This value is printed in the line for node 5 that is labeled SYS-TIME. This is based on 81 observations that occurred during the 480 minute run. The average number of television sets waiting for inspection (INSP-QUE) at Q-node 2 was 0.27 and the average number waiting for adjustment (ADJ-QUE) at Q-node 4 was 1.15. The average number of inspectors busy during this first run (INSPECT) was 1.78 and the fraction of time the adjustor was busy (ADJUST) was approximately 0.72. Further output under server utilization indicates that both servers were idle at one point during the run and both were busy at one point during the run. For the adjustor, his longest idle period was 86.11 minutes whereas his longest consecutive period of being busy was 301.24 minutes. With this type of information, an analyst can assess system performance relative to questions such as: Are the queue storage areas large enough? Is the allocation of manpower between the inspection stations and adjustor stations proper? Is the time to process a television set too long? Additional runs can easily be made to investigate these issues. For this example, these will not be considered. We will look, however, at the statistical adequacy of the final results.

The Q-GERT output for ten 480 minute runs is shown in Figure 4-5. The results averaged over the 10 runs are similar to those for the first run. However, the average values for the utilization of the adjustor and the number of television sets in his queue appear to have a relatively high standard deviation. Because of this, further analysis was performed for the example.

In 480 time units, the average number of television set arrivals should be about 87 (480 divided by 5.5). Since only 15 percent of the arrivals are routed to the adjustor, this means that in 480 time units approximately 13 television sets would be routed to the adjustor. Now 15 percent of those sets adjusted will require a second adjustment which amounts to an additional 2 sets being routed to the adjustor. Therefore, in a run of length 480 minutes, we should expect approximately 15 sets routed to the adjustor. This small number of observations leads to the high variability in the estimates of the average number in the queue for the adjustor and for his utilization. Whether these highly variable estimates are appropriate for the analysis being considered is process dependent.

If the inspection and adjustment system operates in a fashion whereby each 480 minute day is independent of the previous day, the output given in Figure 4-5 provides appropriate estimates for the period of interest. This will be the case if all television sets that require adjustment are adjusted prior to the start of the next day's operation.

GERT SIMULATION PROJECT TV-INS-ADJ-1 BY PRITSKER
DATE 2/ 1/ 1977

FINAL RESULTS FOR   10 SIMULATIONS

AVERAGE NODE STATISTICS

NODE	LABEL	PROBABILITY	AVE.	STD.DEV.	SD OF AVE	MIN.	MAX.	STAT TYPE
5	SYS-TIME	1.0000	19.4758	4.1975	1.3274	13.2068	25.3166	I

AVERAGE NUMBER IN Q-NODE

NODE	LABEL	AVE.	STD.DEV.	SD OF AVE
2	INSP-QUE	.4317	.1816	.0574
4	ADJ-QUE	.8389	.4631	.1464

AVERAGE WAITING TIME

AVE.	STD.DEV.	SD OF AVE
2.0839	.7892	.2496
28.5097	15.3385	4.8505

NUMBER IN Q-NODE

MAX.
3.0000
4.0000

AVERAGE SERVER UTILIZATION

SERVER	LABEL	NO. PARALLEL SERVERS	AVE.	STD.DEV.	SD OF AVE	NO. OF OBS.	MIN.	MAX.
1	INSPECT	2	1.8046	.0462	.0146	10.	1.7543	1.9225
2	ADJUST	1	.7219	.1506	.0476	10.	.4716	.9433

EXTREME VALUES

MAX. IDLE (TIME OR SERVERS)	MAX. BUSY
2.0000	2.0000
131.6808	432.5253

Figure 4-5   Results from 10 runs of Q-GERT analysis program, Example 1.

97

If there is a carryover from one day to the next of television sets that require adjustment, then a longer simulation period can be used to decrease the variability in the estimates. For this example, 5 simulations of 4800 minute durations were run. For these longer runs, the average number in the queue of the adjustor increased to 5.10 and the utilization of the adjustor increased to 0.93.

Clearly, there are many interesting statistical problems relating to the analysis of the output obtained from the Q-GERT Analysis Program (and from simulation studies in general) (40,66,80,120). Only a limited discussion of statistical analysis methods is presented in this book since the main orientation is the presentation of Q-GERT and the modeling of systems using Q-GERT.

EXAMPLE 2. PAINT SHOP

Problem Statement

A paint shop employs six workmen who prepare jobs to be spray painted. The preparation operation is lengthy compared to the spraying operation and, hence, only two spraying machines are available. After a workman completes the preparation of a job, he proceeds to the spraying machine where he waits if necessary for a free spraying machine. The preparation time is normally distributed with a mean of 20 minutes and a standard deviation of 3 minutes. Spraying time is uniformly distributed between 5 and 10 minutes. A Q-GERT model of this situation will be developed to obtain estimates of the utilization of the workmen and the spraying machines for 5 eight hour days. Also to be determined is the length of time required to prepare and paint a job. It is assumed that jobs to be prepared and painted are always available to the workmen.

Q-GERT Model

One way to view this situation is to consider that the workmen are flowing through two operations: the preparation activity and the painting activity. Associated with each workman is a job. Since jobs are always available, they are included implicitly in the model as part of the workman transaction. For the preparation activity, only the workman is re-

quired. For the painting activity, the spraying machine is a required resource. Conceived in this manner, the Q-GERT model must generate six
transactions representing workmen. Each transaction must flow
through a preparation activity and then attempt to spray his job using
the spraying machine. If both spraying machines are in use, the workman transaction (and his job) waits for a machine to become available.

To generate the six workman transactions, a source node with deterministic branching and six branches emanating from it can be used.
Each branch carries a transaction so that six transactions are generated.
(Alternatively a Q-node with five transactions in it initially could have
been used). Each workman transaction then flows through the preparation activity, is processed by the painting service activity, and recycles
for another preparation activity. The Q-GERT network model is shown
in Figure 4-6. In Figure 4-6, the activity from node 3 to node 4
represents the preparation activity. Since it is not a service activity, that
is, it is not preceded by a Q-node, there is no limit to the number of
simultaneous transactions that can flow through the activity. Each
workman transaction arrives and releases node 3 at time 0 and a preparation activity is started for each transaction. The first two workmen to
arrive at Q-node 4 start their painting operations immediately as two
spraying machines are available. If a third workman arrives prior to the
time that the first two complete their painting operations, he would
wait.

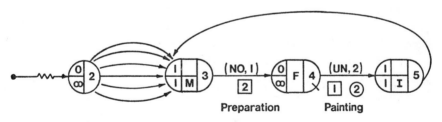

Figure 4-6   Q-GERT model of paint shop, Example 2.

At node 5, the time interval for a workman to go from node 3 (where
he was marked) to node 5 is collected. This represents the time for the
workman to prepare and paint one job. The workman is then routed
back to node 3 with no delay to begin preparing another job.

The input required for the Q-GERT model of Figure 4-6 is given in
Figure 4-7.

```
GEN,PRITSKER,PAINT-SHOP-2,2,5,1977,1,0,0,480.,5*
SOU,2*                          GENERATE WORKMEN
ACT,2,3*                        FIRST WORKMAN TRANSACTION
ACT,2,3*                        SECOND WORKMAN TRANSACTION
ACT,2,3*                        THIRD WORKMAN TRANSACTION
ACT,2,3*                        FOURTH WORKMAN TRANSACTION
ACT,2,3*                        FIFTH WORKMAN TRANSACTION
ACT,2,3*                        SIXTH WORKMAN TRANSACTION
REG,3,1,1,D,M*                  START A JOB CYCLE
ACT,3,4,NO,1,2*                 PREPARATION ACTIVITY
PAR,1,20.,0.,100.,3.*           PREPARATION TIME PARAMETERS
QUE,4/SPRAYQUE*                 WAIT FOR SPRAYING MACHINE
ACT,4,5,UN,2,1/SPRAYER,2*       PAINTING ACTIVITIES
PAR,2,,5,10*                    PAINTING TIME PARAMETERS
STA,5/JOB-TIME,1,1,D,I,25,1*    COLLECT TIME/JOB STATISTICS
ACT,5,3*                        RECYCLE WORKMAN TRANSACTION
FIN*
```

Figure 4-7   Data input for Q-GERT model of a paint shop, Example 2.

Summary of Results

The outputs from the Q-GERT Analysis Program are summarized in Table 4-1. Five runs were made with each run lasting 480 minutes. On the first run, the average time to process a job was 28.542 minutes. The average queue size of workmen waiting for a sprayer was 0.260 and, on the average, 1.57 sprayers were in use. From the Q-GERT report of the first run (not shown), 98 jobs were processed with the standard deviation of the job time being 3.482 minutes. Also, a maximum of three workmen waited for a sprayer at the same time.

The averages over five runs are also given in Table 4-1.

Table 4-1.   Summary of Statistical Outputs for Example 2 (Six Workmen).

	First Run Averages	Five Run Averages				
		Average	Std. Dev.	Std. Dev. of Average	Minimum	Maximum
Average job time	28.542	28.593	0.141	0.063	28.447	28.827
Average queue size	0.260	0.248	0.026	0.012	0.209	0.273
Average sprayers busy	1.570	1.540	0.035	0.016	1.484	1.570

The average job time of 28.593 minutes is an average of the five average values obtained from each run. The standard deviation of the job time, 0.141, is an estimate of the variation about 28.593 obtained from the five observations. The smallest average job time was 28.447 minutes and the largest average job time was 28.827 minutes. If the network were analyzed again for five runs with different random number seeds, the estimated standard deviation of the average would be 0.063. By employing the central limit theorem, we can state with 95 percent confidence that the average over a new five run analysis should be between 28.467 and 28.719.

The statistics for queue size and number of busy sprayers are also given in Table 4-1. On the first run, the average queue size was 0.260. Similar values were obtained on subsequent runs and the average of these averages was 0.248. The standard deviation of the five average values was 0.026 and the minimum average for a run was 0.209 and the maximum average was 0.273. Similarly, the average number of busy servers over the five runs was 1.540 with a standard deviation of 0.035. The minimum average of the number of busy sprayers was 1.484 and the maximum was 1.570. As can be seen from Table 4-1, the average values over the five runs are similar to the first run averages.

The average queue size for this example is extremely small and indicates a very small amount of queueing on the part of the workmen. It also indicates that the item processing time variability can be attributed, in the main, to the variation in the preparation time and spraying time. Any improvement in these times will be reflected directly in the total item processing time.

A histogram of the job times for the first run is presented in Figure 4-8. From Figure 4-8, it can be seen that 14 of the 98 jobs were processed in less than or equal to 25 minutes. This represents 14.3 percent of all jobs processed on the first run. Another important quantity that can be obtained directly from the histogram is the estimate of the probability of the number of jobs that are completed within a specified time. Thus, 63.3 percent of the jobs are processed within 30 minutes. The peak shown in the first cell is due to the fact that all values below 25 are put into the first cell. Also note that three job times were greater than 35 minutes.

In setting the conditions for this example, it was apparent that the number of workmen is a significant component. The Q-GERT model was exercised when 5, 6 and 7 workmen are involved in the preparation and spraying activities. Recall from Figure 4-6 that this involves deleting or adding a branch from node 2 to node 3. Table 4-2 presents the results for five runs for each of these situations. In order to compare the situations, the costs and revenues associated with waiting workmen, idle sprayers and production rates would have to be determined. However, Table 4-2 does show the sensitivity of the outputs to a change in one de-

```
I  STAT HISTOGRAM FOR NODE    5

                  JOB-TIME


     OBSV   RELA   CUML   UPPER         0        20       40       60       80      100
     FREQ   FREQ   FREQ  BOUND OF CELL  I....I....I....I....I....I....I....I....I....I....I
1)   14    .143   .143      25.00      I*******                                          I
      7    .071   .214      26.00      I****    C                                         I
     10    .102   .316      27.00      I*****        C                                    I
     13    .133   .449      28.00      I*******          C                                I
     12    .122   .571      29.00      I******              C                             I
2)    6    .061   .633      30.00      I***                    C                          I
     16    .163   .796      31.00      I********                   C                      I
     10    .102   .898      32.00      I*****                         C                   I
      5    .051   .949      33.00      I***                             C  I
      2    .020   .969      34.00      I*                                 C I
      0     0     .969      35.00      I                                  C I
      1    .010   .980      35.00      I*                                 C I
      0     0     .980      37.00      I                                  C I
      0     0     .980      38.00      I                                  C I
      0     0     .980      39.00      I                                  C I
      0     0     .980      40.00      I                                  C I
      1    .010   .990      41.00      I*                                 CI
      0     0     .990      42.00      I                                  CI
      0     0     .990      43.00      I                                  CI
3)    1    .010  1.000      +INF       I*                                 C
                                       I....I....I....I....I....I....I....I....I....I....I
           ---
TOTAL      98
```

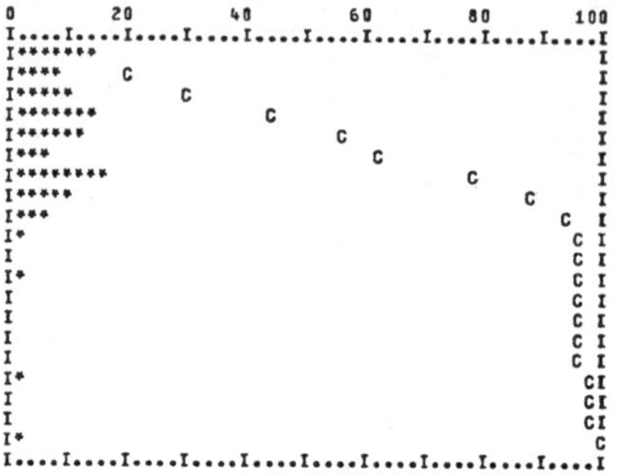

Interpretive statements:
1) 14 of the 98 jobs (0.143) were processed in less than or equal to 25 minutes.
2) 63.3% of the jobs were processed within 30 minutes.
3) one processing time was greater than 43 minutes.

Figure 4-8 Histogram of job times, Example 2.

cision variable, and the increase in job time due to the greater interference among workmen seeking use of the sprayers. The user of Q-GERT should be constantly reflecting on alternative operating procedures and attempting to evaluate their effects on system performance.

Table 4-2. Five Run Statistical Outputs for 5, 6, and 7 Workmen, Example 2.

	Number of Workmen		
	5	6	7
Average Item Processing Time	28.087	28.593	29.740
Average of Average Queue Size	0.109	0.248	0.515
Average of Average Number of Busy Sprayers	1.301	1.540	1.716

EXAMPLE 3. A PRODUCTION SYSTEM INVOLVING MACHINES, SPARE MACHINES AND REPAIRMEN

Problem Statement

The statement for this problem is abstracted from Schriber (121). In a garment factory, fifty sewing machines are operated eight hours a day, five days a week. Each of the machines is subject to failure. When a machine fails, a backup machine is put into production if one is available. A failed machine is serviced by a repairman if one is available.

Management maintains a work force of 50 sewing machine operators to work on the 50 sewing machines in operation. In addition, four backup machines are available and three repairmen have been hired to fix failed machines. This situation is depicted in Figure 4-9. The time between failures of the sewing machines is exponentially distributed with a mean of 157 hours. When a machine fails, the operator goes to a backup machine if one is available and the repairman travels to the failed machine. These travel times are considered to be negligibly small.* The time required to repair a failed machine is uniformly distributed and takes between 4 and 10 hours. No distinctions are made either among repairmen or among sewing machines.

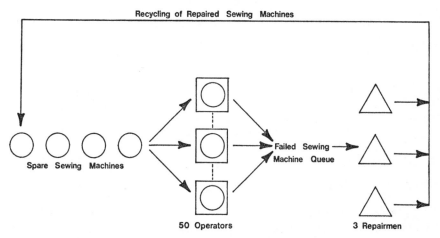

Figure 4-9   Schematic diagram of machine-repairman system, Example 3.

---

*When travel times are not negligible, intermediate Q-GERT concepts are required to model the situation. See Example 8, Chapter 6, for a similar situation in which servers are required to have a break between service operations.

A Q-GERT model will be developed for this system to estimate over a 6240 hour period the average number of operators busy, the average number of repairmen busy, the number of sewing machines in a backup status and the number of sewing machines waiting for repair.

Q-GERT Model

In the system described above, the sewing machines can be considered to flow from an operator (production status) to a repairman (non-productive status) and then back to an available operator to return to production status. Thus, even though a sewing machine stays stationary in the real system, its status is changing and it can be viewed as a transaction moving between two server stations with queues preceding each server station. When viewed in this perspective, the Q-GERT network model for the production situation involving machines, backup machines and repairmen is extremely simple as shown by the network diagram in Figure 4-10.

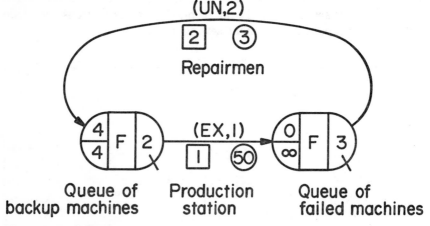

Figure 4-10 Q-GERT network of machine-repairman system, Example 3.

Q-node 2 represents the queue of backup machines which according to the problem statement initially contains four. Since there are four initially in the queue, each server following the queue will be busy initially. Thus, all fifty operators will be busy initially. Activity 1 represents the production time for each operator which, in this case, is the time an operator works until the machine fails. This time is specified as being exponentially distributed using parameter set 1. When a machine fails it is routed to the queue of failed machines as represented by Q-node 3. If a backup machine is available, the operator starts another production cycle which will last until that machine fails.

At Q-node 3, the newly failed sewing machine will wait for a repairman if one is not available. Otherwise, repair will immediately start on the failed machine. When repair is completed on the sewing machine, it is routed back to Q-node 2 to become either a member of the queue of backup machines or to be put directly into production. This completes the description of the Q-GERT model for the production system.

The data input for the Q-GERT network shown in Figure 4-10 is presented in Figure 4-11.

```
GEN,PRITSKER,SEWING-MCH-3,6,22,1977,0,0,0,6240.,1*
QUE,2/SPARE-Q,4,4*            QUEUE OF BACKUP MACHINES
ACT,2,3,EX,1,1/MACHUTIL,50*   PRODUCTION ACTIVITIES FOR 50 OPERATORS
PAR,1,157.,0,1000.*           FAILURE TIME PARAMETERS
QUE,3/FAILED-Q*               QUEUE OF FAILED MACHINES
ACT,3,2,UN,2,2/M-IN-REP,3*    REPAIR ACTIVITIES FOR 3 REPAIRMEN
PAR,2,,4.,10.*                REPAIR TIME PARAMETERS
FIN*
```

Figure 4-11 Data input for machine-repairman system, Example 3.

Summary of Results

The output for Example 3 is shown in Figure 4-12. Only one run was made and the run time was 6240 hours. During this time, on the average, there were 1.4997 backup machines waiting in Q-node 2 to replace the sewing machines in production. At one point in the run, no backup machines were waiting and, at another point, all four were waiting. This latter condition occurs at the beginning of the simulation. By specifying different initial conditions, it could be determined whether this condition actually occurs during a run. For example, 3 machines could be in repair at the beginning of the run. Alternatively, statistics could be collected starting at time 500.

The average number in Q-node 3 represents the average number of machines that failed and had to wait because all repairmen were busy. This value is 0.7318. At one point in the 6240 hour run as many as 8 machines were waiting for a repairman. From the output labeled MACHUTIL, it is seen that the average number of sewing machines in production, server 1, was 49.5956. Under the heading MAX. IDLE for server 1, the value 7 indicates that at one time during the run only 43 parallel servers or sewing machines were in production. This corre-

```
GERT SIMULATION PROJECT SEWING-MCH-3 BY PRITSKER
             DATE  6/ 22/ 1977


        **FINAL RESULTS FOR FIRST SIMULATION**


        TOTAL ELAPSED TIME =    6240.0000




        **NUMBER IN Q-NODE**                    ** WAITING TIME **
                                                    IN QUEUE


 NODE    LABEL       AVE.    MIN.  MAX.     CURRENT      AVERAGE
                                           NUMBER

  2     SPARE-Q     1.4997    0    4.         0         4.8339
  3     FAILED-Q     .7318    0    8.         2         2.3574



        **SERVER UTILIZATION**


 SERVER   LABEL    NO. PARALLEL   AVE.      MAX. IDLE          MAX. BUSY
                     SERVERS             (TIME OR SERVERS) (TIME OR SERVERS)

  1      MACHUTIL      50      49.5956      7.0000             50.0000
  2      M-IN-REP       3       2.1729      3.0000              3.0000
```

Figure 4-12 Results on utilization of sewing machines and repairmen, Example 3.

sponds to 11 sewing machines being in a failed state simultaneously. This value is obtained by subtracting 43 from the 54 sewing machines available. This value also can be obtained from the output for Q-node 3 as 8 machines were waiting while 3 were being repaired. For server 1, it is seen that all 50 servers were busy simultaneously at one point during the simulation. Recall that this was the initial condition.

The values given under server 2 represent the number of busy repairmen labeled M__IN__REP. The estimate of the mean number of repairmen busy is 2.1729. At one point during the run, all three repairmen were idle (initial conditions) and at another point, all three were busy.

This example could be used to demonstrate how the multiple server capability can be used to "size" a needed resource requirement. For example, suppose we asked the question "how many repairmen are needed so that a failed machine never waits to be repaired?" By running the simulation with a large value for the number of parallel servers for activity 2, there would always be a repairman available and the reported value for the maximum number busy will provide an answer to the question posed.

EXAMPLE 4. A CONVEYOR SYSTEM

Problem Statement

A conveyor system involves five servers stationed along a conveyor belt (100). Items to be processed by the servers arrive at the conveyor belt with an interarrival time that is exponentially distributed with a mean of 1 minute. After being placed on the conveyor belt, it takes 2 minutes for the new arrivals to reach the first server. Service time for each server averages 3 minutes and is exponentially distributed. No storage space for items is provided before any server. If the first server is idle, the item is processed by that server. If the first server is busy when the item arrives, the item continues down the conveyor belt until it arrives at the second server. The delay time between servers is 1 minute. If an item encounters a situation in which all servers are busy, it is recycled to the first server with a time delay of 5 minutes. At the completion of service for an item, the item is removed from the system. A diagram of the conveyor system is shown in Figure 4-13. A Q-GERT model will be developed of the conveyor system to collect statistics on the system residence time for an item and the utilization of each server based on the processing of 200 items.

Q-GERT Model

In this example, items are the transactions flowing through the conveyor system. An item arrives and is transferred to the first server with a 2 minute time delay. If the first server is free, the item is taken off the conveyor belt and service is initiated on it. If the first server is busy, then the item must bypass the first server, that is, continue along the conveyor belt, and proceed to the second server. This decision as to whether the item will be processed by the first server can be modeled in Q-GERT using a Q-node with zero capacity. If the server is idle, the item will flow through the Q-node directly to the server. However, if the server is busy, the item cannot stay at the Q-node because it has a zero capacity and, hence, it will balk. In this situation, balking from the server means that the item can continue down the conveyor belt toward the next server. The remainder of the Q-GERT model follows this pattern of attempting to gain access to a server through a Q-node with zero capacity and balking from the Q-node if the server is busy. The Q-GERT model for the conveyor system is shown in Figure 4-14.

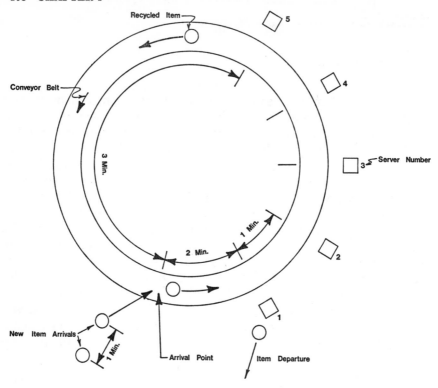

Figure 4-13   Schematic diagram of conveyor system, Example 4.

Arrivals of items are modeled using source node 2 with a self loop branch to represent the interarrival activity. Since it takes 2 minutes for the item to reach the first server, the branch from node 2 to Q-node 3 is prescribed to have a 2 minute delay. Q-node 3 precedes server number 1 and has zero initial transactions in it and a capacity of zero. Balking from Q-node 3 is to node 4. When a transaction arrives at Q-node 3 and server 1 is busy, the transaction balks to node 4. The branch from node 4 to Q-node 5 represents the item staying on the conveyor belt and moving to the next server. A 1 minute time delay is prescribed for the activity as represented by the branch from node 4 to Q-node 5.

Server number 2 is modeled by activity 2 which emanates from Q-node 5. Note that the time for activity 2 is exponential with parameter set 1. This is the identical specification for all servers and illustrates the use of the same parameter set number for different activities. When a transaction arrives at node 13 it has completed service and the time

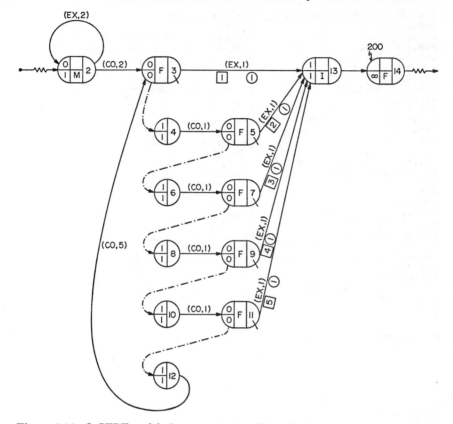

Figure 4-14   Q-GERT model of conveyor system, Example 4.

spent in the conveyor system by the item is collected. The item is then
sent to node 14 to record that one more transaction has been processed
by the conveyor system. Two hundred incoming transactions are required to release node 14 which is the sink node for the system. When
node 14 is released, one run of the conveyor system will have been completed.

When an item balks from the Q-nodes of all servers, it reaches node
12. The activity from node 12 to node 3 represents the recycling of items
which requires 5 minutes. At node 3, the processing of the item through
the 5 server conveyor system is repeated. The data input for the conveyor system model is given in Figure 4-15.

```
GEN,PRITSKER,CONVEYOR-4,9,13,1977,1,1,1,,10*
SOU,2,0,1*                         SOURCE NODE
ACT,2,2,EX,2*                      INTERARRIVAL TIME ACTIVITY
PAR,2,1.00,0.,100.*                INTERARRIVAL TIME PARAMETERS
ACT,2,3,CO,2*                      DELAY TO FIRST SERVER
QUE,3/SERVER-1,0,0,(7)4*           QUEUE OF SERVER 1
ACT,3,13,EX,1,1/SERVER-1,1*        SERVICE TIME, SERVER 1
PAR,1,3.,0.,100.*                  SERVICE TIME PARAMETERS
REG,4,1,1*                         BALK NODE FOR SERVER 1
ACT,4,5,CO,1*                      DELAY TO SERVER 2
QUE,5/SERVER-2,0,0,(7)6*           QUEUE OF SERVER 2
ACT,5,13,EX,1,2/SERVER-2,1*        SERVICE TIME, SERVER 2
REG,6,1,1*                         BALK NODE FOR SERVER 2
ACT,6,7,CO,1*                      DELAY TO SERVER 3
QUE,7/SERVER-3,0,0,(7)8*           QUEUE OF SERVER 3
ACT,7,13,EX,1,3/SERVER-3,1*        SERVICE TIME, SERVER 3
REG,8,1,1*                         BALK NODE FOR SERVER 3
ACT,8,9,CO,1*                      DELAY TO SERVER 4
QUE,9/SERVER-4,0,0,(7)10*          QUEUE OF SERVER 4
ACT,9,13,EX,1,4/SERVER-4,1*        SERVICE TIME, SERVER 4
REG,10,1,1*                        BALK NODE FOR SERVER 4
ACT,10,11,CO,1*                    DELAY TO SERVER 5
QUE,11/SERVER-5,0,0,(7)12*         QUEUE OF SERVER 5
ACT,11,13,EX,1,5/SERVER-5,1*       SERVICE TIME, SERVER 5
REG,12,1,1*                        BALK NODE FOR SERVER 5
ACT,12,3,CO,5*                     RECYCLE TIME TO SERVER 1
STA,13/TIMINSYS,1,1,D,I,2.,2.*COLLECT TIME IN SYSTEM
ACT,13,14*
SIN,14/TOT-TIME,200*               RECORD NUMBER OF TRANSACTIONS PROCESSED
FIN*
```

Figure 4-15   Data input for conveyor system, Example 4.

Summary of Results

The summary statistics for the first run of the conveyor system are shown in Figure 4-16. The total elapsed time for the first run was 205.45 minutes. That is, it required over 205 minutes to process 200 items. Since the average interarrival time is 1.0 minute, we would expect approximately 205 arrivals during this 205 minute interval. Of course, some items that arrived during the 205 minutes have not completed processing.

The statistics given in the row for node 13 labeled TIMINSYS provide the time in the system for an item during the first run. On the average, an item was on the conveyor system 8.26 minutes of which 2 minutes was spent traveling to the first server, an average of 3 minutes was spent in processing and the other 3.26 minutes traveling on the conveyor belt. Since it takes 5 minutes to recycle an item on the conveyor belt, the results indicate that not many items encounter the recycling delay.

```
GERT SIMULATION PROJECT CONVEYOR-4    BY PRITSKER
            DATE  9/ 13/ 1977


        **FINAL RESULTS FOR FIRST SIMULATION**


        TOTAL ELAPSED TIME =    205.4507



            **NODE STATISTICS**

  NODE     LABEL      AVE.      STD.DEV.   NO OF  STAT
                                          OBS.   TYPE

  14     TOT-TIME   205.4507         0      1.   F
  13     TIMINSYS     8.2616    5.7496    200.   I


        **SERVER UTILIZATION**


 SERVER   LABEL    NO. PARALLEL   AVE.      MAX. IDLE         MAX. BUSY
                     SERVERS              (TIME OR SERVERS) (TIME OR SERVERS)

   1     SERVER-1       1        .7431        5.5962          13.1270
   2     SERVER-2       1        .7107        6.0227          15.0012
   3     SERVER-3       1        .7049        6.7575          17.4459
   4     SERVER-4       1        .4706       16.4975          16.2025
   5     SERVER-5       1        .3803       20.6205          12.9509



        **NO. BALKING PER UNIT TIME**


   NODE     LABEL      AVE.

    3     SERVER-1    .9151
    5     SERVER-2    .7009
    7     SERVER-3    .5062
    9     SERVER-4    .3407
   11     SERVER-5    .2093
```

Figure 4-16   Results for first run of conveyor system, Example 4.

The server utilization for each of the five servers is shown in the middle section of Figure 4-16. As expected, server utilization decreases as the server gets farther away from the arrival point of the items. Server 1 who has the first chance to process an item is approximately twice as busy as server number 5. This information is also reflected in the maximum idle time period shown on the output. Since servers would normally be busy for one item at a time, the maximum consecutive busy time essentially represents the largest sample from an exponential distribution obtained during the run. The smaller value for server 5 is due to the fewer number of items processed by server 5.

The third section of the output report for the first run provides estimates of the average number of items balking per unit time. The average number balking from Q-node 3 represents the number of items per minute that arrived at server 1 when he was busy. This balking rate from server 1 also represents the arrival rate to server 2. Thus, the average arrival rate to server 2 for this first run was approximately 0.92 items per minute. The number of items circulated around the conveyor belt is equivalent to the number of items balking from Q-node 11. From the output, it is seen that this number is approximately 0.21 items per minute. Since the run length was a little over 205 time units, the number of items recycled was approximately 41. After the system is operating for awhile, the arrival rate to the first server is the sum of the balking rate from the fifth server and the original arrival rate of items to the system.

A histogram of the time an item spent in the conveyor system for the first run is given in Figure 4-17. This histogram indicates the extensive variability that is obtained when dealing with cyclic or feedback queueing systems. This variability is described quantitatively by the statistics for node 13 given in Figure 4-16 where the mean time in the conveyor system for an item is 8.26 minutes and the standard deviation is 5.75 minutes, and indicates a variable with a high degree of variation relative to the mean value.

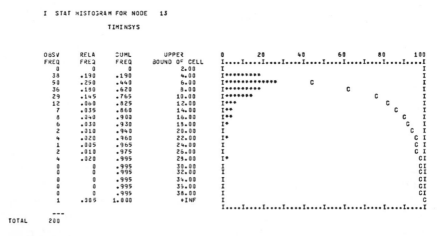

Figure 4-17 Histogram of time in the conveyor system for an item, Example 4, Run 1.

In Figure 4-18, summary statistics for ten runs is provided. The description of the quantities for ten runs would be similar to that provided above for the first run. In all cases, the average values from the first run are within one standard deviation of the average values over ten runs.

FINAL RESULTS FOR 10 SIMULATIONS

AVERAGE NODE STATISTICS

NODE	LABEL	PROBABILITY	AVE.	STD.DEV.	SD OF AVE	NO OF OBS.	MIN.	MAX.	STAT TYPE
14	TOT-TIME	1.0000	206.7593	14.1877	4.4866	16.	181.4785	225.0684	F
13	TIMINSYS	1.0000	9.3058	1.9259	.6090	10.	7.4023	13.7365	I

AVERAGE SERVER UTILIZATION

SERVER	LABEL	NO. PARALLEL SERVERS	AVE.	STD.DEV.	SD OF AVE	NO. OF OBS.	MIN.	MAX.	**EXTREME VALUES** MAX. IDLE (TIME OR SERVERS)	MAX. BUSY
1	SERVER-1	1	.7635	.2329	.0073	10.	.7328	.8143	5.5962	14.6166
2	SERVER-2	1	.7068	.0526	.0166	10.	.6236	.7638	9.9298	18.3141
3	SERVER-3	1	.6375	.1145	.0362	10.	.4802	.8000	15.7174	36.5972
4	SERVER-4	1	.5288	.1643	.0330	10.	.3809	.7217	23.3644	16.2025
5	SERVER-5	1	.3872	.1090	.0345	10.	.2292	.5570	30.9128	22.1643

AVERAGE NO. BALKING PER UNIT TIME

NODE	LABEL	AVE.	STD.DEV.	SD OF AVE	NO. OF OBS.	MIN.	MAX.
3	SERVER-1	1.1534	.2690	.0851	10.	.8042	1.5691
5	SERVER-2	.8308	.2690	.0851	10.	.5732	1.3406
7	SERVER-3	.6415	.2591	.0819	10.	.3777	1.1324
9	SERVER-4	.4677	.2451	.0775	10.	.2249	.9648
11	SERVER-5	.3347	.2213	.0700	10.	.1359	.7973

Figure 4-18   Results for 10 runs of conveyor system, Example 4.

The extreme values obtained over the ten runs are larger as should be expected since extreme values will increase as more observations are made.

The output reports from the Q-GERT Analysis Program for this conveyor situation provide many interesting statistics which illustrate the workings of the system and which could be used for improving system performance.

EXAMPLE 5. WORK STATIONS IN SERIES

Problem Statement

The maintenance facility of a large manufacturer performs two operations (105). These operations must be performed in series; operation 2 always follows operation 1. The units that are maintained are bulky, and space is available for only eight units including the units being worked on. A proposed design leaves space for two units between the work stations, and space for four units before work station 1. The proposed design is illustrated in Figure 4-19. Current company policy is to subcontract the maintenance of a unit if it cannot gain access to the in-house facility.

Historical data indicates that the time interval between requests for maintenance is exponentially distributed with a mean of 0.4 time units. Service times are also exponentially distributed with the first station requiring on the average 0.25 time units and the second service station, 0.5 time units. Units are transported automatically from work station 1 to work station 2 in a negligible amount of time. If the queue of work station 2 is full, that is, if there are two units waiting for work station 2, the first work station is blocked and a unit cannot leave that station. A blocked work station cannot serve other units.

To evaluate the proposed design, statistics on the following variables are to be obtained over a period of 300 time units:
  (1) Work station utilization;
  (2) Time to process a unit through the two work stations;
  (3) Number of units/time unit that are subcontracted;
  (4) Number of units waiting for each work station; and
  (5) Fraction of time work station 1 is blocked.

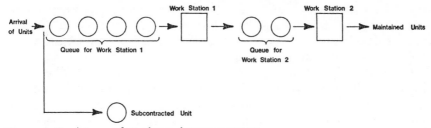

Figure 4-19   A two work station maintenance system.

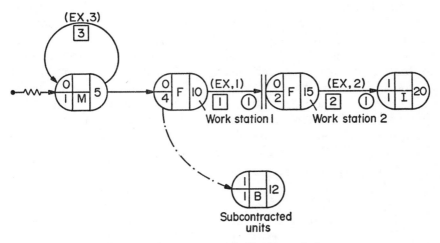

Figure 4-20   Q-GERT model of maintenance facility, Example 5.

Q-GERT Model

The maintenance system described above is a common queueing type
system in which units can be represented by transactions that flow
through the two work stations. The storage area preceding each work
station is represented by a Q-node with the Q-node for work station 2
having a blocking capability to stop the processing of units by work station 1. Each work station is represented by a service activity with one
server associated with each work station. The Q-GERT model for this
system is shown in Figure 4-20.

In Figure 4-20, node 5 is used to generate arrivals to the production
line. Q-node 10 represents the storage area for work station 1. A capac-

ity of 4 is assigned to the Q-node. Transactions that arrive when 4 units are waiting for maintenance at work station 1 balk to node 12. At node 12, the time between balking units is recorded. This represents the time between the subcontracting of units.

Q-node 15 represents the storage area for work station 2. The blocking capability is shown by the two parallel lines preceding Q-node 15. Thus, if a maintenance operation is completed at work station 1 (as represented by activity 1) when there are two transactions at Q-node 15, work station 1 will be blocked and no further processing by it will be allowed until work station 2 completes service on a unit.

Node 20 is used to collect statistics on the time required for a unit to be processed by the maintenance facility involving the two work stations. For this model, the Q-GERT Analysis Program will be instructed to run an analysis for 300 time units in order to collect statistics on the utilization of each work station, the number of units waiting in each queue, the fraction of time that work station 1 is blocked, the number of units per unit time balking from Q-node 10, the time for a unit to be processed by the maintenance facility, and the time between the subcontracting of units. The data input required to get this information from the Q-GERT Analysis Program is shown in Figure 4-21.

```
GEN,PRITSKER,MAINT-FAC-5,6,30,1977,2,0,0,300.,1*
SOU,5,0,1*                      GENERATE TRANSACTIONS
ACT,5,5,EX,3,3*                 INTERARRIVAL TIME ACTIVITY
PAR,3,.4,0.,,100.*              INTERARRIVAL TIME PARAMETERS
ACT,5,10*                       TRANSFER TO WORK STATION 1
QUE,10/WS1-QUE,0,4,(7)12*       QUEUE FOR WORK STATION 1
ACT,10,15,EX,1,1/STATION1,1*    WORK STATION 1 SERVICE ACTIVITY
PAR,1,.25,0.,,100.*             WORK STATION 1 SERVICE TIME PARAMETERS
STA,12/SUB-UNIT,1,1,D,8*        NODE FOR SUBCONTRACTED UNITS
QUE,15/WS2-QUE,0,2,(7)8*        QUEUE FOR WORK STATION 2
ACT,15,20,EX,2,2/STATION2,1*    WORK STATION 2 SERVICE ACTIVITY
PAR,2,.50,0.,,100.*             WORK STATION 2 SERVICE TIME PARAMETERS
STA,20/REP-TIME,1,1,,I*         COMPLETION OF REPAIR NODE
FIN*
```

Figure 4-21   Data input for maintenance facility analysis, Example 5.

Summary of Results

The final results for one run are shown in Figure 4-22. During the 300 time units for the run, 533 units were processed by the maintenance facility. The average time to process a unit through the maintenance facility was 3.09 time units. Since the processing times at work stations 1 and 2 were 0.25 and 0.50 time units on the average, it can be deduced that the waiting time of a unit on the average was 2.34 time units. The reason for this large waiting time is the poor allocation of storage areas before the two work stations. Clearly, more spaces should be allocated before work station 2 which is the slower work station. This will reduce blocking of work station 1.

```
GERT SIMULATION PROJECT MAINT-FAC-5  BY PRITSKER
           DATE  6/ 30/ 1977


      **FINAL RESULTS FOR FIRST SIMULATION**


          TOTAL ELAPSED TIME =    300.0000



             **NODE STATISTICS**

NODE    LABEL        AVE.      STD.DEV.   NO OF  STAT
                                         OBS.   TYPE

20     REP-TIME     3.0940     1.5203     533.   I
12     SUB-UNIT     1.3195     3.2958     224.   B



          **NUMBER IN Q-NODE**                  ** WAITING TIME **
                                                    IN QUEUE


NODE    LABEL       AVE.    MIN.  MAX.   CURRENT      AVERAGE
                                        NUMBER

10     WS1-QUE     2.2223    0    4.       3          1.2346
15     WS2-QUE     1.5137    0    2.       2           .8472



        **SERVER UTILIZATION**

SERVER   LABEL    NO. PARALLEL   AVE.       MAX. IDLE           MAX. BUSY
                   SERVERS             (TIME OR SERVERS)  (TIME OR SERVERS)

1      STATION1       1        .4756       1.5909              4.4962
2      STATION2       1        .9362       3.0177             31.7662



        **BLOCKED TIME PER UNIT TIME**

SERVER   LABEL       AVE.      LONGEST
                            PERIOD BLOCKED

1      STATION1      .4327      4.1380



        **NO. BALKING PER UNIT TIME**

NODE    LABEL       AVE.

10     WS1-QUE      .7506
```

Figure 4-22 Final results for first run of maintenance facility, Example 5.

This same conclusion can be reached by examining the Q-node statistics. The average number of units waiting in the queue of the first work station, Q-node 10, was 2.22. For the second work station, the average number was 1.51. The higher average number in the queue of the first work station is due to the amount of blocking of the first work station by the queue of the second work station. Thus, increasing the number of spaces for work station 2 should decrease the average number in Q-node 10.

The average time for node 12 provides an estimate of 1.32 for the average time between subcontracted units. There were 224 observations associated with node 12 and, therefore, there were 225 units that were subcontracted. Recall the time of first release of node 12 is not included in the "between" statistics calculation because it may not be a representative value.

The last line on Figure 4-22 shows that the average number balking per unit time is 0.75. This corresponds to the 225 units that arrived at node 12 divided by the 300 time units for the run. From this, one might infer that the average time between subcontracted units is 1.33 time units. However, this includes the time until the first balking unit and, hence, differs from the estimate obtained for node 12.

In the statistics for server utilization, it is seen that, on the average, the fraction of time that work station 1 is busy is 0.48. This means that work station 1 is working on units for 48 percent of the time. The output report also indicates that work station 1 is blocked 43 percent of the time. By decreasing the amount of time that work station 1 is blocked, work station 1 will decrease the queue of items waiting for it and reduce the number of units that have to be subcontracted. Work station 2 is busy over 93 percent of the time and, hence, any potential decreases in the processing time for work station 2 would be extremely advantageous.

By changing the storage space allocations at Q-nodes 10 and 15, the Q-GERT Analysis Program could be used for assessing the degree of improvement in system performance obtained by such a procedural change.

EXAMPLE 6. SIMULATION OF A PERT NETWORK

Problem Statement

PERT is a technique for evaluating and reviewing a project consisting of interdependent activities (75). Many books have been written that describe PERT modeling and analysis procedures (3,83,137). A PERT network is a graphical illustration of the relations between the activities of a program. PERT network symbols can be considered a subset of Q-GERT network symbols (17), hence, the Q-GERT Analysis Program can be used for analyzing PERT networks. This example will display a PERT network in Q-GERT network form and will illustrate how estimates for the times to achieve project milestones and project completion can be obtained without making the simplifying assumptions required by PERT analysis procedures.

A PERT network model of a repair and retrofit project is shown in Figure 4-23 and activity descriptions are given in Table 4-3. All activity times will be assumed to be triangularly distributed. For ease of description, activities have been aggregated. The activities relate to power units, instrumentation and a new assembly and involve standard types of operations.

Table 4-3. Description of Activities, Example 6.

Activity Number	Description	Mode	Minimum	Maximum	Average*
1	Disassemble power units and instrumentation	3	1	5	3
2	Install new assembly	6	3	9	6
3	Prepare for retrofit check	13	10	19	14
4	Clean, inspect and repair power units	9	3	12	8
5	Calibrate instrumentation	3	1	8	4
6	Check interfaces	9	8	16	11
7	Check assembly	7	4	13	8
8	Assemble and test power units	6	3	9	6
9	Retrofit check	3	1	8	4

* Assumes activity times are triangularly distributed. The average for the triangular distribution (111) is ⅓ (mode + minimum + maximum).

In the following description of the project, activity numbers are given in parentheses. At the beginning of the project, three parallel activities can be performed that involve: the disassembly of power units and instrumentation (1); the installation of a new assembly (2); and the preparation for a retrofit check (3). Cleaning, inspecting and repairing the power units (4) and calibrating the instrumentation (5) can only be done after the power units and instrumentation have been disassembled. Thus, activities 4 and 5 must follow activity 1 in the network. Following the installation of the new assembly (2) and after the instruments have

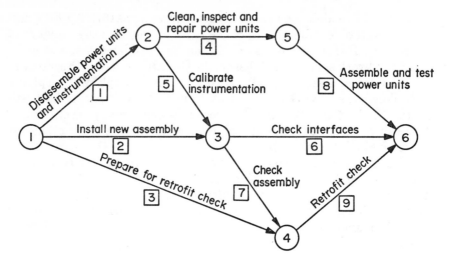

Figure 4-23   PERT network model of a retrofit project, Example 6.

been calibrated (5), a check of interfaces (6) and a check of the new assembly (7) can be made. The retrofit check (9) can be made after the assembly is checked (7) and the preparation for the retrofit check (3) have been completed. The assembly and test of power units (8) can be performed following the cleaning and maintenance of the power units (4). The project is considered completed when all 9 activities are completed. Since activities 6, 8 and 9 require the other activities to precede them, their completion signifies the end of the project. This is indicated on the network by having activities 6, 8 and 9 incident to node 6, the sink node for the project.

Q-GERT Model

The Q-GERT network model corresponding to the PERT network is shown in Figure 4-24. The Q-GERT network is similar to the PERT network with the addition of: 1) the number of first releases (equal to the number of incoming branches); 2) an infinite number for the number of subsequent releases; and 3) a specification that F statistics are to be collected at each node but the source node.

PERT network models have a very simple structure as indicated by

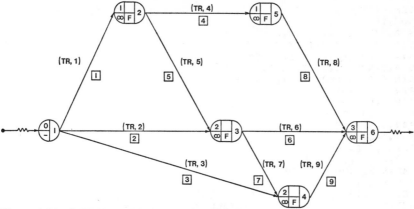

Figure 4-24   Q-GERT model of retrofit project, Example 6.

the following list of requirements imposed on the modeler using PERT networks:

1. The number of transactions to release a node is equal to the number of branches ending at the node.
2. All branching is done on a deterministic basis.
3. No Q-nodes are included in the network.
4. No cycles are allowed in the network.
5. The concept of a transaction is not employed in PERT.
6. Projects as represented by PERT networks will always be completed successfully as no failures can be modeled in the network. Thus, the analysis to be performed deals entirely with the time (or other additive variable) at which nodes of the network are released. In fact, PERT deals only with the time of first release of a node and does not consider delay type statistics for a node.

As can be seen from the above list, the PERT symbol set is quite restrictive. The data input for the Q-Gert Analysis Program for the PERT network given in Figure 4-24 is shown in Figure 4-25. Four hundred runs for the network analysis will be made. Additional fields for the GEN card are used to obtain a trace. Definitions for the additional fields are given in Chapter 6.

Summary of Results
A trace of the first run of this project is shown in Figure 4-26. At time zero, activities 1, 2 and 3 are started and their estimated times of com-

```
GEN,PRITSKER,RETRO-NET-6,6,23,1977,4,1,1,,400,(15)1,2*
SOU,1*
STA,2/NODE-2,1,(7)0,0.5*
STA,3/NODE-3,2,(7)3,0.5*
STA,4/NODE-4,2,(7)10,0.5*
STA,5/NODE-5,1,(7)12,0.5*
SIN,6/PROJCOMP,3,(7)15,0.5*
PAR,1,3,1,5*
PAR,2,6,3,9*
PAR,3,13,10,19*
PAR,4,9,3,12*
PAR,5,3,1,8*
PAR,6,9,8,16*
PAR,7,7,4,13*
PAR,8,6,3,9*
PAR,9,3,1,8*
ACT,1,2,TR,1,1*          DISASSEMBLE POWER UNITS
ACT,1,3,TR,2,2*          INSTALL NEW ASSEMBLY
ACT,1,4,TR,3,3*          PREPARE FOR RETROFIT
ACT,2,5,TR,4,4*          CLEAN, INSPECT, AND REPAIR POWER UNITS
ACT,2,3,TR,5,5*          CALIBRATE INSTRUMENTATION
ACT,3,6,TR,6,6*          CHECK INTERFACES
ACT,3,4,TR,7,7*          CHECK ASSEMBLY
ACT,4,6,TR,9,9*          RETROFIT CHECK
ACT,5,6,TR,8,8*          ASSEMBLE AND TEST POWER UNITS
FIN*
```

Figure 4-25   Data input for PERT network of retrofit project, Example 6.

pletion are 2.58, 4.91 and 11.68 respectively. At time 2.58, activity 1 is completed and since node 2 only requires one incoming transaction to release it, node 2 is released. (The trace highlights the occurrence of a transaction reaching a node by placing three asterisks in the start node column). Since statistics are collected at node 2, this release time is recorded. Activities 4 and 5 emanating from node 2 are now scheduled, and from the trace their completion times are 8.90 and 3.89 respectively. The next activity completion occurs at time 3.89 and is for activity 5. Since this is the first activity completion incident to node 3, node 3 is not released. The next activity completion is for activity 2 which releases node 3 at time 4.91. This time is recorded for later statistical output. The activities leaving node 3 are now scheduled. As shown on the trace, activity 4 is completed which releases node 5. Activity 8, from node 5 to node 6, is then started and scheduled to be completed at time 13.71. Activity 7 is completed at time 9.90 and activity 3 is completed at time 11.68. Thus, node 4 which requires both activities 7 and 3 to be completed is released at time 11.68. Activity 9 is scheduled from node 4 to be completed at time 16.95. Since the largest completion time of an activity incident to node 6 is 16.95, node 6 is released at time 16.95. Thus, on the first run, the time to perform the project is 16.95.

** TRACE **

	START NODE	END NODE	START TIME	END TIME	ACTIVITY NUMBER	MARK TIME	TRANS. NUMBER
RUN NO. 1							
	1	2	0	2.58	1	0	1
	1	3	0	4.91	2	0	2
	1	4	0	11.68	3	0	3
	***	2		2.58	1	0	1
	2	5	2.58	8.90	4	0	1
	2	3	2.58	3.89	5	0	4
	***	3		3.89	5	0	4
	***	3		4.91	2	0	2
	3	6	4.91	16.24	6	0	2
	3	4	4.91	9.90	7	0	4
	***	5		8.90	4	0	1
	5	6	8.90	13.71	8	0	1
	***	4		9.90	7	0	4
	***	4		11.68	3	0	3
	4	6	11.68	16.95	9	0	3
	***	6		13.71	8	0	1
	***	6		16.24	6	0	2
	***	6		16.95	9	0	3

Figure 4-26   Trace of activity start and end times for Run 1, Example 6.

The results from this first simulation run of the time to release each node is shown in Figure 4-27. This output provides, in summary form, the statistics collected as described in the explanation of the output trace.

GERT SIMULATION PROJECT RETRO-NET-6   BY PRITSKER
DATE   5/ 23/ 1977

FINAL RESULTS FOR FIRST SIMULATION

TOTAL ELAPSED TIME =   16.9478

NODE STATISTICS

NODE	LABEL	AVE.	STD.DEV.	NO OF OBS.	STAT TYPE
6	PROJCOMP	16.9478	0	1.	F
5	NODE-5	8.8972	0	1.	F
4	NODE-4	11.6813	0	1.	F
3	NODE-3	4.9128	0	1.	F
2	NODE-2	2.5802	0	1.	F

Figure 4-27   Times to release nodes in a retrofit project on Run 1, Example 6.

In Figure 4-28, another run for the network is traced to show how the random sampling for the activity times can produce a different pattern of completion times and nodal releases.

TRACE

	START NODE	END NODE	START TIME	END TIME	ACTIVITY NUMBER	MARK TIME	TRANS. NUMBER
RUN NO. 2							
	1	2	0	4.54	1	0	1
	1	3	0	4.90	2	0	2
	1	4	0	13.37	3	0	3
	***	2		4.54	1	0	1
	2	5	4.54	9.56	4	0	1
	2	3	4.54	7.80	5	0	4
	***	3		4.90	2	0	2
	***	3		7.80	5	0	4
	3	6	7.80	20.51	6	0	4
	3	4	7.80	19.26	7	0	2
	***	5		9.56	4	0	1
	5	6	9.56	14.25	8	0	1
	***	4		13.37	3	0	3
	***	6		14.25	8	0	1
	***	4		19.26	7	0	2
	4	6	19.26	22.37	9	0	2
	***	6		20.51	6	0	4
	***	6		22.37	9	0	2

Figure 4-28   Trace of activity start and end times for Run 2, Example 6.

The final summary report for 400 simulation runs of the network is shown in Figure 4-29. The average time to complete the project is 20.74 time units with a standard deviation of 2.05 time units. Four hundred independent observations were made on the project completion time and the estimate of the standard deviation of the average time to complete the project is approximately 0.10 time units. By the central limit theorem, the average project duration is approximately normally distributed and we estimate with 99.7% confidence that the project duration would be between 20.44 and 21.04 time units by using three standard deviation confidence limits.

The average values for nodes 5, 4, 3 and 2 provide estimates of the average starting times for activities emanating from these nodes. Additional information concerning all nodes is available on the histograms obtained as part of the standard Q-GERT output. The histogram for project completion, node 6, is shown in Figure 4-30. From Figure 4-30, estimates of the probability that the project will be completed by a certain time can be made. Thus, it is estimated that the probability of the project being completed by 19 time units is 0.222, and, hence, the probability of the project taking more than 19 time units is 0.778.

GERT SIMULATION PROJECT RETRO-NET-6   BY PRITSKER
DATE 6/ 23/ 1977

FINAL RESULTS FOR   400 SIMULATIONS

AVERAGE NODE STATISTICS

NODE	LABEL	PROBABILITY	AVE.	STD.DEV.	SD OF AVE	NO OF OBS.	MIN.	MAX.	STAT TYPE
6	PROJCOMP	1.0000	20.7389	2.0498	.1025	400.	15.3113	27.8492	F
5	NODE-5	1.0000	10.9607	1.9748	.0987	400.	6.1025	15.6519	F
4	NODE-4	1.0000	16.0487	1.9842	.0992	400.	10.5848	22.5087	F
3	NODE-3	1.0000	7.2893	1.3700	.0685	400.	4.1636	11.0536	F
2	NODE-2	1.0000	2.9350	.7876	.0394	400.	1.0326	4.7145	F

Figure 4-29   Final summary report for 400 simulation runs of retrofit project, Example 6.

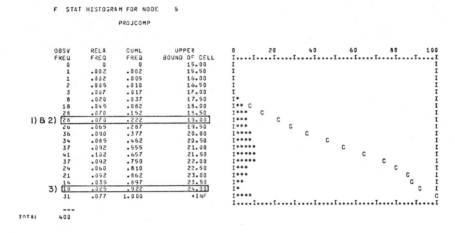

Interpretive statements:
1. Probability of project completion by 19 time units = 0.222.
2. Probability of project taking more than 19 time units = 1 − 0.222
   =   0.778.
3. Probability of project taking more than 24 time units = 1 − 0.922
   =   0.078.

Figure 4-30   Histogram of retrofit project completion time, Example 6.

A PERT analysis for this project is presented in Table 4-4. In the PERT analysis, deterministic times were assumed for each activity equal to the average value of the triangular distribution. Values for the early start and early finish time for each activity are computed first. The start time of each activity leaving the source node is specified as zero and the early finish time for each of these activities is then computed by adding the duration time to the early start time. The early start time of activities released due to the completion of other activities is then recorded. Since a completion of activity 1 releases node 2 at time 3, the early start time for activities 4 and 5 is inserted in Table 4-4 with a value of 3. The early finish time for these activities is then computed by adding the duration to the early start time. This gives the values 11 and 7 in the column headed Early Finish for activities 4 and 5. When activity 5 and activity 2 are completed, node 3 is released and activities 6 and 7 can be started. Node 3 is released at time 7 (the maximum of 6 and 7) and the early finish time for activities 6 and 7 is computed as 18 and 15 respectively. Activity 8 can be started when node 4 is completed which is at time 11, and its early finish time is then 17. Activity 9 can be started when activities 3 and 7 are completed which occurs at time 15 and the completion of activity 9 occurs at time 19. The maximum of the completion times for activities 6, 8 and 9 is 19, and this is defined as the expected project duration.

Table 4-4.   PERT Analysis of Network of Example 6.

Activity Number	Duration	Early Start ES	Early Finish EF	Late Start LS	Late Finish LF	Total Float (LF–EF)	Activity on Critical Path
1	3	0	3	0	3	0	*
2	6	0	6	1	7	1	
3	14	0	14	1	15	1	
4	8	3	11	5	13	2	
5	4	3	7	3	7	0	*
6	11	7	18	8	19	1	
7	8	7	15	7	15	0	*
8	6	11	17	13	19	2	
9	4	15	19	15	19	0	*

The late start times and late finish times presented in Table 4-4 are obtained by working backwards through the network starting at node 6 and assigning a late finish time of 19 to those activities that are incident to node 6. The late start time is obtained by subtracting the duration from the late finish time. The late finish time for other activities in the network is computed as the minimum of the late start times. The late finish time for activities 3 and 7 are equal to the late start time of activity 9, that is, 15. The late start time for activity 7 then is 15–8=7. The late finish time for activities incident to node 3 is then the minimum of 7 and 8 and is equal to 7. Thus, for activities 2 and 5, the late finish time is 7. The other values for late start and late finish times presented in Table 4-4 are computed in a similar manner.

The total float for an activity is defined as the late finish time minus the early finish time (or equivalently the late start time minus the early start time). This represents the amount of time the activity could be delayed without affecting the total project duration based on constant activity times. If an activity has zero total float, it is said to be on the critical path. Those activities on the critical path for the network of Example 6 are indicated by an asterisk in Table 4-4.

From the above analysis, PERT estimates the average project completion time as 19 and Q-GERT estimates a value of 20.74. From the histogram presented in Figure 4-30, the estimated probability of completing the project by the PERT estimate of 19 time units is only 0.222. Thus, Q-GERT estimates there is a 77.8 percent chance that the PERT estimate is optimistic.

The expected node release times for PERT and Q-GERT are listed in Table 4-5. The Q-GERT estimates are taken directly from Figure 4-29. The PERT values are obtained from Table 4-4, and are the early start times for activities leaving the node.

Table 4-5. Expected Node Release Times

Node	PERT	Q-GERT
2	3	2.94
3	7	7.29
4	15	16.05
5	11	10.96
6	19	20.74

In Table 4-5, it is seen that the node release times for nodes 2 and 5 compare favorably. The reason for this is that only one activity is required to release these nodes, and the release time is the sum of the times of a sequence of activities. Thus, the time to release node 2 is the time to complete activity 1. The expected release time for node 2 should then be the expected time to complete activity 1 which is 3. Similarly, the time to release node 5 is the sum of the times to complete activities 1 and 4. Thus, the expected time to release node 5 is the sum of the expected times to complete activities 1 and 4. For the other node release times, more than one activity must be completed to release the node and a maximum of activity times must be obtained to determine the node release time. The PERT analysis assumes that the maximum of the expected times is a good estimate of the expected value of the maximum time. As the Q-GERT analysis shows this is not always a good assumption.* The values obtained by the Q-GERT Analysis Program are better estimates of the node release times and can be used to provide improved project planning and analysis.

This example illustrates the use of Q-GERT in project planning. Two other examples of the use of Q-GERT in project planning are given in this book. The computation of criticality indices for this example is described in Example 10. The procedure for including costs for activities and for performing a cost analysis for a GERT network are described in Chapter 9, Example 14.

*Better estimation procedures for project duration than the PERT procedure have been developed (31,43,67).

EXERCISES

4-1. Modify the Q-GERT model of the inspection and adjustment stations, Example 1, to accommodate the following changes:

a) an arrival of television sets to the inspection station involves two television sets to be inspected;

b) the adjustor routes 40% of the adjusted sets directly to packing and 60% back to the inspectors;

c) by adding a step to the inspection process, it is felt that the probability of sending a set to the adjustor can be decreased to 0.10; the added step takes 5 minutes.

Redraw the network to indicate these changes. For one of the above situations, run the Q-GERT Analysis Program and analyze the results.

4-2. In the paint shop example, the operations of preparation and painting were required. Consider now that a drying operation following painting is to be performed. Drying requires 15 minutes and does not require a workman. Include this embellishment on the Q-GERT network presented in Figure 4-6. With this addition, what changes would you expect in the statistical quantities of interest.

4-3. Based on the statistical summary for 5, 6 and 7 workmen presented in Table 4-2, what changes would you expect as the number of workmen is increased to 8, 9 and 10? Develop a cost (profit) structure by which you could ascertain the number of workmen that should be hired.

4-4. For the production system example involving sewing machine breakdowns and repair, Example 3, redevelop the Q-GERT network and run the Q-GERT Analysis program to obtain estimates of the following quantities:

a) time between breakdowns of sewing machines;

b) time in operation for a sewing machine;

c) the cycle time of a sewing machine where the cycle time is the sum of waiting times, sewing time and repair time.

4-5. For Example 3, assume that no spare sewing machines are available at the beginning of the run, that is, all 4 spares are in a failed state. Draw the Q-GERT network for this situation.

4-6. For the sewing machine example, assume that management has decided to operate with only two repairmen. To compensate for the decrease in the number of repairmen, the subcontracting of the repair of sewing machines has been established. Whenever the queue of failed machines reaches 2, the repair of sewing machines will be subcontracted to an outside agency. When this occurs, 20 to 30 hours, uniformly distributed, are required until the machine is again available to be placed into production. Draw the Q-GERT network for this situation and employ the Q-GERT Analysis Program to assess the statistical quantities associated with such subcontracting. What financial considerations must be given when evaluating this new mode of operation compared to the original procedures?

4-7. For the conveyor situation presented in Example 4, assess the increased performance obtained by allowing a one item buffer before each server. Based on the results of this study, specify how you would allocate ten buffer spaces to the five servers.

4-8. Discuss how you would evaluate the tradeoffs involved between reducing the number of servers in the conveyor systems versus increasing the buffer size associated with each server.

4-9. For the conveyor system, discuss and test the ramifications of increasing the speed of the conveyor belt. Modify the network to count the number of items that are recycled and the congestion on the branch from node 12 to node 3.

4-10. For the maintenance facility situation involving work stations in series, Example 5, analyze the results and redistribute the six storage spaces to work station 1 and work station 2. Test your alternative design using the Q-GERT Analysis Program. If you were to begin a research and development program for improving the production line, on what quantity would you place your initial efforts?

4-11. For Example 5, suppose the company only has twenty-five units that require maintenance. The time between maintenance operations for each of these 25 units is exponentially distributed with a mean of 0.4 time units. Redraw the Q-GERT network for this situation assuming that units subcontracted require 4 time units before being returned to operation.

4-12. Simulate the activities of the PERT network described below 400 times. Compute statistics and prepare a histogram on the time to reach each node of the network. Compare the results with the PERT calculations for the network (111).

Activity Number	Start Node	End Node	Distribution Type	Mean	Variance
1	10	2	Lognormal	10	4.00
2	10	3	Exponential	6	36.00
3	2	4	Uniform	7	3.00
4	2	9	Gamma	14	21.00
5	3	2	Beta	8	4.71
6	3	4	Uniform	13	5.33
7	3	6	Normal	5	1.00
8	4	9	Erlang	8	32.00
9	6	5	Constant	7	0.00
10	6	7	Normal	4	2.16
11	6	7	Normal	4	3.00
12	5	4	Normal	2	1.20
13	5	8	Normal	6	10.40
14	7	8	Normal	8	26.40
15	8	9	Normal	5	2.00

4-13. Based on the Q-GERT simulation of a PERT network, Exercise 4-12, develop a schedule of early start times and late start times for the activities in the network.

4-14. Simulate the network of example 6 assuming each activity time is Beta distributed with the same mode, minimum and maximum.

4-15. Use the Q-GERT Analysis Program to simulate a PERT network in which activities have a probability of failing.

CHAPTER 5

INTERMEDIATE Q-GERT CONCEPTS

In this chapter, intermediate Q-GERT concepts are presented. The concepts described are translated into network symbols for use in network modeling. The procedures for describing these new symbols to the Q-GERT Analysis Program are specified, and examples of the modeling and input procedures are included. The intermediate Q-GERT concepts presented in this chapter relate to the following characteristics.

1. Associating attributes with transactions.
   a) Assigning attributes to transactions.
   b) Ranking transactions in Q-nodes based on attribute values.
   c) Routing transactions based on attribute values.
2. S-nodes: Nodes to select from among available servers and/or queues.
   a) Routing transactions to parallel Q-nodes.
   b) Removing transactions from parallel Q-nodes.
   c) Selecting from among parallel nonidentical servers.
   d) Assembling different transactions prior to service.
3. Match node: A node that halts the flow of transactions until a set of transactions with a common attribute value has arrived to it.
4. Nodal modification: The conditional replacement of a node by another node.

The presentation of intermediate Q-GERT concepts completes the description of the network symbols available in Q-GERT. The advanced concepts presented in Chapter 7 relate to the procedures for including programming inserts into Q-GERT and the subprograms available to assist the user in writing such inserts.

ATTRIBUTES OF TRANSACTIONS

In the chapter on basic Q-GERT concepts, it was stated that transactions can have attributes. One attribute that every transaction has is its mark time. As previously described, the mark time is the time at which a transaction passes through a node that performs the marking function. *All source nodes automatically mark transactions.* Thus, every transaction leaving a source node is marked with the time it leaves the source node.

The values assigned to attributes give a transaction an identity. Therefore, attributes can be used to distinguish between types of transactions and to differentiate between transactions of the same type. Attributes are used to affect three fundamental aspects of network logic:
  1. The specification of the time required for an activity to process the transaction;
  2. The ranking of transactions in queues; and
  3. The routing of transactions (branching).
By using attributes, a modeler can incorporate a significant amount of flexibility in a Q-GERT network. This flexibility results from having a network process transactions differently based on the attribute values of the transactions.

Q-GERT provides procedures that allow the modeler to assign attributes to transactions at different nodes in the network. The procedures for assigning attributes to transactions and the building of networks to process transactions in accordance with their attribute values is discussed in the following sections.

Assigning Attribute Values to Transactions

The number of attributes associated with each transaction in the network is defined by the modeler through data input. In addition to the user defined attribute values, a transaction's mark time is automatically considered as one of its attribute values. Just as with the mark time, the assignment of attribute values to a transaction is made at a node. *Any node in a Q-GERT network can be used to perform this assignment function.* Only when a transaction passes through the node will the values be assigned.

When specifying an assignment of an attribute value to a transaction, the attribute number and the computational procedure for obtaining the value for the attribute are prescribed. The attribute number to which a value is to be assigned is set by the modeler based on the situation that he is modeling. The modeler prescribes the value to be assigned in the same manner as he prescribes the time to perform an activity. That is, he specifies a function type and a parameter identifier. Thus, attribute values can be obtained from any of the following functions:

BE, beta distribution;
BP, beta distribution fitted to three parameters;
CO, constant;
ER, Erlang distribution;
EX, exponential distribution;
GA, gamma distribution;
IN, incremental function;
LO, lognormal distribution;
NO, normal distribution;
PO, Poisson distribution;
TR, triangular distribution;
UF or US, user function or subroutine; and
UN, uniform distribution.

The symbolism associated with *value assignment* (VAS) is placed in the central portion of the node just prior to the node number. For each assignment to be made, three items of information are required: the attribute number; the label for the function type; and the parameter identifier.

Examples of Attribute Assignments

Let us look at some examples of attribute assignments. Suppose we desire to assign a value to attribute 1 at node 6. The value assigned is to be a sample from a normal distribution that has parameters as given in parameter set number 3. The symbolism for node 6 is given on page 135.
Every transaction passing through node 6 receives a new value for attribute 1. The value assigned is a sample from a normal distribution. Any previous value of attribute 1 associated with the transaction is lost. The values of other attributes are unaffected by this value assignment. Furthermore, transactions that do not flow through node 6 are not affected by the specification given at node 6. Recall there is no passage of time at a node, and it is presumed that the assignment of values is made

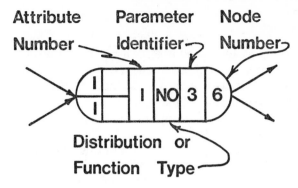

Attribute Parameter Node
Number Identifier Number

Distribution or
Function Type

instantaneously. Every transaction leaving node 6 will have an attribute 1 value that was obtained as a sample from a normal distribution.

To illustrate the symbolism for multiple attribute assignments at a node, suppose it is desired to assign at node 7 a value of 10 to attribute 1 and a value of 30 to attribute 3. Further assume that interval statistics are collected at node 7.

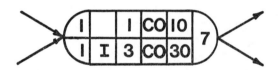

From this symbolism, it is seen that the value assignment information is placed in the middle of the node after the specification that node 7 is a statistics node. (The blank space above the statistics code would be used to specify the choice criterion which is only needed if input requirements are greater than 1.) Assignments are made in the order specified on input which normally corresponds to the top to bottom specification used at the node. The above notation indicates that attribute 1 is assigned a value of 10 and then a value of 30 is assigned to attribute 3.

It should be clear that attributes are associated with transactions. Each transaction has a unique set of attributes that flow along with it through the network. A node can be used to define or change attribute values as a transaction passes through it. As stated above, the values assigned at a node changes only those attributes for which a VAS specification is made. If assignments for attributes 1 and 3 are to be made at a node, then every transaction passing through the node will retain its previously assigned value for attribute 2.

The Use of Attributes

Before describing other procedures for assigning values to attributes, a brief discussion of the use of attribute values seems appropriate. If, in a highway model, attribute 1 is set to 1 to indicate that a vehicle is a car and to 2 to indicate that a vehicle is a truck, then as transactions flow through the network, the testing of attribute 1 could be used to distinguish between cars and trucks. By using the conditional branching features of Q-GERT to be presented later in this chapter, different routings of cars and trucks can be modeled directly into the network structure. In this way, different types of transactions that require the same server at one time but specialized service at another time can be modeled in Q-GERT.

Another use of attribute values is to differentiate between transactions of the same type. For example, trucks may be characterized by size. There can be twenty-ton trucks and fifty-ton trucks. By assigning the value 20 to attribute 2 in the above example, a twenty-ton truck can be defined. If attribute 2 has the value 50, the transaction would represent a fifty-ton truck.

Another use of attribute values is to store the service times associated with transactions. As we shall see shortly, the time to perform an activity can be taken directly from an attribute value of a transaction flowing through a branch. When service times are prescribed as an attribute of a transaction, then the transactions can be ranked in queues based on the service time and processed in the order of shortest service time first or largest service time first. Other examples of the use of attribute values will be presented in the following chapter which presents applications that use intermediate Q-GERT concepts.

Special Procedures for Assigning Attributes

A plus sign appended to the attribute number specifies that the modeler desires to add a value to the current value of the attribute. If the modeler appends a negative sign to the attribute number then a value is to be subtracted from the current value of the attribute.

Suppose it is desired to assign a sample from a triangular distribution with parameters as specified by parameter set 4 to attribute 2. In addition, it is desired to add the value 3 to attribute 4. These value assignments are to be made at node 8 which is also used to collect interval statistics. The symbolism for node 8 is shown below.

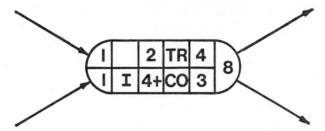

A new value is assigned to attribute 2 using the (TR,4) specification. The second value assignment specification indicates an addition is to be made to the current value of attribute 4. The specification of (CO,3) causes the value 3 to be added to the current value of attribute 4.

A special function that assigns a sequential value to each transaction flowing through a node has been included in Q-GERT. The functional type is called "incremental assignment" and is abbreviated as IN. The specification (IN,1) assigns the value 1 to the first transaction passing through the node, the value 2 to the second transaction passing through the node, and so on. The parameter identifier is used here to specify the initial number assigned to the first transaction passing through the node. An assignment value indexed by 1 is then assigned for each subsequent transaction passing through the node. Thus, the notation (IN,-3) would produce the following sequence of assignments to transactions: -3, -2, -1, 0, 1, . . .

Another function included in Q-GERT involves the direct use of an attribute value. The function is abbreviated as AT. The attribute value can be used as either an activity time or in a value assignment. First, consider its use in assigning a new value to an attribute. Suppose it is desired to assign a sample from an exponential distribution using parameter set number 3 to attribute 1. In addition, it is desired to add the value assigned to attribute 1 to the current value of attribute 2. These assignments are to be made at node 9. At node 9, shown below, a new value that is a sample from an exponential distribution is given to attribute 1.

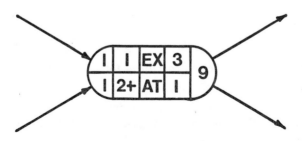

This specific sample is then added to the current value of the transaction's attribute 2. Recall that the order of assignment is determined on input. The notation here indicates that in a given transaction, attribute 1 is added to attribute 2 after attribute 1 has been defined for that transaction.

As stated above, attribute values can be used directly as activity times. This is accomplished by using the AT specification for a branch. Thus, if the specification (AT,1) is assigned to a branch, then the time for a transaction to traverse the branch is the value of attribute 1 of the transaction.

Data Input of Value Assignments to Attributes

Value assignment information for the Q-GERT Analysis Program is prepared on a separate data input card. The code letters for this card are VAS and the field descriptions are listed below:

Field	Description	Default Value
1	Card Type, VAS	none
2	Node number at which assignment is to be made	none
3	Attribute number	1
4	Distribution or function type	CO
5	Parameter identifier	0.0

Fields 3, 4 and 5 can be repeated as: Fields 6, 7 and 8; Fields 9, 10 and 11; and so on to make up to eight value assignments at the node specified by Field 2. Only one VAS card for each node is permitted.

Examples of the VAS data input are shown below for the illustrations in the previous section.

Example Illustrating Special Procedures for Assigning Attributes

Consider the situation where there are two classes of arrivals that seek service. Suppose that the service activity represents a numerically con-

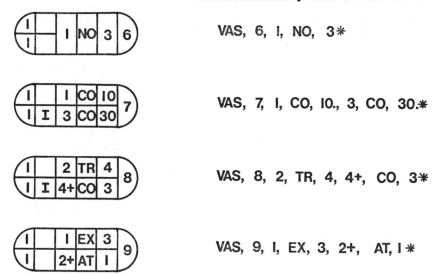

VAS, 6, I, NO, 3*

VAS, 7, I, CO, IO., 3, CO, 30.*

VAS, 8, 2, TR, 4, 4+, CO, 3*

VAS, 9, I, EX, 3, 2+, AT, I *

trolled machine tool that has the capability of performing several operations. Jobs arrive that require either one or two operations. From past data, it has been determined that 20 percent of the arriving jobs require two operations and 80 percent require one operation. The time required to perform the first operation is normally distributed using parameter set number 2. If a second operation is required, the time to perform it is uniformly distributed using parameter set number 3. Thus, 80 percent of the jobs that seek service from the numerically controlled machine tool will have a processing time that is normally distributed and 20 percent of the arriving jobs will have a processing time that is the sum of a normally distributed value and a uniformly distributed value. The network model of this situation is shown below. Again the system is easily

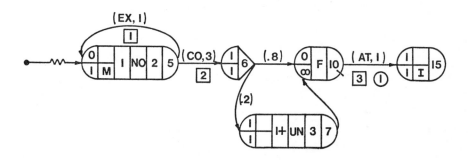

modeled by adapting the one server, single queue system. Jobs are represented by the transactions flowing through the system. At node 5, the time to perform operation 1 is assigned to attribute 1. The transaction representing the arriving job is then routed to node 6. The branch from node 5 to node 5 (activity 1) models the interarrival time of jobs. At node 6, 80 percent of the transactions are routed directly to Q-node 10 and 20 percent of the jobs are routed to node 7 where the value of attribute 1 is increased by a sample from a uniform distribution. Following node 7, the transactions are routed to node 10; however, attribute 1 now contains the sum of the two operation times. The branch from node 10 to node 15 represents the service activity of the numerically controlled machine. Note that there are no times on the branches from node 6 to node 10, node 6 to node 7, and node 7 to node 10. These branches are only used to segregate transactions according to whether one or two operations are required. Therefore, zero time delays are associated with these branches.

Another model of the numerically controlled machine tool system can be made. Instead of knowing the fraction of arriving jobs that require one or two operations, data may be available on the interarrival time of jobs of a given class. When this is the case, the system can be modeled with two source nodes: one source node generates jobs that require only one operation and the other source node generates jobs that require two operations. Transactions representing either type of job are routed directly to node 10 for processing. The network model of this system is shown below. Note in this case, the basic queueing system (nodes 5, 10

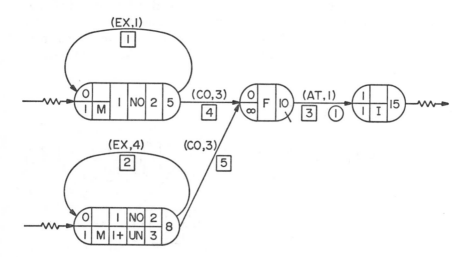

and 15) remains intact and only a source node and two branches are added to the network to represent the alternate arrival of jobs. At node 8, the processing time for jobs requiring two operations is generated by assigning first a sample from a normal distribution to attribute 1 and then adding a sample from a uniform distribution to attribute 1. The transaction is then routed to node 10. At the same time, the next job that requires two operations is scheduled with the interarrival time of such jobs being exponentially distributed with parameters as given in parameter set number 4.

Attribute Assignments at Q-Nodes

As stated earlier, the assignment of attribute values to transactions can be made at any node of the network. In particular, value assignments can be made at Q-nodes. For example, if it is desired to record the order in which transactions are removed from a queue, the incremental assignment function can be used. This is illustrated below. At Q-node 12,

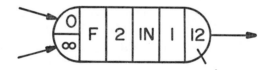

transactions are ranked in the queue on a first-in, first-out basis. When a transaction is removed from the queue, just before it is put into service, a new value is assigned to attribute 2. This new value is obtained from the incremental function and essentially prescribes a value for attribute 2 equal to the order in which the transaction is removed from the queue. Thus, if attribute 2 equals 1, the transaction was the first one taken from the queue at Q-node 12 and put into service. If attribute 2 of a transaction equals 4, it was the fourth transaction taken from the queue and put into service. This information could be used in a later portion of the network model if it is necessary to process jobs in the same order. Input information to the Q-GERT Analysis Program would be made using a VAS card that references node 12. The next section describes the procedures for ranking transactions in queues based on an attribute value.

Attribute Based Queue Ranking

Attributes can be used to govern the ranking of transactions in queues. Recall from Chapter 2 that transaction were ranked either *first*-in, first-out or *last*-in, first-out. In this chapter, we introduce the capability to rank queues with priority given to *big* or *small* values of a specified attribute.

To introduce the notation involved in designating attribute based queue ranking, consider a construction system where we are modeling transactions that represent twenty-ton and fifty-ton trucks. Suppose we wish to rank a maintenance area queue so that fifty-ton trucks are serviced before twenty-ton trucks. If the queue of trucks is represented by Q-node 4 and attribute 2 is 20 for the small trucks and 50 for the large trucks, the notation would be:

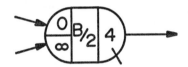

The B/2 ranking specifies that transactions with *big* values of attribute 2 are given priority. For Q-node 4, this means the transactions are ordered so that the transaction with the largest value of attribute 2 is always first in the queue. The second transaction in the queue will have the second largest value of attribute 2. The third will have the third largest and so on. Should a transaction arrive at the queue with a value of attribute 2 greater than the currently ranked second transaction but less than the first ranked transaction, then the new arrival will assume second place in the queue. If two or more transactions have the same value for the ranking attribute, then the order within this group of transactions is determined by the time of arrival to the queue. Priority goes to the early arrivals. That is to say, the secondary ranking rule, or tie breaking rule, is first-in first-out (FIFO).

If queue ranking is based on small values of attribute 2, the notation is S/2 (small-value-first on attribute 2). The tie breaking rule is again FIFO.

To rank transactions in a queue based on their mark times,* the attribute specification should be B/M or S/M.

---

* Mark times are carried as the largest attribute number plus 1. Thus, if 5 attributes are specified for transactions, the mark time is stored as attribute 6 of the transaction.

Data Input for Ranking Transactions in Q-nodes

In Chapter 3, the QUE card was discussed for specifying the characteristics of a Q-node to the Q-GERT Analysis Program. Field 6 of the QUE card is used for specifying the ranking procedure of a Q-node. Previously, only F → FIFO and L → LIFO procedures were discussed (since attribute values had not yet been introduced). As discussed above, transactions can be ranked in a Q-node based on *big* (B) values or *small* (S) values of an attribute. Thus, the choices for Field 6 of the QUE card are expanded to: F → FIFO, L → LIFO, B → Big and S → Small. If Field 6 is prescribed as B or S, then the attribute associated with the ranking is prescribed by following the B or S with a slash (/) and specifying the attribute number after the slash. The specification, S/2, for Field 6 indicates that ranking is based on small values first of attribute 2. For Q-node 4 presented in the previous section, the QUE card would be

   QUE,4,0,,D,B/2*

The flexibility that exists in assigning values to attributes, combined with the capability to rank queues on attribute values, introduces additional modeling power into Q-GERT. The following examples embellish the single server queueing system to incorporate attribute assignment, attribute based queue ranking and attribute defined activity times.

Example Illustrating Queue Ranking

In our previous models of the one server, single queue system, a first-in, first-out queue discipline rule was used. It is now desired to model the system using a shortest processing time rule, that is, to serve the transactions that have the smallest processing time first. In order to include this rule in the model, it is necessary to assign the processing time of a transaction prior to encountering the service operation. This will be accomplished by assigning the service time of a transaction to attribute 1 of the transaction. Transactions will then be ranked at Q-node 10 based on the smallest value of attribute 1 and the processing time for the service activity will be taken from attribute 1 of the transaction. Again, we will assume that interarrival times are exponentially distributed with parameter set number 1 and that service times are normally distributed with parameter set number 2. The network model and data input for this situation is shown below.

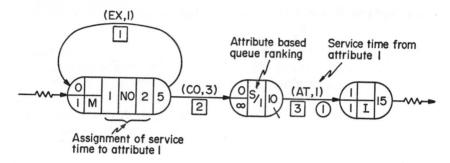

GEN,PRITSKER,111,7,19,1977,0,1,100,10,(14)1*
SOU,5,0,1,D,M*
VAS,5,1,NO,2*
PAR,2,10.,0.,100.,2.*
ACT,5,5,EX,1,1*
PAR,1,15.,0.,100.*
ACT,5,10,CO,3.,2*
QUE,10,0,,D,S/1*
ACT,10,15,AT,1,3,1*
SIN,15,1,1,,I,5.,2.*
FIN*

For this model, note that the *structure* of the network has not been altered. The only addition is the value assignment made at node 5. Other changes are the ranking rule specified for Q-node 10 and the function specification for the service time for server number 3. The ease of changing the model specification illustrates the versatility of Q-GERT. The transactions could be processed with the largest value of service time first by specifying a B/1 ranking rule (*big* value first on attribute 1) at node 10.

Conditional Branching and the Use of Attributes in Transaction Routing

The routing of transactions through a network using deterministic branching and probabilistic branching has been discussed. To review, with deterministic branching, transactions with identical attribute values are generated and multiple routings are accomplished. With probabilistic branching, one of a set of branches is selected and the transaction is routed over the branch selected. Neither of these methods for routing transactions involves the assessment of the current status of the system or the attribute values associated with the transaction being routed. To take advantage of this additional information, two other branching types are available in Q-GERT. These branching types are *conditional branching - take first* and *conditional branching - take all.*

For conditional branching, a condition is specified that must be satisfied if the transaction is to be routed through the branch. Conditions are specified in terms of four system or transaction attributes:

1. the time at which routing is to occur;
2. the prior release of a node;
3. the value of an attribute in comparison to a criterion value; and
4. the value of an attribute in comparison with another attribute value.

These four types of conditions result in twenty-eight different possible specifications for a branch. A description of the condition codes to describe the alternatives is given in Table 5–1.

To specify graphically a condition for a branch, the condition code is placed above the branch in the same position as is done for the probability value when probabilistic branching is performed. Note that the specification of a probability to a branch excludes the possibility of assigning a condition code and vice versa. Condition codes are only specified on branches emanating from nodes for which conditional-take first or conditional-take all branching has been prescribed. A node with conditional-take first branching is drawn as $\square$. A node with conditional-take all branching is drawn as $\square$. For conditional-take first branching, the conditions specified on the branches are evaluated in order and the transaction is routed along the first branch for which the condition is satisfied. As soon as one condition is found that is satisfied, the activity on that branch is scheduled and the other conditions are not evaluated. For conditional-take all branching, *every condition* is evaluated and a duplicate of the transaction is routed along each branch for which the condition is satisfied. If no condition is satisfied for either type of conditional branching, a warning message is printed and the program continues.

Table 5–1. Condition Codes for Routing Transactions over Branches

<u>Condition Codes *</u>

> T.R.V
> T.R.Ak
> Aj.R.V
> Aj.R.Ak
> Ni.R
> Ni.NR
> NAj.R
> NAj.NR

where

> T is the current simulation time (TNOW), that is, the time at which conditional branching is taking place
>
> V is a constant value
>
> Aj and Ak are the values of attributes j and k of the transaction for which routing is being determined
>
> R is a relational operator. The possible operators are: LT; LE; EQ; NE; GT; and GE
>
> Ni is node number i
>
> NAj is the node number specified by the value of attribute j of the transaction for which routing is being determined
>
> R stands for released
>
> NR stands for not released

<u>Examples</u>

Specification	Route Transaction Through Branch if
T.LT.10.0	Current time less than 10
T.GT.A3	Current time greater than attribute 3
A2.EQ.4.0	The value of attribute 2 is equal to 4
A2.NE.A3	The value of attribute 2 is not equal to the value of attribute 3.
N5.R	Node 5 has been released
NA3.NR	Node number specified by attribute 3 has not been released

* There are 28 possible condition codes that can be specified for a branch.

146

An example of conditional-take first branching is given below:

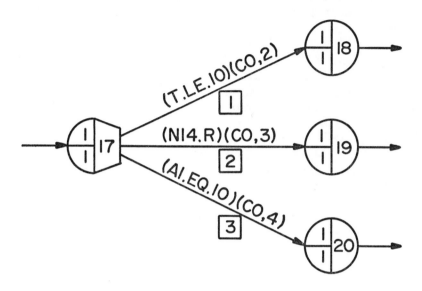

When a transaction arrives at node 17, it causes node 17 to be released since only one incoming transaction is required. Since the output side of node 17 indicates that conditional-take first branching is to occur, the condition on each branch emanating from node 17 is evaluated. Typically, the modeler draws the branches in the order in which he desires the evaluations to be made, starting with the topmost branch and proceeding downward (the order in which the branches are evaluated by the Q-GERT program is specified in Field 8 of the ACT input card by the user).

For our purposes, consider that the graphical convention described above is used by the modeler. The transaction will be routed through activity 1 to node 18 if the current time is less than or equal to 10. The current time is the time the transaction reached node 17. This condition is represented by the notation (T.LE.10.): time less than or equal to the value of 10. If this is the case, the transaction will encounter a two time unit delay (CO,2) and be routed to node 18. No further evaluations of conditions at node 17 would occur. If the current time is greater than 10, then the condition on the branch from node 17 to node 19 is evaluated. The condition specified here (N14.R) indicates that the transaction should be routed through this branch if node 14 has been released prior to the release of node 17. If this is the case, the transaction is routed through activity 2 where it incurs a time delay of three time units (CO,3) before it arrives at node 19. The condition specified on the branch from node 17 to node 20 indicates that the transaction should be routed through this branch if the value of attribute 1 of the transaction is equal to 10 (A1.EQ.10.). If this is the case, the transaction is routed through activity 3 where it incurs a time delay of 4 time units (CO,4) before it arrives at node 20. If a transaction arrives at node 17 and none of the conditions is satisfied, a warning is printed and the transaction is destroyed. The Q-GERT program warning is a message that no activity could be scheduled for the transaction when it reached node 17. The message printed is as follows: "SCHAT CALLED AT xxxxx.xx ACTIVITY COULD NOT BE SCHEDULED FROM NODE xxxxx".

An example of conditional-take all branching that illustrates some of the other branching conditions is shown below. In this network segment,

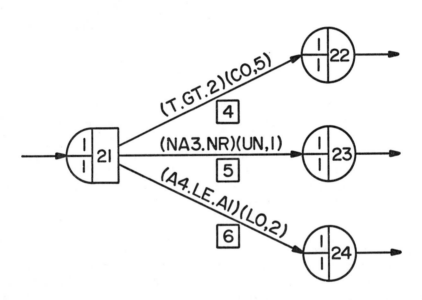

a transaction arriving at node 21 is routed according to the conditions specified on the branches emanating from node 21. The squared-off symbol on the output side of node 21 indicates that conditional-take all branching is to be used. If the time of arrival of a transaction to node 21 is greater than the specified constant value of 2.0 (T.GT.2.), then the transaction is routed to node 22 via activity 4. The transaction may also be routed from node 21 to node 23 if the node prescribed by attribute 3 of the transaction has not been released (NA3.NR). Thus, if attribute 3 is equal to 7, activity 5 will be selected only if node 7 was not released prior to the release of node 21. If the transaction is routed along activity 5, the time delay encountered by the transaction is uniformly distributed with parameters as specified by parameter set number 1. The condition (A4.LE.A1) specified on the branch between node 21 and node 24 indicates that the transaction or its duplicate should be routed along activity 6 if attribute 4 of the transaction is less than or equal to the value of attribute 1 of the transaction. If this condition is satisfied, then the transaction incurs a log-normally distributed time delay before arriving at node 24. Note that any combination of activities 4, 5 and 6 may be initiated for each transaction. This could result in the generation of transactions as in the case of deterministic branching. The above examples should clarify the condition codes and their use for routing transactions through a network. The reader is again referred to Table 5–1 for a complete description of the condition codes available in Q-GERT.

Data Input for Conditional Branching

In Chapters 2 and 3, the branching type was limited to deterministic (D) and probabilistic (P). For Q-nodes, these branching types are still the only ones permitted. However, for other node types (SOU, REG, STA, SIN), conditional branching is permitted. A branching type is specified in Field 5 of these card types. Conditional-take *first* branching is specified by an F and conditional-take *all* branching by an A. Thus, the possibilities for branching type are: D, P, F or A.

Branches emanating from nodes having an F or A branching type must have a condition associated with them that specifies the test to be made when the node is released. The condition is placed in Field 9 of the ACT card in the same manner as shown in Table 5–1. When employing conditional-take first branching from a node, it may be important to test the conditions in a prescribed order. Field 8 on the ACT card* is used to prescribe the relative order for testing conditions using a low-value-first priority rule, that is, 1 is preferred to 2 which is preferred to 3.

---

*Field 8 is also used to prescribe probability values for activities. Since a probability value is not associated with activities emanating from nodes using conditional branching, Field 8 can be used to specify the order in which conditions associated with activities should be tested.

Note that the data input for conditional branching comes last on the ACT card yet the information on the branch of the network comes first. Conceptually, selection of a branch occurs before the delay involved in taking the branch. However, many branches will not have conditions associated with them and, in the interest of simpler data input procedures, the condition specification was placed last on the ACT cards. The default value for a condition code is that the start node was released which is equivalent to assuming that the condition of the branch is satisfied.

Examples

Let us consider some common uses for conditional branching. Conditional branching can be used for introducing a finite number of transactions into a network. If no transactions are to arrive after time 100, the following network segment can be used. Node 5 has been prescribed

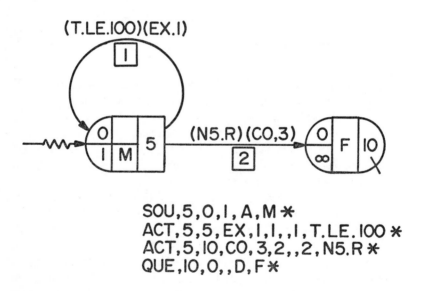

```
SOU,5,0,1,A,M*
ACT,5,5,EX,1,1,,1,T.LE.100*
ACT,5,10,CO,3,2,,2,N5.R*
QUE,10,0,,D,F*
```

with conditional-take all branching. Since node 5 is a source node, a transaction is generated and the conditions for routing the transaction are evaluated. With branching type A specified for node 5, the condition codes of activities whose start node is 5 are tested. Since the current time is less than 100, the transaction is routed back to node 5 after incurring an exponentially distributed delay. The T.LE.100 in Field 9 of the ACT card for activity 1 provides the necessary values. This branch will be tested first because a "1" is prescribed for Field 8. Since conditional-take all branching is employed, the condition on the branch from node 5 to node 10 is then evaluated. This condition specifies that the transaction should be routed to node 10 if node 5 has been released, that is, this branch will always be taken when a transaction is to be routed from node 5. *This condition is the default condition used if no condition is specified for a branch.* As long as transactions arrive prior to or at 100 time units, a transaction is routed back to node 5 to generate another arrival. The first transaction that arrives at node 5 after 100 time units is not returned to node 5 and, hence, the arrival process is stopped. Note that the first arrival after time 100 is routed to node 10. To eliminate this one arrival after time 100, the condition for activity 2 should be changed to (T.LE.100.)

A similar example that involves the origination of transactions is shown below. In this case, it is desired to generate three trucks into the

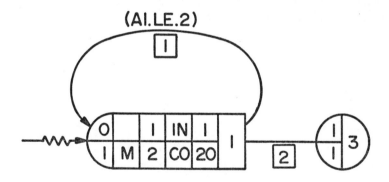

system, identified as trucks number 1, 2 and 3, each of which has a carrying capacity of twenty tons. At source node 1, the first transaction generated has a value of 1 assigned to attribute 1 and a value of 20 assigned to attribute 2. Conditional-take all branching is specified for node 1 and the transaction is routed through activity 1 back to node 1 if attribute 1 has a value less than or equal to 2 (A1.LE.2). Since the first transaction meets this condition, activity 1 is taken. This first transaction is also routed to node 3 through activity 2 since no condition was specified. Recall the default condition would be node 1 released (N1.R). When the transaction returns to node 1, the attribute 1 value is changed to 2 since node 1 has been released once before. The incremental function (IN) adds the number of prior releases of the node to the starting value and assigns this as the new attribute value of the transaction passing through the node. Attribute 2 is again assigned the value of 20. The transaction is routed again through activity 1 back to node 1, since attribute 1 has a value of 2. A transaction with attribute 1 equal to 2 is also routed to node 3. When the transaction returns to node 1, attribute 1 is incremented to 3 and now the transaction is not rerouted to node 1 since the attribute value is not less than or equal to 2. However, the transaction is routed to node 3 since the default condition is automatically satisfied. Thus, without any passage of time, since no activities shown incur a time delay, three transactions arrive at node 3 with the values of attribute 1 equal to 1, 2 and 3, respectively. The value of attribute 2 for each transaction is 20.

Now suppose that attribute 1 identifies a truck number and that trucks are assigned specific routes but are required to make deliveries from a common warehouse. A node in the network would be used to route trucks from the warehouse according to the truck number, that is, according to attribute 1. This would be accomplished by the network segment shown below. The branching at node 10, which represents the warehouse, is conditional-take first.

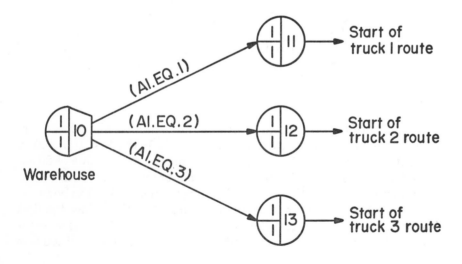

The transaction is routed to node 11 if its attribute 1 value is equal to 1 (A1.EQ.1). If the transaction is routed to node 11, no further conditions are tested. If the transaction's attribute 1 is not equal to 1, the next branch is tested and the transaction is routed to node 12 if its attribute 1 value is equal to 2. If this does not occur, then the condition on the branch to node 13 is evaluated and the transaction is sent to node 13 if its attribute 1 value is equal to 3. If a transaction arrives at node 10 with a value of attribute 1 greater than 3, no routing will occur and a message to this effect will be printed. Other examples of the use of conditional branching will be given in Chapter 6 which contains applications of intermediate Q-GERT concepts.

Probabilistic Branching Based on Attribute Values

Another way to use attributes for routing is by assigning probabilities to the attributes of a transaction and then routing the transaction through a node with probabilistic branching. Since probabilistic branching is involved, no new symbol for the output side of the node is required and the symbol, $\triangleright$, is employed. It is the activity description which instructs the program to probabilistically select activities based on attribute values, rather than fixed probabilities. On the branches emanating from the node, the letter A and the attribute number are prescribed for this type of branching. For example, the network shown below specifies

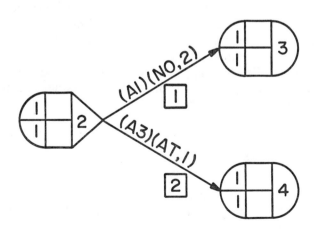

that activity 1 is taken with probability equal to the value of attribute 1 (A1) and activity 2 is taken with probability equal to the value of attribute 3 (A3). [Note: The symbols AT1 and AT3 are not used to avoid possible confusion with the designators (AT,1) and (AT,3)]. It is the user's responsibility to ensure that the sum of A1 and A3 equals one.

Probabilistic branching based on attribute value is useful when the path of a transaction determines the probabilities associated with future routings. The following partial network indicates this concept.

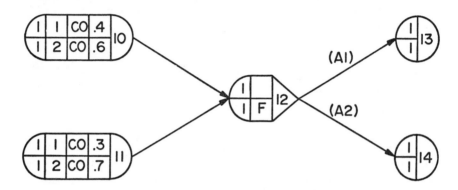

The transaction passing through node 10 has assigned to attribute 1 and 2 the values 0.40 and 0.60 respectively. For such transactions, the probability of branching from node 12 to node 13 is 0.40 and from node 12 to node 14 is 0.60. For transactions that pass through node 11, 30 percent are routed from node 12 to node 13 and 70 percent are routed from node 12 to node 14.

The data input requirements for probabilistic branching based on attribute value are straight forward. Recall that Field 8 of the ACT card can be used to specify fixed probabilities for probabilistic branching. Field 8 can also be used to specify the attribute number from which the probability is to be taken. Thus, if the node from which the activity emanates is specified to have probabilistic branching and if Field 8 contains an integer value, I, then the probability of taking the activity is obtained as the value of attribute I.

SELECTOR NODES (S-NODES)

In the discussion of queueing situations, no mention has been made of parallel queues forming before a service center. Also, no mention has been made of nonidentical servers that obtain their transactions from the same queue. The reason for this omission is that parallel queues and parallel servers in a system necessitate decision rules regarding their selection when a choice exists. Specifically, the decisions to be made are the following:

1. When a transaction is routed to a set of parallel queues, what rule should be used to select the queue to which the transaction should be routed?
2. When a transaction arrives at a queue that has two nonidentical servers drawing transactions from it, what rule should be used for selecting the server to process the transaction?
3. When a service activity completes the processing of a transaction, what rule should be used for selecting the next transaction to be assigned to the server if the parallel queues that feed the server both have transactions waiting in them?
4. What rule should be used to select from a set of parallel queues so that the transactions in the queues can be assembled by a service operation?

The answers to all of the above questions are modeled in Q-GERT through the specification of rules that are prescribed for a *selector node*. A selector node is referred to as an S-node and is given the following symbol.

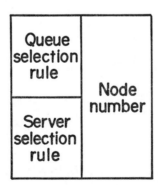

S-nodes have node numbers that are placed on the right hand side of the node. On the left hand side of the node, a queue selection rule and a server selection rule are specified. The queue selection rule specifies the procedure by which a transaction is routed to or from a queue based on the status of the network. The procedure is invoked when a transaction arrives at an S-node or when a service activity emanating from an S-node completes the service on a transaction. The server selection rule is invoked when a transaction arrives at a Q-node and a choice from among free servers is necessary. Before describing these procedures in detail, we will examine more closely the situations in which an S-node is required.

Routing Transactions to Parallel Queues

Consider a drive-in bank situation that involves two tellers. Cars line up before each teller and, hence, each teller has a separate queue. Customers arrive in cars, and these are the transactions flowing through the system. When cars arrive at the drive-in bank, a decision must be made by the customer as to which teller subsystem to join. In a network model, this requires information beyond the node that the transaction has reached, that is, a look-ahead capability. S-nodes provide this look-ahead capability by evaluating the subsystems linked to the S-node and selecting one according to a selection rule specified by the modeler. The network model of an S-node routing arriving transactions to one of two subsystems is shown below. In this situation, transactions arrive at the

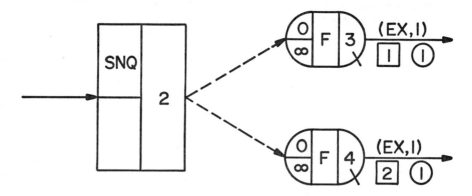

S-node which immediately attempts to route the transaction to one of the Q-nodes that follow it. At S-node 2, the modeler has selected the queue selection procedure SNQ, which is the shorthand notation for selecting the queue that has the smallest number in the queue. Q-nodes 3 and 4 are the possible choices to which the transaction can be routed. Dashed lines connect the S-node to the Q-nodes to indicate the possible routings for the transaction. *The dashed lines are not activities and*

must not be defined as such on input. The lines are used to indicate the possible routing for transactions arriving at S-node 2. S-node 2 evaluates the number of transactions waiting in Q-nodes 3 and 4 and routes the arriving transaction to the Q-node with the smallest number in it. The complete list of queue selection rules and their codes are given in Table 5–2.

Several observations can be made about the use of an S-node to route transactions to a set of parallel Q-nodes.

1. No server selection rule is required as no servers are associated with the S-node (no servers emanate from the output side of the S-node).
2. It is not feasible to have Q-nodes associated with both input and output sides of an S-node.
3. The routing of a transaction to a Q-node is performed instantaneously. When an S-node selects a Q-node in this manner, no activity description is required between the S-node and the Q-node.
4. A set of Q-nodes can be associated with an S-node.

Selecting From Q-nodes in Order to Initiate Service Activities

Consider next the situation in which transactions can wait in two separate queues for a single server. In this case, the Q-nodes are placed before the selector node and there is a single service activity emanating from the S-node. This situation is depicted in network form below.

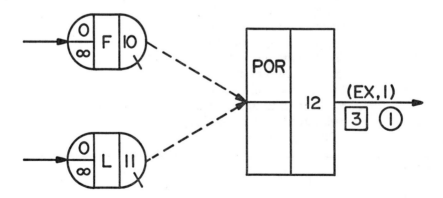

Table 5–2. Priority rules associated with S-nodes for selecting from a set of parallel queues.

Code	Definition	Numeric Code
POR	Priority given in a preferred order.	1
CYC	Cyclic Priority—transfer to first available Q-node starting from the last Q-node that was selected	2
RAN	Random Priority—assign an equal probability to each Q-node that can be selected.	3
LAV	Priority given to the Q-node which has had the largest average number of transactions in it to date.	4
SAV	Priority is given to the Q-node which has had the smallest average number of transactions in it to date.	5
LWF	Priority is given to the Q-node for which the waiting time of its first transaction from its last marking is the longest	6
SWF	Priority is given to the Q-node for which the waiting time of its first transaction from its last marking is the shortest	7
LNQ	Priority is given to the Q-node which has the current largest number of transactions in it.	8
SNQ	Priority is given to the Q-node which has the current smallest number of transactions in it.	9
LNB	Priority is given to the Q-node which has had the largest number of balkers from it to date.	10
SNB	Priority is given to the Q-node which has had the smallest number of balkers from it to date.	11
LRC	Priority is given to the Q-node which has the largest remaining unused capacity.	12
SRC	Priority is given to the Q-node which has the smallest remaining unused capacity.	13
ASM	Assembly mode option—all incoming queues must contribute one transaction before a processor may begin service (this can be used to provide an "AND" logic operation).	–14

For this network segment, one class of transactions arrives at Q-node 10 and another class arrives at Q-node 11. When a transaction arrives at either Q-node and the server is idle, it immediately is put into service by S-node 12. If a transaction arrives while the server is busy, it is placed in the queue represented by the node to which it arrived. When the service activity completes the processing of a transaction, the next transaction to be processed is determined by S-node 12. If only one queue is non-empty, then a transaction is selected from that queue. If both queues are empty, again no choice exists and the server becomes idle. However, if there are transactions in both queues, a choice must be made. At S-node 12, the queue selection rule, preferred order (POR), has been designated. This means that the queues will be examined in a specified order to select the transaction to be routed to the server. The preferred order is specified on the input for the S-node where the Q-nodes associated with the S-node are listed. Other queue selection rules involve examination of waiting times, unused capacity and number of balkers.

For the above example, no choice exists with regard to the selection of a server, since only one server is associated with the S-node. This would also be the case if service activity 3 was modeled to portray two identical servers, that is, a 2 was placed in the circle underneath the service activity. No selection would be required in this case since the two servers are identical and there cannot be a selection between identical units.

Assembly of Transactions Prior to Service

Another type of selection procedure involves two or more queues feeding a server where the server works on an assembled transaction.* In this case, the selection process requires that at least one transaction be in each Q-node prior to the start of the service activity. An example of this assembly selection procedure is the requirement for both an aircraft transaction and a cargo transaction before aircraft loading can begin. Below a Q-GERT network segment is shown for this situation where aircraft wait at Q-node 10, cargo waits at Q-node 11, and aircraft loading is modeled as activity 3. S-node 12 does not allow activity 3 to start until

---

*The reader is cautioned that this Q-GERT assembly terminology is different from that used in GPSS. The ASSEMBLE block in GPSS accumulates transactions at a node before releasing a transaction from a block. In Q-GERT, this corresponds to a regular node which has the number of incoming transactions requirement greater than one and only one branch emanating from the node. If the number of branches emanating from the node is set equal to the number of transactions to be assembled, the equivalent of a GATHER block in GPSS is obtained. The assembly (ASM) queue selection rule allows the combining of different types of transactions by selecting the transactions to be assembled from those waiting at specified Q-nodes.

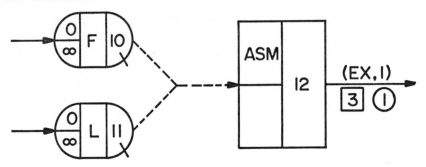

there are transactions in Q-nodes 10 and 11. Two notational changes have been incorporated in the previous network segment. The queue selection procedure has been prescribed as ASM which stands for *Assembly Mode Selection*. The dashed lines preceding the S-node have been joined prior to the S-node to indicate that a transaction is required at each Q-node before any transaction is sent to the server. Thus, if a transaction arrives at Q-node 10 and no transactions are in Q-node 11, no transaction will be sent to service activity 3. If a transaction arrives at the empty Q-node 11 when there are transactions in Q-node 10, it is immediately combined with the transaction that is first in the queue at node 10 and a single transaction is routed to service activity 3. If during the service operation, another transaction arrives at Q-node 11, it will be placed in the queue waiting for the server to become free. When service activity 3 ends, S-node 12 will examine Q-nodes 10 and 11 and find transactions in both. The first transaction in each queue will be removed, assembled, and routed to service activity 3 for processing. Thus, an S-node using the ASM queue selection rule provides a means for merging transactions. An S-node can merge transactions from 2 or more queues.

When transactions are assembled in this manner by an S-node, it is necessary to specify a criterion by which the appropriate attributes of one of the transactions can be maintained when the assembled set of transactions are routed to the service activity. The concept is similar to the one presented earlier for regular nodes that require two or more incoming transactions in order to release the node.

An example of the assembling of three transactions for which the attributes of the transaction that has the biggest value of attribute 1 are maintained is shown below. In this subnetwork, there are two identical servers available for processing the assembled transaction. Note that the ranking of transactions in the Q-nodes is based on the biggest value of attribute 1 for Q-node 20, smallest value of attribute 2 for Q-node 21,

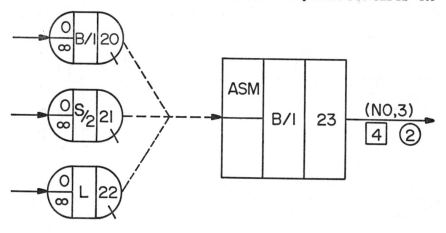

and last-in, first-out for Q-node 22. The three transactions, one from each queue, are assembled into one transaction which enters the service activity emanating from node 23. The attribute set passed on with this assembled transaction will be the set possessed by one of the three transactions that were assembled. For this example, the choice criterion is as specified on S-node 23, and the attribute set associated with the transaction that has the biggest value of attribute 1 is assigned to the assembled transaction.

Selecting Servers

Consider now the situation in which a single queue holds transactions for two parallel nonidentical servers. An example of this situation is a machine shop in which jobs can be processed either on a numerically controlled machine tool or on a conventional machine. The arriving jobs are transactions and each machine is represented by a service activity. If a choice exists as to which machine will process the job, the numerically controlled machine is preferred. However, if the numerically controlled machine tool is working when a job arrives, the job will be processed by the conventional machine if it is available. The network model of this machine shop is shown on the next page. For this situation, no queue selection rule is specified since a single queue is used before S-node 25. The server selection rule is prescribed as POR (preferred order) so that service activity 1 is always selected over service activity 2 if both servers are idle. It is important to note that *server selection rules apply only to a choice among free servers.* If one of the servers is idle and the other is

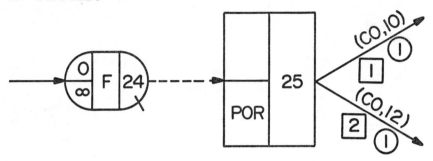

busy, then no choice exists and a transaction arriving at Q-node 24 is routed immediately to the free server. The complete list of server selection rules is given in Table 5–3.

Table 5–3. Priority rules associated with S-nodes for selecting from a set of parallel service activities.

Code	Definition	Numeric Code
POR	Select from free servers in a preferred order.	1
CYC	Select servers in a cyclic manner.	2
RAN	Select servers by a random selection of free servers.	3
LBT	Select the server that has the largest amount of usage (busy time) to date.	4
SBT	Select the server which has the smallest amount of usage (busy time) to date.	5
LIT	Select the server who has been idle for the longest period of time.	6
SIT	Select the server who has been idle for the shortest period of time.	7
RFS	Select randomly from free servers according to preassigned probabilities.	8

Example

Consider the case of two terminals being served by two communication lines. Each terminal has a limited amount of storage space and can maintain only five messages. Messages are maintained on a first-in, first-out basis. The network model of this situation is shown below.

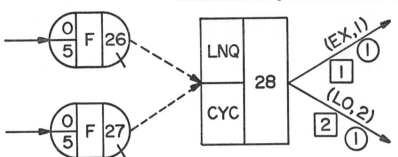

For this situation, S-node 28 performs a selection of a server when both servers are free and also selects a Q-node from which to draw a transaction when transactions are queued at both Q-nodes and a server has become available. The selection rules given for S-node 28 specify the following:

1. When determining which Q-node from which to draw a transaction, the Q-node with the largest number of transactions in it will be the one selected (LNQ);
2. When assigning a transaction to an available server, when both servers are available, it will select the server on a cyclic basis (CYC). This means that the server selected will be the first available one following the last server selected.

To illustrate the working of the cyclic selection rule, consider that the first transaction arrives at time 1 to node 26 and that both servers are available. This transaction is routed to server 1 (presuming that server 1 has priority over server 2). Suppose the service time for this transaction is 2 time units and, hence, server 1 will become available again at time 3. Further assume that another transaction arrives at node 27 at time 6. At this time, both servers are free. However, since the last selection made by S-node 28 was to server 1, the newly arriving transaction at time 6 is routed to server 2 because of the cyclic selection rule prescribed for S-node 28.

By using the *largest number in queue* (LNQ) selection rule at S-node 28, the maximum number of transactions waiting at the terminals (Q-nodes 26 and 27) is kept low. This simple network segment models an extremely complex queueing situation. Note that it is not necessary to specify a criterion for saving attribute values at S-node 28. At S-node 28, no assembly operation is performed and each transaction is treated individually. Transactions from node 26 are routed to either server 1 or 2. No combining of transactions is modeled in this queueing situation. The S-node performs the functions of selecting between the servers when a choice exists and selecting between the Q-nodes when a server becomes available.

Parallel Identical Servers Following an S-node

Parallel identical servers following an S-node are permitted. However, *only one branch can follow an S-node when multiple servers are associated with an activity.* The number of parallel servers is placed in a circle below the branch emanating from the S-node as shown below.

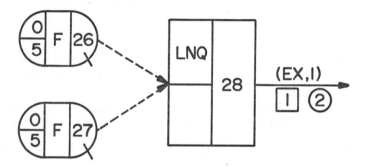

Since the two servers associated with activity 1 are identical, no server selection rule is required. The S-node is only used to select from the Q-nodes when a choice exists.

Balking from an S-node

Let us embellish the two queue, two server situation given above by routing incoming transactions to the terminals, that is, routing transactions to Q-node 26 or 27 upon their arrival. This would be accomplished by an additional S-node placed before nodes 26 and 27 that routes transactions to the Q-nodes based on a queue selection rule. In this case, we will route arriving transactions to the Q-node that has the largest remaining unused capacity. (Since in this instance, Q-nodes 26 and 27 both have a capacity of 5, this rule corresponds to routing to the Q-node with the smallest number of transactions in it.) As a further embellishment, assume that arriving transactions that cannot join either queue because they are at their capacity, balk to node 30. The model of this situation is shown below.

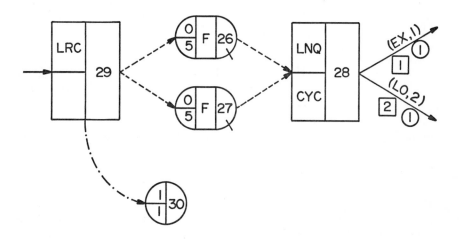

In this network model, S-node 29 routes transactions to the appropriate queue or, if a routing cannot be made because both queues are full, incoming transactions balk (are routed) to node 30. When a transaction is routed to one of the Q-nodes by S-node 29, a test on the availability of one of the servers is made. S-node 28 is used to look ahead to determine if one of the servers is available. S-node 28 is also used following the completion of a service to select a transaction from Q-node 26 or Q-node 27.

Blocking by an S-node

In addition to being able to balk from an S-node, it is also possible for an S-node to block service activities. Thus, if there is no remaining space in Q-nodes that follow an S-node, the S-node can block a service activity that is routing transactions to it. The symbolism for blocking at an S-node is shown below. Service activity 4 routes transactions to S-node 32. S-node 32 selects between Q-node 33 and Q-node 34 and routes transactions to the Q-node that has the smallest number of transactions in it. Q-nodes 33 and 34 have finite capacities. When service activity 4 completes the processing of a transaction it attempts to route it to S-

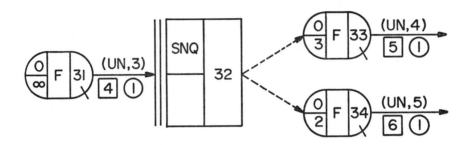

node 32. If S-node 32 encounters a situation in which there are three transactions at Q-node 33 and two transactions at Q-node 34, S-node 32 blocks server 4. A blocking of server 4 causes the transaction upon which service was just completed by server 4 to remain associated with the server. The transaction is not routed and server 4 cannot start the processing of another transaction until it is unblocked. Server 4 becomes unblocked when either server 5 or 6 completes the servicing of a transaction. For this blocked situation, let's trace the events following a completion of service by server 5. First, a transaction is removed from Q-node 33 and service is initiated on it by server 5. Then S-node 32 unblocks server 4 by removing the transaction that is blocking it and routes the transaction to Q-node 33 which now has an available space for it. Also occurring at this time is the removal of a transaction from Q-node 31 if one exists and the scheduling of an end of service for server 4. The Q-GERT Analysis Program updates all aspects of the network model as described above.

Multiple S-nodes Associated with a Q-node

One other situation deserves illustration. Suppose there are three types of transactions in a system. Transaction types 1 and 2 can be processed by server 7 and transaction types 2 and 3 can be processed by server 8. However, server 7 cannot process transactions of type 3 and server 8 cannot process transactions of type 1. In this situation, transactions of type 2 must be associated with two different servers, each of which can perform only for special types of transactions. One way to model this situation in Q-GERT involves the segregation of transactions into queues by transaction type and the use of S-nodes to select from the Q-nodes so that servers will have transactions routed to them which they can process. The network model of this situation is shown below.

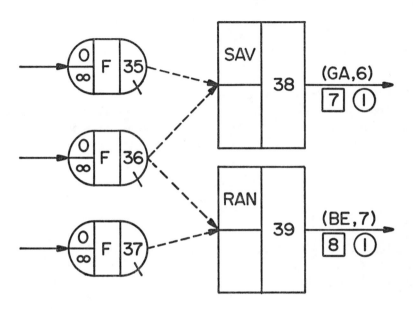

Associated with Q-node 36 are S-nodes 38 and 39. S-node 38 selects transactions for server 7. The processing time for server 7 is gamma distributed. When server 7 becomes available, S-node 38 selects a transaction from Q-node 35 or Q-node 36. If both Q-nodes have transactions waiting for server 7, S-node 38 selects the transaction from the queue that has had the smallest average number of transactions in it (SAV selection rule). Similarly, S-node 39 selects transactions for server 8 for which the processing time is beta distributed. S-node 39 selects transactions from Q-nodes 36 and 37. When both Q-nodes 36 and 37 contain a transaction, then S-node 39 selects a transaction from one of these queues on a random basis, that is, it assigns a 50–50 chance to selecting from either of the two nodes. The significant feature of this illustration is the association of two S-nodes (S-node 38 and S-node 39) with a single Q-node (Q-node 36). When a transaction arrives at Q-node 36, it checks *both* S-node 38 and S-node 39 (in a preferred order as specified on input) to determine if it can be serviced by either server 7 or server 8.

This section has illustrated the concepts and use of the S-node. The S-node provides the important function of routing transactions to Q-nodes and to servers when a choice exists. The S-node performs a decision function and no time delay is associated with the processing of a transaction through S-nodes. Attribute value assignments can be made at S-nodes.

Data Input for S-nodes

To describe an S-node to the Q-GERT Analysis Program, a SEL input card is used. S-node numbers associated with Q-nodes are defined starting in Field 10 of the QUE card. The information on the SEL card is organized in the following fields with default values as shown.

Field	Description	Default
1	Card Type (SEL)	none
2	S-node Number	none
3	Queue Selection Rule (see Table 5-2)	POR
4	Server Selection Rule (see Table 5-3)	POR
5	Choice Criterion for Assembly Nodes (needed only if ASM is prescribed for Field 3)/Attribute number for choice criterion	B/1
6	Balking and Blocking Information	Balking Transactions Lost
7–16	Q-nodes associated with S-node through dashed lines. The preferred order rule (POR) assumes the Q-nodes are listed in the preferred order starting with the first Q-node number	At least one required

Examples of the data input required to describe S-nodes are given below.

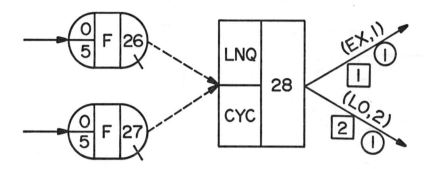

SEL,28,LNQ,CYC,(7)26,27 *

In the above illustration, the S-node selects transactions from Q-nodes 26 and 27 and routes transactions to service activities 1 or 2. No choice criterion and no balking node are specified and default values are used. The servers associated with the S-node are not defined on the SEL card as this information would be included on the ACT cards for activities 1 and 2.

The next illustration indicates how blocking is specified by an S-node.

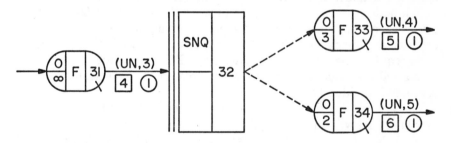

SEL,32,SNQ,(6)B,33,34 *

Q-nodes 33 and 34 are associated with S-node 32 as shown on the data input. Since Q-nodes cannot be associated with both sides of an S-node*, Fields 7-16 are now used to associate the Q-nodes to which the S-node is routing transactions.

---

*An S-node cannot be used to route transactions from one Q-node to another without an intervening activity.

A third illustration shows the data input for an S-node that employs the assembly (ASM) queue selection procedure. Other than providing the choice criterion, no special inputs are required.

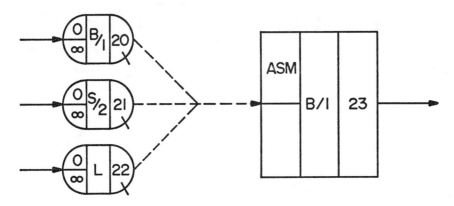

SEL,23,ASM, ,B/I, ,20,21,22 ✳

MATCH NODES

Match nodes in Q-GERT are nodes that match transactions residing in specified Q-nodes that have equal values for a specified attribute. The match node removes these matched transactions from the Q-nodes and routes each transaction to a node specified on input. A match node differs from an S-node with the ASM queue selection rule in that the match node requires that the transactions in the different queues have a common attribute value. In addition, when a match occurs, each transaction is routed individually.

The Q-GERT symbolism for a match node is presented below. The attribute that will be "matched" is placed in the left-hand portion of the symbol. No choice criterion is necessary as each transaction is routed separately when a match occurs. The Q-nodes associated with the match node are connected to the input side of the match node with a dashed line. The nodes to which the transactions are to be sent are connected to the output side of the match node with a dashed line. Recall dashed lines are not considered activities and separate input cards are *not* used for non-solid Q-GERT symbols.

There may be up to 5 Q-nodes associated with the input side of a match node. The nodes to which the transactions are to be sent following a match may be of any type. However, if a transaction is routed to a

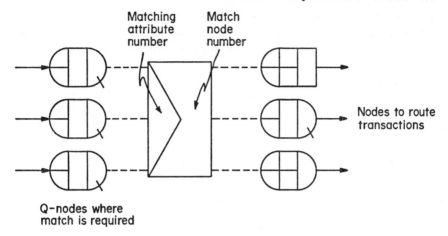

Q-node or a selector from a match node, the Q-node or S-node may not have the blocking capability since only service activities may be blocked.

A Q-node associated with the input side of a match node may *not* be associated with an S-node. However, a Q-node can be associated with more than one match node. For a match, the QUE cards for the Q-nodes associated with the match node will have the number of the match node placed in Field 10. *The initial number in the queue for a Q-node associated with a match node must be zero.*

The description of a match node for the Q-GERT Analysis Program is prescribed on a MAT input card as shown below.

Field	Description	Default
1	Card Type (MAT)	None
2	Node Number	None
3	Attribute on which match is to be based	Mark time
4	Input Q-node number/node number to which transaction from input Q-node is to be sent	None/ No routing
5–8	Repeats of Field 4 with at least 1 repeat required and not more than 4 repeats allowed.	None

Examples of Match Node

Match nodes can be used as logic switches which are only set when two transactions have reached specified Q-nodes in the network. For example, if it is desired to force a transaction to wait until another transaction achieves a particular status, a match node can be used as shown below. Transactions that arrive to Q-node 6 wait before proceeding to

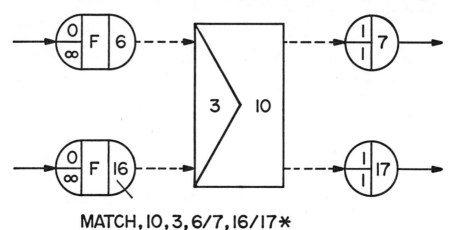

MATCH, 10, 3, 6/7, 16/17∗

node 7 until a transaction arrives at Q-node 16 that has the same value for attribute 3. If, at its time of arrival, a transaction was waiting at Q-node 16 with the same attribute 3 value, then the arriving transaction would be routed directly to node 7 and the matching transaction at Q-node 16 would be routed to node 17. When a match occurs only one transaction from each Q-node is routed through the match node. The ranking rule at the Q-node prescribes which transaction is to be routed as the transaction with the highest priority in the Q-node is routed.

Another view of a match node is that it models the situation in which a transaction must wait for a signal before proceeding in the network. This situation is shown below. For this network, a unique number is as-

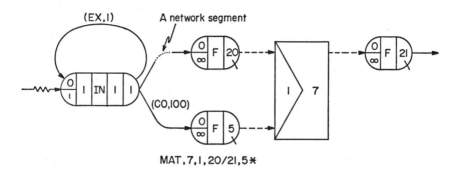

MAT, 7, 1, 20/21, 5∗

signed to attribute 1 at node 1. A transaction is routed to node 20 through a network segment as indicated by the . . .. A timing transaction with the same value of attribute 1 is routed to node 5 with a 100 time unit delay. In this way, transactions are prohibited by MATCH node 7 from arriving at Q-node 21 until 100 time units after they leave node 1. The "timing" transaction at Q-node 5 is eliminated from the network following a match as no routing node is associated with Q-node 5.

A third use of a MATCH node is to match transactions and cause them to be assembled. This is shown below. When transactions with the

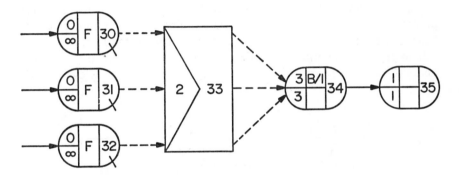

MAT, 33, 2, 30/34, 31/34, 32/34 ∗

same value of attribute 2 reside in Q-nodes 30, 31 and 32, MATCH node 33 takes each of them from the Q-nodes and routes each one to node 34. At node 34, the transactions are assembled and a single transaction is routed to node 35. The attributes of the routed transaction are set equal to the attributes of the transaction which has the *biggest* value of attribute 1.

NODE MODIFICATION

We have discussed how a transaction can be routed through a network based on its attribute values (conditional branching) or based on the status of servers and their associated queues (through S-nodes). In some systems, the routing of a transaction may be based on whether an activity has been completed or which of a set of activities was last performed. To permit the routing of a transaction that is dependent on the sequence in which activities are performed, the concept of nodal modification is included in Q-GERT. Nodal modification involves the replacement in the network of one node by another node when an activity is completed. The replacement of a node specifies that the functions performed at the node *after it is released* are replaced by a new node. Only nodes that are released can be modified, that is, *Q-nodes, S-nodes, and MATCH nodes cannot be modified.* The functions that are replaced involve the collection of statistics, the assignment of values to attributes, and the method for routing transactions. For example, if node 7 is replaced by node 10, any transaction that causes node 7 to be released is transferred to node 10 and the functions and branching specified for node 10 are applied to the transaction. A dotted line from the node being replaced is used to indicate nodal modification with an arrow pointing toward the node being inserted. The activity number causing the modification is placed in a square next to the dotted line.

The graphical symbolism indicating that node 7 is to be replaced by node 10 when activity 3 has been completed is shown below. For the

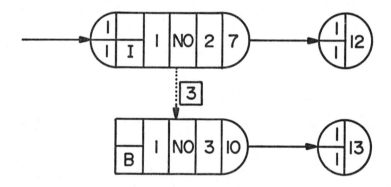

above network segment, activity 3 is not shown but is presumed to be part of the total network. A transaction arriving to node 7 releases node 7. If activity 3 has not been completed, interval statistics are collected, and a value is assigned to attribute 1 of the transaction that is a sample from a normal distribution having parameters as specified by parameter set number 2. The transaction is then sent to node 12. However, if activity 3 was completed prior to the time that the transaction arrived at node 7, node 7 is released, but the functions associated with node 7 are now replaced by the functions specified by node 10. Thus, between statistics are collected, and a value is assigned to attribute 1 of the arriving transaction that is normally distributed with parameters as specified by parameter set number 3. The transaction is then routed to node 13 from node 10.

In the above illustration, the input side of node 10 has not been drawn to indicate that the input functions performed at a node are not replaced when a nodal modification occurs. This example illustrates how a new value can be assigned to an attribute of a transaction and how the routing of a transaction can be changed, based on the completion of an activity. From an applications standpoint, activity 3, the instigator of the modification, could be modeling the passage of time or a learning process after which transactions are processed in a more efficient manner.

Data Input for Nodal Modifications

To describe a nodal modification to the Q-GERT Analysis Program, a MOD input card is used. The information on the MOD card is organized in the following fields (no default values are prescribed):

Field	Description
1	Card Type (MOD)
2	Activity number causing modification
3	Number of the node to be replaced
4	Number of the node to be inserted
5–26	Repeats of Fields 3 and 4

If one activity causes many modifications, Fields 3 and 4 can be repeated on the card. Thus, if activity 3 causes node 10 to be replaced by node 11 and node 20 to be replaced by node 30, the MOD card would be
MOD,3,10,11,20,30*

Examples of Simple Nodal Modification

As an example of the use of nodal modification, consider a banking system that includes drive-in tellers and inside tellers. Assume the drive-in tellers start processing customers at 9 o'clock but the inside tellers do not begin processing customers until 10 o'clock. Also, there is a finite queue for the drive-in teller, and an arriving customer who finds the queue full for the drive-in teller balks from the drive-in portion of the system and seeks service from the inside teller. This situation is modeled in the network given below. Arrivals to the drive-in portion of the

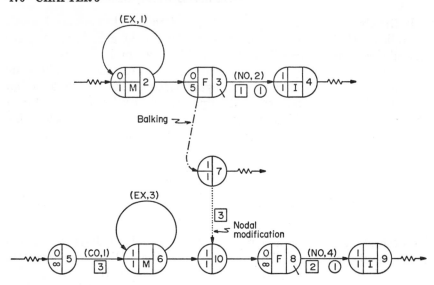

bank are modeled by node 2. As long as Q-node 3 is not at capacity, transactions arriving and seeking service from the drive-in portion of the bank are processed by activity 1 and depart the system at node 4. When a transaction arrives at Q-node 3 and there are five transactions waiting at Q-node 3, the arriving transaction balks to node 7. If node 7 has not been replaced in the network, the arriving transaction departs the system. If activity 3 has been completed, the transaction is routed to node 10 which further routes it to Q-node 8 which is the queue of the inside teller. Activity 3 is modeled as the branch from node 5 to node 6. The time required for activity 3 is one hour, and represents the delay in opening the inside portion of the bank. When activity 3 is completed, the arrival process to the inside portion of the bank as modeled by node 6 is activated, that is, transactions arriving at node 7 will be routed to node 10. Note that in the above illustration, the input side of node 10 was included to illustrate that a node can be replaced by an existing node in the network. The data input describing the above nodal modification would be

MOD,3,7,10*

Example of Multiple Nodal Modification

Nodal modifications are essentially a means of modeling switches that are set or reset as activities are completed. To illustrate the resetting capability permissable with nodal modifications, consider the situation in which transactions arrive at a system during the first sixteen hours of operation, do not arrive during the next eight hours, arrive during the next sixteen hours and so on. This arrival process, which is a function of the time of day, is modeled in Q-GERT in the manner shown below.

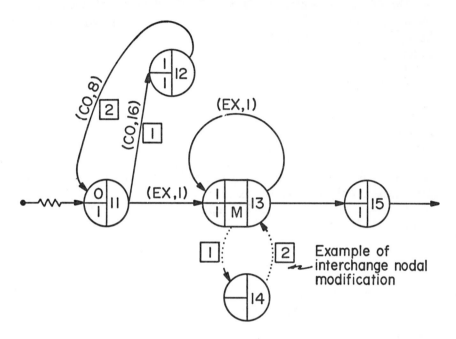

At source node 11, a transaction is sent with an exponentially distributed delay to node 13. At the same time, a transaction is also sent to node 12 with a sixteen hour time delay. This time delay, as modeled by the branch from node 11 to node 12, has been labeled as activity 1. The arrival process is modeled by node 13 and the branch from node 13 back to node 13 represents the time between arrivals. As shown, an exponentially distributed interarrival time is used. Transactions arriving at node 13 are routed to node 15 for further processing as long as activity 1 has not been completed. When activity 1 is completed, that is, after sixteen hours, node 13 is removed from the network and transactions arriving at node 13 are routed to node 14. This nodal modification stops the arrival process, as no branching occurs from node 13 after activity 1 has been completed.

The completion of activity 1 also releases node 12; thus activity 2, which requires eight hours, is started. When activity 2 is completed, node 14 is replaced by node 13 and node 11 is released. When node 11 is released, the activities represented by the branches from node 11 to node 13 and from node 11 to node 12 are started. Since node 13 is back in the network, branching from node 13 back to node 13 and from node 13 to node 15 is reinitiated. Hence, the arrival process is reactivated. This sixteen hour on and eight hour off schedule is continued throughout the life of the system. This example illustrates that nodes can be modified and remodified, that is, on-off switches or flip-flop devices can be modeled in Q-GERT. The modification data input for this illustration would be

MOD,1,13,14*
MOD,2,14,13*

Serial Nodal Modifications

It may be desired to construct a network involving a series of nodal modifications which specifies that node 7 is replaced by node 8 when activity 1 is completed and node 8 is replaced by node 9 when activity 2 is completed. These serial modifications are shown below. For this specifi-

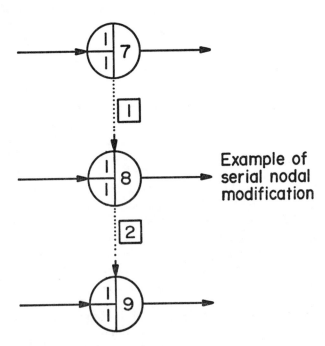

Example of serial nodal modification

cation, the order in which activities 1 and 2 are completed affects the nodes kept in the network*. If activity 1 is completed before activity 2, then a transaction arriving at node 7 is processed at node 9 and routed from node 9. However if a transaction arrives at node 7 after both activities have been completed and activity 2 is completed before activity 1, the transaction is processed at node 8 and is routed from node 8.

If, in the above example, it is desired to have node 9 in the network when activities 1 and 2 are completed regardless of the order in which the activities are completed, it is necessary to construct the Q-GERT network segment as shown below. In this case, when activities 1 and 2

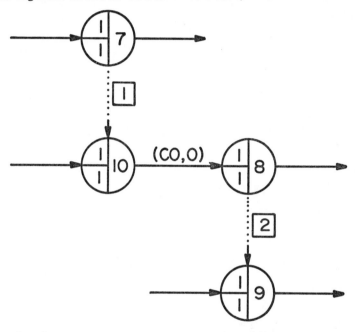

are completed, a transaction arriving at node 7 is processed and routed from node 9 independent of the order in which the activities were completed.

Three final comments regarding nodal modification are listed below:
1. Nodal modifications are indicated by dotted lines and are not considered activities in the network. Thus, no activity description for the dotted modification lines is permitted.
2. Nodal modifications can be prescribed to occur based on one of a set of activity completions. This is illustrated below where node 16

---

*There is a technical incompatability between a serial modification and an interchange modification where one node is modified to the other and the reverse can occur.

is to be replaced by node 17 whenever activities 3, 4 or 5 are completed.

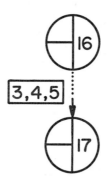

3. The terminology used with nodal modifications depends on the system being modeled. All of the following statements are equivalent:
   a) Node 16 is replaced by node 17;
   b) Node 16 is removed and node 17 is inserted;
   c) Node 16 goes into node 17 when a modification occurs;
   d) Node 16 is switched to node 17; and
   e) Node 17 replaces node 16.

SUMMARY OF INTERMEDIATE Q-GERT SYMBOLS

A summary of the symbols defined in this chapter is presented in Table 5-4. This completes the description of the graphical elements included in Q-GERT. Examples of the use of Q-GERT to model specific situations are presented in Chapter 6.

Table 5-4. Summary of Intermediate Q-GERT Symbols.

Symbol	Concept	Definition
	Value Assignment	A is the attribute number to which a value is to be assigned; if A+ is specified, add value to attribute A; if A– is specified, subtract value from attribute A. D is the distribution or function type from which assignment value is to be determined. PS is the parameter set number.
	Queue Ranking	R is the ranking procedure for ordering transactions at the Q-node. R can be specified as: F → FIFO; L → LIFO; B/i → Big value of attribute i. S/i → Small value of attribute i. If i= M, ranking is based on mark time.
	Conditional, Take-First Branching	indicates conditional-take first branching from the node.
	Conditional, Take-all Branching	indicates conditional-take all branching from the node.
(C) (D, PS) →	Condition Specification for Branch	C is the condition specification for taking the activity (see Table 5-1).
(P) (D,PS)	Attribute Based Probabilistic Branching	If P<1.0, P is the probability of taking the activity. If P≥1, P is an attribute number.

Table 5-4 (continued)

Symbol	Concept	Definition
	Selector node or S-node	QSR is the queue selection rule for routing transactions to or from Q-nodes (see Table 5-2). SSR is the server selection rule for deciding which server to make busy if a choice exists (see Table 5-3). # is the S-node number.
	Routing Indicator	Routing indicator for transaction flow to or from Q-nodes to S-nodes or Match nodes
	Assembly by S-nodes	ASM is the queue selection rule that requires transactions to be assembled from two or more queues.
	Blocking	Blocking at an S-node.
	Balking	Balking from an S-node.
	Match Node	# is the match node number. Transactions are routed from N_1 to N_3 and N_2 to N_4 when a match occurs. A is the attribute number on which the match is to be made

Table 5-4 (continued)

Symbol	Concept	Definition
	Nodal Modification	# is the activity number causing nodal modification. N_1 is the node number to be replaced when activity # is completed. N_2 is node number to be inserted when activity # is completed.

EXERCISES

5-1. Customers arrive to a barber shop in an exponential fashion with the mean time between arrivals equal to 15 minutes. Seventy percent of the arrivals only desire to have their hair cut. Twenty percent of the arrivals desire a haircut and a shave, and ten percent desire to have their hair cut and washed. The time to cut an individual's hair is normally distributed with a mean of 10 minutes and a standard deviation of 1 minute. The time to shave a customer is independent of the time to cut his hair and takes between 7 and 13 minutes uniformly distributed. The time to wash a person's hair is normally distributed with a mean of 12 minutes and a standard deviation of 2 minutes. The barber shop employs two barbers.

Draw a Q-GERT network for the above problem statement corresponding to each of the following conditions:

a) both barbers are considered to be equivalent and can cut and wash hair and shave customers;

b) both barbers can perform all functions, however, customers prefer barber 1 to barber 2;

c) barber 1 only cuts and washes hair, and barber 2 has an allergy to water which does not allow him to wash hair.

Customers queue for the barber that can perform the operations they require. Barbers select the customer waiting who has the longest waiting time.

d) customers join separate queues depending on the service they desire. Barbers process customers who require two operations first and then will serve customers who only desire hair cuts.

5-2. Embellish Example 1 of Chapter 4, the television inspection and adjustment situation so that television sets requiring a third adjustment are sent to a rebuild operation. The rebuild operation is not to be modeled. For this embellishment develop the network so that the adjustor spends more time on a television set on the second time it is adjusted, say (UN,4). Because of this added time, the probability of requiring a third adjustment is reduced to 0.10.

5-3. For the television inspection and adjustment situation modeled in Example 1, management is considering the combining of the inspection and adjustment operations. In this proposal, 3 servers would man the inspection and adjustment station. Inspection time is not changed when the stations are combined but the adjustment time is increased by 20 percent due to the non-specialized operations involved. Assume the probability that a television set will require an adjustment is still 0.15. When a television set requires adjustment, it is placed back in the queue of the inspector and adjustor station so that the individual who performed the inspection and adjustment is not biased by the knowledge that he has just adjusted the set. (The sets are similar so that he would not recognize a set after it has been in the queue.) Develop the Q-GERT network model for this situation.

5-4. For the paint shop situation, Example 2, in which workmen prepare and paint items, incorporate into the situation a 15-minute break for a workman after he has finished the painting of five items. Change the network model so that the workman who has painted the most items since his last break has priority in gaining access to an available paint spraying machine.

5-5. (From Schriber (121)) A production shop is comprised of six different groups of machines. Each group consists of a number of identical machines of a given kind as indicated below.

Machine Group Number	Kind of Machines in Group	Number of Machines in Group
1	Casting units	10
2	Lathes	4
3	Planers	3
4	Drill presses	4
5	Shapers	12
6	Polishing machines	3

Three different types of jobs move through the production shop. These job-types are designated as Type 1, Type 2, and Type 3. Each job-type requires that operations be performed at specified kinds of machines in a specified sequence. All operation times are exponentially distributed. The visitation sequences and average operation times are shown below.

Visitation Sequences and Mean Operation Times for the Three Types of Jobs

Job Type	Total Number of Machines to be Visited	Machine Visitation Sequence	Mean Operation Time (minutes)
1	4	Casting Unit	125
		Planer	35
		Lathe	20
		Polishing machine	60
2	3	Shaper	105
		Drill press	90
		Lathe	65
3	5	Casting unit	235
		Shaper	250
		Drill press	50
		Planer	30
		Polishing machine	25

Jobs arrive at the shop in a Poisson stream at a mean rate of 50 jobs per 480 minute day or, equivalently, with exponential interarrival times with a mean of 9.6 minutes. Twenty-four percent of the jobs in this stream are of Type 1, 44 percent are of Type 2, and the rest are of Type 3. The type of arriving job is independent of the job type of the preceding arrival. Build a Q-GERT model which simulates the operation of the production shop for five separate 40-hour weeks to obtain: 1) the distribution of job residence time in the shop, as a function of job-type; 2) the utilization of the machines; and 3) queue statistics for each machine group.

5-6. Consider a system consisting of three components in parallel. The time to failure for each component is lognormally distributed with parameter sets 1, 2 and 3. Draw the Q-GERT network from which the following quantities can be obtained: the probability that the system fails before 10, 20, 30, 40 and 50 time units where system failure occurs when all three components fail.

5-7. Given three components in series, each with a lognormal failure time distribution, develop the Q-GERT network from which the probability that the system does not fail beyond a specified time can be obtained. (Note that the failure of any one component causes system failure.)

5-8. Draw a Q-GERT network of a system involving one component in series with three components in parallel to estimate the failure time distribution.

5-9. A power generation station has three generators that must work in parallel. When one of the generators fails, a spare generator (which is not as good as the original equipment) is automatically switched on and remains on until the failed generator is fixed. When the failed generator is repaired, it is placed back in operation and the spare generator is returned to standby status. The distribution of the time to failure of the repaired generator is the same as its original failure time. Develop a Q-GERT network to estimate the time to system failure or, equivalently, the time until two generators have concurrently failed. Embellish this network by including a probability p that the automatic switching device for turning on the spare generator does not work. The time to failure distribution for all generators is lognormal. For the three on-line generators, the mean time is 1000 hours with standard deviation of 25 hours. For the spare generator, the mean is 300 hours with a standard deviation of 75 hours. Repair time is exponentially distributed with a mean of 50 hours.

5-10. In quality control sampling plans, the acceptance and rejection of a lot is based on a sample of size n. If, in the sample of size n, c+1 defective units are found, the lot is rejected (c is called the acceptance number). Assuming that the fraction of defective units in the lot is p, draw the Q-GERT network from which you can estimate: 1) the probability of accepting and rejecting a lot; and 2) the number of samples tested when a lot is rejected.

5-11. For the single sampling plan described in the previous exercise, embellish the situation so that in the inspection process there is a probability of q of declaring a good unit bad (a Type I error) and a probability of s of declaring a bad unit good (a Type II error).

5-12. Develop a Q-GERT network of the following double sampling inspection plan: n_1 samples are taken, and if the number of defectives in the first n_1 samples is less than or equal to c_1 the lot is accepted. If the number of defectives in the first n_1 samples is greater than c_2 the lot is rejected. If the number of defectives is greater than c_1 but less than or equal to c_2 a second sample of size n_2 is taken. If the number of defectives in $n_1 + n_2$ samples is less than or equal to c_3, accept the lot. Draw the Q-GERT network first assuming that $c_3=c_2$. Redraw the network then assuming c_3 is greater than c_2

5-13. At an airline terminal, five ticket agents are employed and current practice is to allow queues to form before each agent. Time between arrivals to the agents is exponentially distributed with a mean of 5 minutes. Customers join the shortest queue at the time of their arrival. The service time for the ticket agents is uniformly distributed between 0.5 and 1.5 minutes. The queues of the ticket agents are not allowed to exceed two customers each. If the queues of all ticket agents are full, the customer goes directly to his gate to be served by a stewardess. Develop the Q-GERT network from which the total time a customer spends at the ticket agent windows, the utilization of the ticket agents, and the number of customers per minute that cannot gain service from the ticket agents can be determined.

5-14. The airline company described in Exercise 5-13 has decided to change the procedures involved in processing customers by the ticket agents. A single line is formed and customers are routed to the ticket agent that becomes free next. A tenth of a minute service time is added to the processing time of each ticket agent. Space available in the single line for waiting customers is ten. Develop the Q-GERT network for this revised situation.

5-15. Based on the analysis of service times of ticket agents (see Exercise 5-13), it has been found that a subset of the customers purchasing tickets are taking a long period of time. By segregating ticket holders from non-ticket holders, improvements can be made in the processing of customers. To accomplish this segregation, four ticket agents are used for checking in customers and one agent is used for purchases. The time to check in a person is uniformly distributed between 0.2 and 1 minute and the time to purchase a ticket is exponentially distributed with a mean of 5 minutes. Assuming that 15 percent of the customers will be purchasing tickets, develop the Q-GERT network for this situation. The time between all customer arrivals is exponentially distributed with a mean of 5 minutes. (Advanced) Embellish your Q-GERT model so that the ticket agent assigned to writing tickets processes customers that desire to check-in when no purchasers are waiting for his services and only after he has completed a service. That is, a check-in customer cannot be routed to the special ticket agent upon arrival.

Chapter 6

DATA INPUT AND EXAMPLES: INTERMEDIATE CONCEPTS

In Chapters 3 and 5, the data input procedures for describing basic and intermediate Q-GERT networks were presented. In Appendix 1, a complete listing of each input card is provided including all default values, editing performed and associated errors for each input field. In the next section, a Q-GERT input short form is provided that contains the information to translate a Q-GERT network into the data requirements for the Q-GERT Analysis Program. A section is also provided to assist the user in determining a distribution type to represent an activity duration. At the end of this chapter, three examples are given of Q-GERT models that contain intermediate concepts.

DATA INPUT

Figure 6-1 presents a revised Q-GERT input short form that includes the field specifications for describing S-nodes on a SEL card; match nodes on a MAT card; value assignments at a node on a VAS card, and nodal modifications on a MOD card. Also, a SEE card for initializing the random number seeds for different streams and a TRA card for tracing the transaction flow through specified nodes of the network are described. Random number streams and tracing will be discussed later in this section.

Fields*

1	2	3	4	5	6	7	8	9	10
REG or SOU	Node number	Initial number to release [1]	Subsequent number to release [∞]	Branching (D,P,F,A) [D]	Marking (M) [M if SOU, no M if REG]	Choice criterion (F,L,S,B) [L]/ Attribute [M]			
SIN or STA	Node number/ label	Initial number to release [1]	Subsequent number to release [∞]	Branching (D,P,F,A) [D]	Statistics desired (F,A,B,I,D) [F]	Upper limit of first cell [N]	Width of histogram cell [N]	Choice criterion (F,L,S,B) [L]/ Attribute [M]	
QUE	Node number/ label	Initial number in queue [0]	Capacity of Q-node [∞]	Branching (D,P) [D]	Ranking (F,L,S,B) [F]/ Attribute [M]	Block or node number for balkers (B) [balkers destroyed]	Upper limit of first cell [N]	Width of histogram cell [N]	Following S-nodes or match nodes or allocate nodes
SEL	Node number/ label	Queue selection rule [POR]	Server selection rule [POR]	Choice criterion (S, B) [B]/ Attribute [M]	Block or node number for balkers (B) [balkers destroyed]	Associated Q-nodes	(Repeats of Field 7)		
MAT	Node number	Matching attribute [POR]	Q-node/ Routing node	(Repeats of Field 4)					

190

Fields*

1	2	3	4	5	6	7	8	9	10
SEE	Stream number	Seed[0]/ -------- Initialization (I, N) [N]		(Repeats of Fields 2 and 3)					
VAS	Node number	Attribute number [1]	Distribution type [CO]	Parameter set [0]		(Repeats of Fields 3, 4 and 5)			
PAR	Parameter set number	Parameter 1 [0]	Parameter 2 [-10^{20}]	Parameter 3 [10^{20}]	Parameter 4 [0]	Stream number [10]			
ACT	Start node	End node	Distribution or function type [CO]	Parameter set or constant [0.0]	Activity number/ -------- label	Number of parallel servers [1]	Probability or attribute number or order [.5]	Condition code [Ni:R] i=start node	
MOD	Activity number	Node out	Node in	(Repeats of Fields 3 and 4)					
TRA	Node number/ subnetwork ID	(Repeats of Field 2)							

* Default values are given in parentheses ( ). A slash (/) and dashed line indicate the field may contain two entries where the slash and second entry are optional.

* Default values are given in brackets [ ]. If no default is indicated, data for the field is required. Options for a field are given in parentheses ( ). A slash (/) and dashed line indicate the field may contain two entries where the slash and second entry are optional.

Figure 6-1 Q-GERT input short form.

191

With the addition of intermediate concepts, general project information that is included on the GEN card is increased and it no longer conveniently fits on the short form. The information for the GEN card is discussed separately. As an aid to the Q-GERT user, Table 6-1 has been prepared that provides in one place the codes available for the options relating to distribution and function types; parameter values for distribution and function types; conditional branching codes; queue selection rules; and server selection rules. Definitions are not included in Table 6-1 in order that all codes can be included on one page. References to the table numbers where the definitions of the options are included are given in Table 6-1. After using Q-GERT for problem solving, the codes for the various options become familiar and it is handy to have a one page table for them.

The random number seed initialization card, SEE, is used to specify a first or starting value for each random number stream. In Field 2, the stream number is given for which a seed value is to be prescribed. The next field, Field 3, consists of a seed value and, if desired, a specification that the same seed value should be used on each simulation run.* This latter specification is made by having a slash (/) and 'I' follow the seed value. If no slash is used in a field or an 'N' follows the slash, no resetting of the seed value is performed. For example,

SEE,1,328751329/I,2,41389777,10,/I*

prescribes that: stream 1 have an initial seed value of 328751329 and be reset at the beginning of each run; stream 2 have a seed value for the first run of 41389777 and should not be reset; and stream 10 should take the default seed value and should be reset for each run. Streams 3 through 9 will take default seed values and will not be reset.

A TRA card is used for specifying a set of node numbers for which every event associated with the nodes is to be printed. The runs for which such nodal traces are to be obtained are defined on the GEN card in Fields 17 and 18. Examples of the outputs from event tracing and nodal tracing are given in Example 9, Figure 6-23.

A BEG card is used in the data input to segregate network descriptions. Thus, multiple networks can be analyzed for one submission of the program. After a complete network description is given, a BEG card is used to indicate the end of data for the network and that the beginning of the data for the next network is to follow.

Table 6-2 presents a description of the fields for the GEN card. Fields 12 through 20 have been added to those described in Chapter 3. These new fields are used to define the number of attributes for a transaction,

---

* Using the same seed on different runs is a commonly used variance reduction technique (40,66).

Table 6-1. Code Options for Q-GERT Specifications

Distribution and Function Types (See Table 2-1)		Parameter Values* (See Figure 3-2)			
Code	Key	1	2	3	4
AT	Attribute	–	–	–	–
BE	Beta	μ	a	b	σ
BP	Beta PERT	m	a	b	–
CO	Constant	μ	–	–	–
ER	Erlang	μ/k	a	b	k
EX	Exponential	μ	a	b	-
GA	Gamma	μ	a	b	σ
IN	Incremental	–	–	–	–
LO	Lognormal	μ	a	b	σ
NO	Normal	μ	a	b	σ
PO	Poisson	$\mu-a$	a	b	–
TR	Triangular	m	a	b	–
UF	User Function	–	–	–	–
UN	Uniform	–	a	b	–

* —→not used; $\mu\to$ mean; $\sigma\to$ standard deviation; m → mode; a → minimum or optimistic time; b → maximum or pessimistic time.

Branching Condition Codes (See Table 5-1)		Queue Selection Rules (See Table 5-2)		Server Selection Rules (See Table 5-3)	
Code	Key	Code	Key	Code	Key
T.R.V.	Time .R. Value	POR	Preferred order	POR	Preferred order
T.R.Ak	Time .R. Attribute k	CYC	Cyclic	CYC	Cyclic
Aj.R.V.	Attribute j.R. Value	RAN	Random	RAN	Random
Aj.R.Ak	Attribute j.R. Attribute k	LAV	Largest average number	LBT	Largest busy time
where R={LT;LE;EQ;NE;GT; or GE}		SAV	Smallest average number	SBT	Smallest busy time
		LWF	Longest waiting of first	LIT	Longest idle time
Ni.R	Node i Released	SWF	Shortest waiting of first	SIT	Shortest idle time
Ni.N	Node i Not Released	LNQ	Largest number in queue	PFS	Probabilistic from
NAj.R	Node Aj Released	SNQ	Smallest number in queue		free servers
NAj.N	Node Aj Not Released	LNB	Largest number of balkers		
		SNB	Smallest number of balkers		
		LRC	Largest remaining capacity		
		SRC	Smallest remaining capacity		
		ASM	Assembly mode		

special output reporting procedures such as tracing a set of runs, and a list of run time options. Run time options include the specification of an indicator as to whether the input cards should be listed, conditions under which the execution of the program should be performed, and the time from which statistics are to be kept. If the time from which statistics are to be kept is specified as a value other than zero, the Q-GERT Analysis Program will reinitialize all statistical storage arrays at the time specified (Field 13 of GEN card). In essence, all data values collected up to this specified time are discarded and will not be included in the computation of run or summary statistics.

The output report option allows the user to obtain individual run statistics and cumulative run statistics. On each run, averages for the run are computed and each average is considered as one observation for a multiple run analysis. A summary report contains a statistical analysis of the run averages. In addition, statistics on the individual release time of nodes are maintained for the first run. A special report on these first run values is printed whenever the user requests an output report for individual runs. The reporting options are:

F → a report for the first run and a summary of all runs [default value]

E → a report for each run and a summary of all runs

C → a report for each run and a cumulative report up to the end of each run

S → only a summary report for all runs

Two types of tracing are included in Q-GERT: event and nodal. An event trace is a printout of all start and completion times of activities for a specified set of runs (Fields 15 and 16 of the GEN card). When a trace is obtained, information on the transaction associated with the event is also printed. A nodal trace is a printout of start and completion times of activities for selected nodes as specified on a TRA card, and for selected runs (Fields 17 and 18). An event trace portrays the sequence in which activities are performed. A nodal trace portrays the decisions, value assignments and branching that occurs at a given node. Both event and nodal traces can be obtained for any run of the network.*

Illustrations of the data input, tracing and the various options for the GEN card will be given in the three examples contained in the last sections of this chapter. Before presenting the examples, a discussion on selecting a random variable type for describing an activity duration is given.

*A trace for a specific time period during a run can be obtained by setting the Q-GERT variable ITRAC=1 to start the trace and setting ITRAC=0 to stop the trace.

Table 6-2. Description of Data Fields for the General Project Information Card (GEN).

Field Number	Description	Default Value
1	Card type, GEN	Required
2	Analyst name consisting of up to 12 alpha-numeric characters	12 blanks
3	Project name or number up to 12 significant characters	12 blanks
4	Month number	1
5	Day number	1
6	Year number	2001
7	Number of STAtistics nodes	0
8	Number of SINk nodes	0
9	Number of sink node releases to end a run of the network	value in Field 8
10	Time to end one run of the network	1.E20
11	Number of runs of the network	1
12	Indicator for output reports in addition to the final summary report (F → first run, E → each run, C → cumulative summary reports at end of each run, S → summary only)	F
13	Time from which statistics will be kept on each run	0.0
14	Maximum number of attributes associated with each transaction flowing through the network (not including the mark time attribute)	0
15	Run number for beginning of event tracing	0 (no tracing)
16	Run number for ending of event tracing	value of Field 15
17	Run number for beginning of nodal tracing (If other than zero, a TRA card is required)	0 (no tracing)
18	Run number for ending of nodal tracing	value in Field 17
19	Indicator that only input cards with errors are to be listed (E → cards with errors to be listed)	all input cards listed
20	Execution option (E1 → no execution and only input is to be examined; E2 → no execution if any input discrepancies; E3 → no execution if fatal input discrepancies; E4 → same as E1 with the echo check suppressed)	E3

SELECTING A DISTRIBUTION TYPE TO REPRESENT AN ACTIVITY TIME

This section is presented to provide a discussion and description of random variables and when a particular type may be appropriate. The procedures for fitting a distribution to a set of data are described in many books and manuals (48,81,94) and need not be gone into in this text. Any of the goodness-of-fit packages (94) can be used for testing the adequacy of a distribution with regard to a specific set of data. Goodness-of-fit tests such as Chi-square, Kolmogorov-Smirnov (K-S), Cramér-Von Mises, and matching moments can all be used for this purpose. For a test of normality, the Shapiro-Wilk test can be applied.

In this section, the characteristics of density functions that would lead a modeler to select a particular random variable type to represent an activity are described. For a formal discussion and graphical description of density functions, the book "Statistical Methods in Engineering" by Hahn and Shapiro is highly recommended (48). The procedures for obtaining random samples in the Q-GERT Analysis Program are similar to those employed in the GASP IV simulation language. The GASP IV book provides the details of these procedures (111).

Throughout the discussion, the following variable definitions will be used:

$$
\begin{aligned}
x &= \text{the random variable} \\
f(x) &= \text{the density function of x} \\
a &= \text{minimum;} \\
b &= \text{maximum;} \\
m &= \text{mode;} \\
\mu &= \text{mean} = E[x] \\
\sigma^2 &= \text{variance} = E[(x-\mu)^2] \\
\sigma &= \text{standard deviation} \\
\alpha &= \text{a parameter of the density function} \\
\beta &= \text{a parameter of the density function}
\end{aligned}
$$

For those density functions which are not expressed in terms of μ and σ, formulas for μ and σ will be given.

Uniform Distribution

The uniform density function specifies that every value between a minimum and maximum value is equally likely. The use of the uniform distribution often implies a complete lack of knowledge concerning the time to perform an activity other than that it is between a minimum value and a maximum value. Another way of saying this is that the probability that an activity duration is in a specified interval is proportional to the length of the interval. Another name for the uniform distribution is the rectangular distribution. Figure 6-2 gives the density function for the uniform distribution and its graph. Samples are obtained using the probability-integral transformation (111).

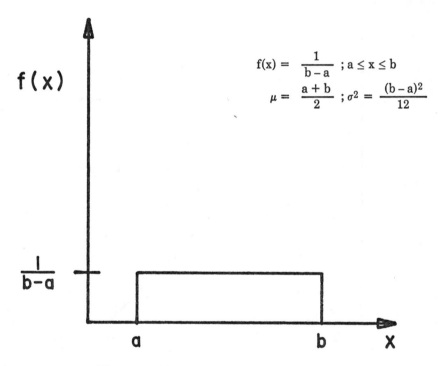

$$f(x) = \frac{1}{b-a} \; ; a \le x \le b$$

$$\mu = \frac{a+b}{2} \; ; \sigma^2 = \frac{(b-a)^2}{12}$$

Figure 6-2   Uniform density function and illustration.

Triangular Distribution

The triangular distribution is one step up from the uniform distribution. For this distribution, three values are specified: a minimum, mode and a maximum. The density function consists of two linear parts: one part increases from the minimum to the mode value; and the other part decreases from the mode value to the maximum. The average associated with a triangular density is the sum of the minimum, mode and maximum divided by 3. The triangular distribution is used when a most likely value can be ascertained along with minimum and maximum values, and a piecewise linear density function seems appropriate. Figure 6-3 gives the density function for the triangular distribution and its graph. Samples are obtained using the probability-integral transformation (111). The triangular distribution is easy to use and explain, and should be given serious consideration when hypothesizing a form for a random variable.

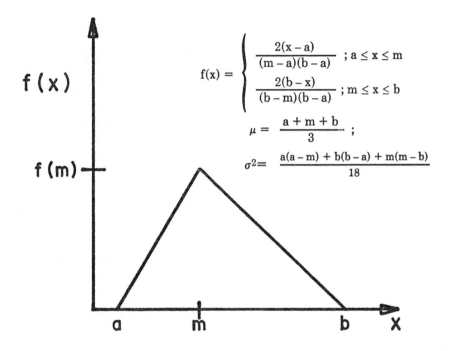

$$f(x) = \begin{cases} \dfrac{2(x-a)}{(m-a)(b-a)} & ; a \le x \le m \\[2ex] \dfrac{2(b-x)}{(b-m)(b-a)} & ; m \le x \le b \end{cases}$$

$$\mu = \frac{a+m+b}{3} \; ;$$

$$\sigma^2 = \frac{a(a-m) + b(b-a) + m(m-b)}{18}$$

Figure 6-3 Triangular density function and illustration.

Exponential Distribution

If the probability that one and only one event will occur during a small time interval Δt is proportional to Δt and if the occurrence of the event is independent of the occurrence of other events, then the time interval between occurrences of events is exponentially distributed. Another way of saying the above is that the activity characterized by an exponential distribution has the same probability of being completed in any subsequent period of time Δt. Thus, if the activity has been ongoing for t time units, the probability that it will end in the next Δt time units is the same as if it had just been started. This lack of conditioning of remaining time on past time expended is called the Markov or forgetfulness property. There is direct association between the assumption of an exponential activity duration and Markovian assumptions. The use of an exponential distribution assumes a large variability in activity times. If the expected duration of an activity is μ, then the variance of the time to perform the activity is μ^2. The exponential distribution has one of the largest variances associated with it of the common distribution types. The exponential distribution can be manipulated mathematically with ease and is assumed for many studies because of this property.

Figure 6-4 gives the density function for the exponential distribution and its graph. Samples are obtained using the probability-integral transformation (111).

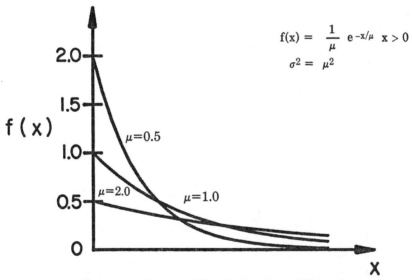

$$f(x) = \frac{1}{\mu}\, e^{-x/\mu} \quad x > 0$$

$$\sigma^2 = \mu^2$$

Figure 6-4 Exponential density function and illustrations.

Poisson Distribution

The Poisson distribution is different from the distributions discussed above in that it usually pertains to a number of events occurring in a

specified time period. If the duration of time between events is exponentially distributed and events occur one at a time, then the number of
events that occur in a fixed time interval can be shown to be Poisson
distributed. Thus, if the interarrival distribution is exponential, the
number of arrivals during a run will be Poisson distributed. The Poisson
distribution is frequently used as a limiting case approximation to the
binomial distribution where the binomial distribution is used to represent a series of independent Bernoulli trials (an outcome of a trial is go-
no go, success-failure, yes-no). For large mean, the normal distribution
is used to approximate the Poisson distribution.

Figure 6-5 gives the Poisson probability mass function and illustrates
its form. Samples are obtained using a derived scheme involving the
generation of exponential samples (111).

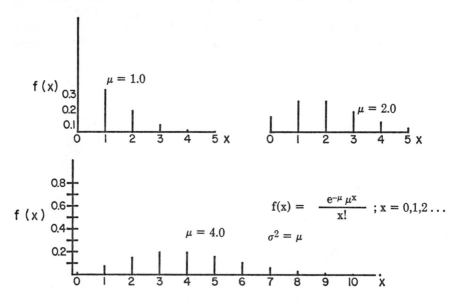

Figure 6-5   Poisson probability mass function and illustrations.

Normal Distribution

The normal or Gaussian distribution is the most prominent distribution
in probability and statistics. Justification for the use of the normal distribution comes from the Central Limit Theorem which states that
under very broad conditions the distribution of the average or sum of n
independent observations from any distribution approaches a normal

distribution as n becomes large. Thus, when dealing with phenomena that are related to sums of random variables, approximation by a normal distribution should be considered.

Because of the Central Limit Theorem, it is easy to see why the normal distribution has received a great amount of attention and use in applications of probability and statistics. There is another reason for the heavy use of the normal distribution. The normal distribution also has the advantage of being mathematically tractable and consequently many techniques of statistical inference such as regression analysis and analysis of variance have been derived under the assumption of an underlying normal density function.

As discussed above, for large mean, the normal distribution is a good approximation to the Poisson distribution, which in turn is a limiting distribution for the binomial distribution.

Figure 6-6 gives the density function for the normal distribution and illustrates the distribution for selected values of the mean and standard deviation. Samples are obtained by summing 12 pseudo-random numbers.

Lognormal Distribution

The lognormal distribution is the distribution of a random variable whose natural logarithm follows the normal distribution (60). The lognormal distribution is appropriate for a multiplicative type process in the same manner that the normal distribution is applicable for additive type processes. By use of the Central Limit Theorem, it can be shown that the distribution of the product of independent positive random variables approaches a lognormal distribution under very general conditions.

If a set of data is transformed by taking the logarithm of each data point, and if the transformed data points are normally distributed, then the original data is said to be lognormally distributed. The lognormal distribution has been used as an appropriate model in a wide variety of situations from biology to economics. It is an appropriate model for processes where the value of an observed variable is a random proportion of the previous observed value. Examples of such processes include the distribution of personal incomes, inheritances and bank deposits, and the distribution of particle sizes.

Figure 6-7 gives the density function for the lognormal distribution and illustrates the distribution for selected values of the mean and variance. Samples are generated by transforming a sample from a normal distribution.

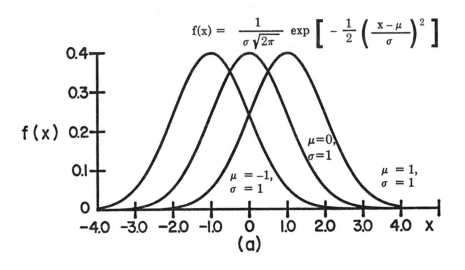

$$f(x) = \frac{1}{\sigma \sqrt{2\pi}} \exp\left[-\frac{1}{2}\left(\frac{x-\mu}{\sigma}\right)^2\right]$$

(a)

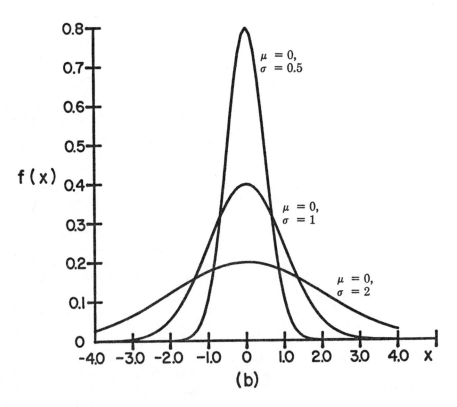

(b)

Figure 6-6 Normal density function and illustrations.

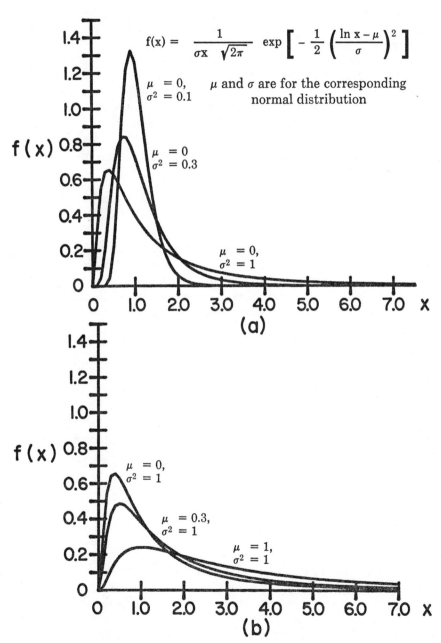

$$f(x) = \frac{1}{\sigma x \sqrt{2\pi}} \exp\left[-\frac{1}{2} \left(\frac{\ln x - \mu}{\sigma} \right)^2 \right]$$

$\mu = 0,$
$\sigma^2 = 0.1$

μ and σ are for the corresponding normal distribution

$\mu = 0$
$\sigma^2 = 0.3$

$\mu = 0,$
$\sigma^2 = 1$

(a)

$\mu = 0,$
$\sigma^2 = 1$

$\mu = 0.3,$
$\sigma^2 = 1$

$\mu = 1,$
$\sigma^2 = 1$

(b)

Figure 6-7 Lognormal density function and illustrations.

Erlang Distribution

The Erlang distribution is derived as the sum of independent and identically distributed exponential random variables. It is a special case of the gamma distribution, and the density function, illustrations and remarks concerning the gamma distribution apply to the Erlang distribution. The Erlang distribution is used extensively in queueing theory when an activity or service time is considered to occur in phases with each phase being exponentially distributed. Samples are generated by summing exponential samples. It is more efficient to generate a sample from an Erlang distribution than from a gamma distribution.

Gamma Distribution

The gamma distribution is a generalization of the Erlang distribution where conceptually the number of sums of exponentials included need not be integer valued. Gamma distributed times can take on values between 0 and infinity. By different parameter settings, the gamma distribution can be made to take on a variety of shapes and, hence, can represent many different physical processes.

The gamma distribution is related to the normal distribution as the sum of squares of normal random variables, which is the chi-squared distribution, is a special case of the gamma distribution. Thus, special cases of the gamma are the chi-squared distribution, the Erlang distribution, and, hence, the exponential distribution.

Figure 6-8 gives the density function for the gamma distribution and illustrates the density function for selected values of its parameters. Samples are generated using a scheme developed by Jöhnk (58) and Fox (41).

Beta and Beta-PERT Distributions

The beta distribution is defined over a finite range and can take on a wide variety of shapes for different values of its parameters. It can be bell shaped, symmetric or asymmetric, or it can be U-shaped within the finite range. For U-shaped beta functions, the value of the density function goes to infinity as the ends of the range are approached. A simple variant of the beta distribution is referred to as the Pareto distribution

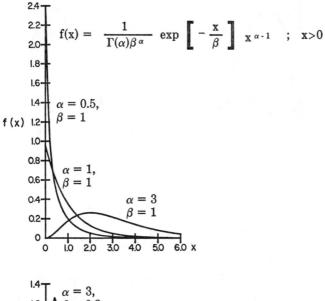

$$f(x) = \frac{1}{\Gamma(\alpha)\beta^{\alpha}} \exp\left[-\frac{x}{\beta}\right] x^{\alpha-1} \quad ; \quad x > 0$$

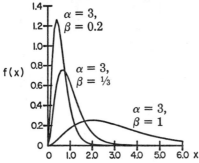

Figure 6-8   Gamma density function and illustrations.

which is used to characterize income distributions. Due to the wide variety of shapes obtainable for the beta distribution, it has been used to fit many different types of data.*

Since the beta distribution is defined over a finite interval, it has been used to describe situations which have a finite range. Examples of this are density functions related to percentages and probability estimates.

---

* In this regard, the warning given by Feller (39) with regard to the law of logistic growth should be mentioned: "... the only trouble with the theory is that not only the logistic distribution but also the normal, the Cauchy and other distributions can be fitted to the same material with the same or better goodness-of-fit ... Most contradictory theoretical models can be supported by the same observational material."

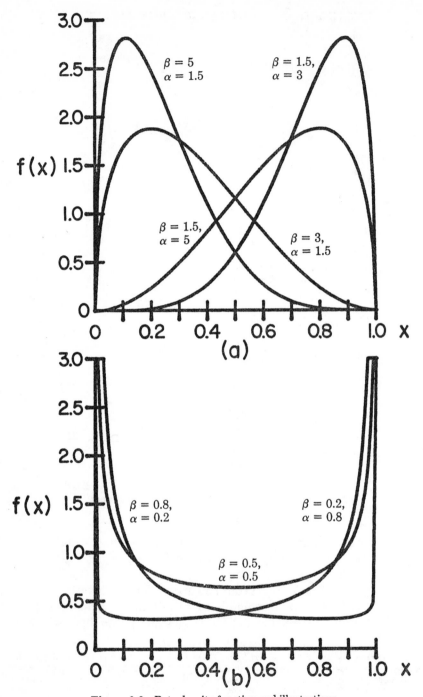

Figure 6-9 Beta density function and illustrations.

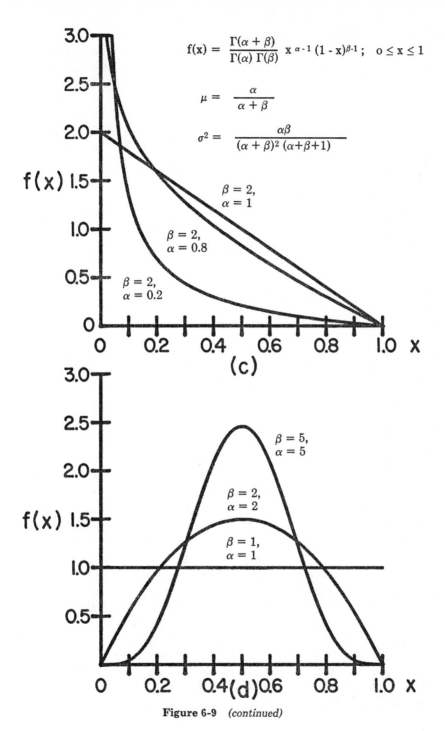

$$f(x) = \frac{\Gamma(\alpha + \beta)}{\Gamma(\alpha)\,\Gamma(\beta)}\, x^{\alpha-1}\,(1-x)^{\beta-1}\,; \quad 0 \le x \le 1$$

$$\mu = \frac{\alpha}{\alpha + \beta}$$

$$\sigma^2 = \frac{\alpha\beta}{(\alpha+\beta)^2\,(\alpha+\beta+1)}$$

$\beta = 2,\ \alpha = 1$

$\beta = 2,\ \alpha = 0.8$

$\beta = 2,\ \alpha = 0.2$

(c)

$\beta = 5,\ \alpha = 5$

$\beta = 2,\ \alpha = 2$

$\beta = 1,\ \alpha = 1$

(d)

Figure 6-9 *(continued)*

207

Frequently, the beta distribution is used as the a priori distribution of the parameter of a binomial process by Bayesian statisticians. Another use of the beta distribution is as the descriptive density function associated with an activity duration in PERT. Subjective estimates of the activity duration based on optimistic (a), pessimistic (b), and most likely (m) values are combined to estimate the mean and variance of the beta distribution as $(a+4m+b)/6$ and $(b-a)^2/36$ respectively. The beta-PERT function of Q-GERT uses these estimates in conjunction with the beta distribution to obtain samples.

Figure 6-9 gives the density function for the beta distribution and illustrates the density function for selected values of its parameters. The ratio of gamma random variables are beta distributed, and samples in Q-GERT are obtained by taking the ratio of gamma samples.

Truncated Versus Mixed Distributions

The samples obtained for the random variables included in Q-GERT are values from a distribution with a minimum and maximum specified. The probability associated with values less than the minimum is concentrated at the minimum value. Similarly, the probability of obtaining a sample greater than the maximum value is concentrated at the maximum value. Any sample drawn from the distribution which is outside the range specified by the minimum and maximum values is set at the minimum or maximum value. Within the minimum and maximum values, the density function prescribed for the random variable is used to portray the probability associated with values within the range. The distribution of a random variable as described above is referred to as a mixed distribution in that there are discrete probabilities associated with the minimum and maximum points and a continuous density function is used for intermediate points. *Note that the mean and standard deviation associated with a mixed distribution may be different from the values commonly associated with the density function.*

If samples are desired from the entire density function, then a small value for the minimum and a large value for the maximum should be used. If samples are desired from a truncated distribution, then the probabilities associated with obtaining samples outside the range specified by the minimum and maximum value need to be distributed over the entire allowed range for the random variable. Two procedures are available for doing this in Q-GERT, both of which require the use of advanced Q-GERT concepts (see Chapter 7). First, a sample can be drawn using one of the generator functions included in Q-GERT through a call to the appropriate function. The user should then make a test to see if the obtained sample is either less than the minimum or greater than the maximum value. If it is, the sample is rejected and another sample is generated by another call to the generator. This process is continued until a sample within the prescribed range is obtained. A second procedure is to include a generator as a user built function that obtains samples from a truncated distribution. This specially built function can be patterned after the Q-GERT generator with the exception that samples are rejected if they are outside the range prescribed. This second procedure will be more efficient, but requires the adaptation of the Q-GERT generators.

Subprograms for obtaining samples from truncated distributions were not included in Q-GERT because of the possible confusion between obtaining samples from truncated and mixed distributions. Mixed distributions were selected over truncated distributions to avoid the possibility of a user specifying a narrow range from which samples would be accepted. The rejection of samples if done excessively can lead to long execution times. The open ended design of Q-GERT allows new sample generators to be added at any time.

EXAMPLE 7. A BANKING SYSTEM (110)

Problem Statement

Figure 6-10 depicts schematically a banking system involving two inside tellers and two drive-in tellers. Arrivals to the banking system are either for the drive-in tellers or for the in-house tellers. The drive-in tellers have limited waiting space. Queueing space is available for only three cars waiting for one of the tellers and four cars waiting for the other teller. If a car arrives when the queues of both drive-in tellers are full, the customer balks and seeks service from one of the inside bank tellers. However, the inside bank system opens one hour after the drive-in bank.

Customers who directly seek the services of the inside tellers arrive through a different arrival process. However, they join the same queue as the balkers from the drive-in portion. A single queue is used for both inside tellers. A maximum of seven customers can wait in this single queue. Customers who arrive when there are seven in the inside queue balk and do not seek banking service. In this description of the banking system, the times to serve customers and the interarrival times of customers were purposefully omitted. These times are not required to understand or model the structure of the system. These times will be inserted during the discussion of the Q-GERT network model.

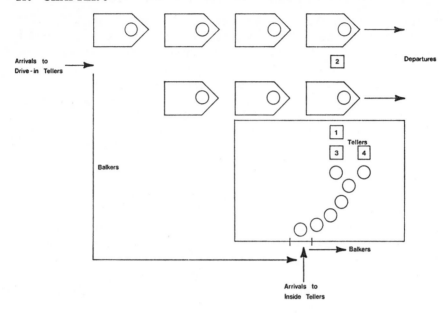

Figure 6-10   Pictorial representation of a banking system, Example 7.

Q-GERT Model

Figure 6-11 presents the Q-GERT network representing this banking system. Nodes 2 and 9 are source nodes for the network. Node 2 signifies the arrival of a customer (transaction) to the drive-in portion of the banking system. Since the output side of node 2 is deterministic, both branches emanating from node 2 are taken. The branch from node 2 back to node 2 depicts an exponential time between arrivals of customers to the drive-in portion of the bank. The time of arrival of each customer is "marked" at node 2, and this time is associated with the transaction that represents the customer. The branch between node 2 and node 3 (activity 1) involves a time delay of 1 minute for the customer after his arrival.

Node 3 is an S-node to select between the two queues of the drive-in tellers. The queue selection code SNQ signifies that the transaction will be routed to the shorter queue when a difference in the queue lengths exists. If both queues are full, the customer balks from S-node 3 and the dot-dash line from node 3 to node 8 illustrates this balking. The dashed lines from node 3 to node 4 and from node 3 to node 5 indicate the queue selection alternatives. The queue for the first teller is indicated by Q-node 4 which initially has 0 in the queue, allows a maximum of 3

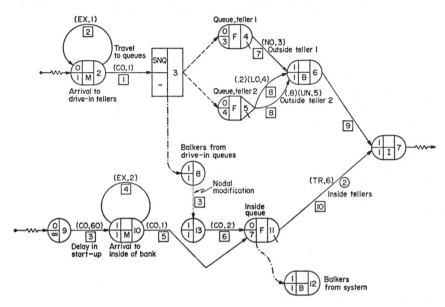

Figure 6-11 Q-GERT network model of a banking system, Example 7.

customers, and ranks customers on a *FIFO* basis. The service time for this teller is indicated by the branch from node 4 to node 6, that is, activity 7.

Q-node 5 also has no one in it initially, has a limit of 4 waiting spaces, and uses a *FIFO* ranking. The service time for the second teller is dichotomized into two types. The triangle on the output side of Q-node 5 indicates that probabilistic branching is prescribed and that either one or the other of the branches will be taken. Probabilities are assigned to the branches representing the activities. These two branches represent the service time for the same server (activity 8) and no matter which one is taken, the server is assumed to be busy. Thus, only one of the two branches from node 5 to node 6 can be ongoing at a given time. From the Q-GERT network, service time by this teller will be lognormally distributed 20 percent of the time and uniformly distributed 80 percent of the time.

Node 6 is inserted into the network in order to collect statistics on the time between departures from the drive-in system. This is indicated by the B in the central portion of node 6. The time between departures from the drive-in bank is important if an analysis is to be made of the

ability of the highway to accept departures from the drive-in system.*
The branch from node 6 to node 7 represents an information transfer
activity. At node 7, the customer has departed the system and the interval of time from when he was marked until he reaches node 7 is recorded
as indicated by the "I" in node 7.

Next, the internal operations of the bank are modeled in network
form. The branch from node 9 to node 10 delays the starting time for
the inside bank tellers. The sixty minute time specified for activity 3
represents this delay. At node 10, the arrival time for customers is
marked. The branch from node 10 back to node 10 represents the time
between arrivals of customers for the inside bank system. The activity
from node 10 to Q-node 11 represents the time it takes a customer to
travel from his arrival to the queue of the inside tellers.

The network modification which indicates that node 8 is replaced by
node 13 when activity 3 (the activity from node 9 to node 10) is completed indicates that balking from the drive-in system to the inside system cannot occur until after the inside system is open. The branch from
node 13 to node 11 represents the delay involved between the arrival
time of the customers at the drive-in system and the time they enter the
queue inside the bank. Q-node 11 represents the queue for the two inside tellers which initially has 0 in it and allows 7 as its maximum. Customers are ranked on a *FIFO* basis. Customers balk from Q-node 11
when it is full to node 12 and statistics are collected on the time between
balkers from the inside bank system. These balking customers are not
served by the bank system.

At the completion of service, the customers depart the system
through node 7 and interval statistics will be collected on their time in
the system. Note that the mark time given at either node 2 or node 10 is
associated with the customer and this time is used at node 7 to determine the interval of time that was spent in the system. By using one statistics node, node 7, all customers for the drive-in tellers and for the inside tellers are collected together. If separate statistics were desired,
then separate nodes would be required. A run will be ended when 300
customers have been processed by the banking system. This corresponds to 300 releases of sink node 7.

Descriptions of the activities of the banking network model are given
in Table 6-3. The time specifications for the activities are also given in
the table. The data input for the Q-GERT Analysis Program follows directly from the Q-GERT network and is shown in Figure 6-12. On the

---

*By modeling the bank exit as a server, the effect of exit rates on customer time in the
system could be obtained. This extension to the model could use the blocking capability of
Q-GERT to model the stoppage of service due to exit blockages.

Table 6-3. Activity Descriptions for Banking Network Model of Example 7.

Activity Number	Start Node	End Node	Description of Activity Times
1	2	3	One minute delay time to the drive-in waiting lines
2	2	2	Time between arrivals to drive-in bank. Exponentially distributed with a mean of 0.75 minutes.
3	9	10	Sixty minute delay time between opening of drive-in bank and inside bank.
4	10	10	Time between arrivals to inside bank. Exponentially distributed with a mean of 0.5 minutes.
5	10	11	One minute delay time to the inside waiting line.
6	13	11	Two minute delay time for drive-in arrival to balk to inside waiting line.
7	4	6	First drive-in teller service time: Normally distributed with a mean of 1.4 minutes and standard deviation of 0.3.
8	5	6	Second drive-in teller service, type 1: Lognormally distributed with a mean of 1.4 minutes and a standard deviation of 0.3.
8	5	6	Second drive-in teller service, type 2: Uniformly distributed between 1.0 and 2.0 minutes.
9	6	7	Information transfer.
10	11	7	Service times for the two inside tellers: Triangularly distributed between 0.5 and 1.6 minutes with a mode of 0.9 minutes.

GEN card, the stopping condition is specified as the release of 300 sink nodes. Since node 7 is the only sink node, this corresponds to 300 releases of it. In Field 13 of the GEN card, the time to begin collecting statistics is set to 60 because the in-house tellers will be idle until time 60. For this example, the 'C' report option is specified which causes a run report and a cumulative summary report at the end of each run to be printed. A SEEDS card is used to reinitialize random number streams 1 and 2 for each run. These streams are used to generate the customer arrival pattern and, hence, customer arrival times will be the same for all runs.

```
GEN,PRITSKER,BANK-7,4,11,1977,2,1,300,,5,C,60.*
SEEDS,1,479315/I,2,911823/I*       SET AND REINIT STREAMS 1 AND 2
SOU,2,0,1*                         GENERATE CUSTOMERS FOR DRIVE-IN BANK
ACT,2,2,EX,1,2*                    INTERARRIVAL TIME FOR DRIVE-IN BANK CUSTOMERS
PAR,1,0.75,0.,100.,,,1*            PARAMETER VALUES FOR INTERARRIVAL TIME
ACT,2,3,CC,1,1*                    DELAY OF DRIVE-IN BANK CUSTOMERS
SEL,3/SLECTQ,SNQ,(6)8,4,5*         SELECT BETWEEN DRIVE-IN TELLER QUEUES OR BALK
REG,8,1,1*                         NODE TO WHICH DRIVE-IN CUSTOMERS BALK
REG,13,1,1*                        REPLACEMENT FOR NODE 8
MOD,3,8,13*                        ALLOW BALKING TO INSIDE TELLERS
ACT,13,11,CO,2,6*                  DELAY FOR BALKERS TO INSIDE TELLERS
QUE,4/TELLER1Q,0,3,0,F*            DRIVE-IN TELLER QUEUE
ACT,4,6,NO,3,7/TELLER-1,1*         DRIVE-IN TELLER SERVICE ACTIVITY
PAR,3,1.4,0.8,2.5,0.3*             PARAMETER VALUES FOR SERVICE TIME
QUE,5/TELLER2Q,0,4,P*              DRIVE-IN TELLER QUEUE
ACT,5,6,LO,4,8/TELLER-2,1,0.2*     DRIVE-IN TELLER SERVICE ACTIVITY
PAR,4,1.4,0.8,2.5,0.3*             PARAMETER VALUES FOR SERVICE TIME
ACT,5,6,UN,5,8/TELLER-2,1,0.8*     DRIVE-IN TELLER SERVICE ACTIVITY
PAR,5,,1.,2.*                      PARAMETER VALUES FOR SERVICE TIME
STA,6/T-BETDEP,1,1,0,B*            COLLECT STATISTICS ON TIME BETWEEN DEPARTURES
ACT,6,7,(6)9*                      INFORMATION TRANSFER
SIN,7/CUST-TIM,1,1,0,I,1.,2.*      COLLECT STATISTICS ON CUSTOMER TIME IN SYSTEM
SOU,9*                             SOURCE NODE FOR INSIDE BANK OPERATIONS
ACT,9,10,CO,60,3*                  DELAY IN OPENING INSIDE BANK
REG,10,1,1,0,M*                    GENERATE CUSTOMERS FOR INSIDE BANK
ACT,10,10,EX,2,4*                  INTERARRIVAL TIME FOR INSIDE BANK CUSTOMERS
PAR,2,0.50,0.,100.,,,2*            PARAMETER VALUES FOR INTERARRIVAL TIME
ACT,10,11,CO,1,5*                  DELAY FOR CUSTOMERS FOR INSIDE TELLERS
QUE,11/INSIDE-Q1,0,7,0,F,12*       QUEUE FOR INSIDE TELLERS
ACT,11,7,TR,6,10/INS-TELL,2*       SERVICE TIME FOR TWO INSIDE TELLERS
PAR,6,0.9,0.5,1.6*                 PARAMETER VALUES FOR SERVICE TIME
STA,12/T-B-BALK,1,1,,B*            COLLECT STATISTICS ON TIME BETWEEN BALKERS
FIN*
```

Figure 6-12   Data input for Q-GERT network model of a banking system, Example 7.

Summary of Results

The final results for five simulation runs for the Q-GERT model of the banking situation are shown in Figure 6-13.

The statistical estimates are based on the time period from 60 minutes to the end of the simulation run. Thus, all data values collected up to time 60 are not included in the statistics presented.

FINAL RESULTS FOR   5 SIMULATIONS

AVERAGE NODE STATISTICS

NODE	LABEL	PROBABILITY	AVE.	STD.DEV.	SD OF AVE	NO. OF OBS.	MIN.	MAX.	STAT TYPE
7	CUST-TIM	1.0000	4.3151	.1663	.0744	5.	4.0950	4.4879	I
12	T-B-BALK	1.0000	4.1280	2.6213	1.1723	5.	.6147	6.6291	B
6	T-BETDEP	1.0000	.7235	.0191	.0085	5.	.7099	.7543	B

AVERAGE NUMBER IN Q-NODE

NODE	LABEL	AVE.	STD.DEV.	SD OF AVE	MIN.	MAX.	NUMBER IN Q-NODE MAX.
4	TELLER1Q	2.2134	.0683	.0305	2.1492	2.3049	3.3333
5	TELLER2Q	2.2772	.0926	.0414	2.1421	2.3878	4.3000
11	INSIDE-Q	1.9149	.3680	.1646	1.3625	2.3300	7.0000

AVERAGE WAITING TIME

AVE.	STD.DEV.	SD OF AVE	NO. OF OBS.	MIN.	MAX.
3.0943	.2677	.1197	5.		
3.4234	.1759	.0787	5.		
1.0691	.2079	.0930	5.		

AVERAGE SERVER UTILIZATION

SERVER	LABEL	NO. PARALLEL SERVERS	AVE.	STD.DEV.	SD OF AVE	NO. OF OBS.	MIN.	MAX.
7	TELLER-1	1	.9991	.0021	.0009	5.	.9953	1.0000
8	TELLER-2	1	.9956	.0085	.0038	5.	.9805	1.0000
10	INS-TELL	2	1.6781	.0458	.0205	5.	1.6031	1.7161

EXTREME VALUES

MAX. IDLE (TIME OR SERVERS)	MAX. BUS (TIME OR SERVERS)
.3604	77.9476
1.4977	77.1915
2.0000	2.0000

AVERAGE NO. BALKING PER UNIT TIME

NODE	LABEL	AVE.	STD.DEV.	SD OF AVE	NO. OF OBS.	MIN.	MAX.
11	INSIDE-Q	.0648	.0311	.0139	5.	.0392	.1155
3	SLECTQ	.0961	.0368	.0165	5.	.0648	.1411

Figure 6-13   Results for five runs of Q-GERT model of a banking system, Example 7.

The statistics on average number in the Q-nodes and server utilization provide standard information of interest regarding the tellers' operations. The balking statistics illustrate that 0.10 customers per minute balked from the drive-in portion of the bank system (S-node 3). Since the average time between arrivals is 0.50 minutes, the customer arrival rate is 2.0 per minute. It appears that one out of twenty customers arriving to the drive-in portion of the bank are balking to the inside portion of the bank.

Selected averages from the run and cumulative summary reports are presented in Table 6-4. From this table, it is seen that the outputs from each run are similar. One reason for this similarity is the use of common randon number streams to generate the same arrival pattern for each run.

EXAMPLE 8. MODELING OF A TRUCK HAULING SITUATION

Problem Statement

This example illustrates the use of the S-node for an assembly operation. The problem statement is taken from a paper by Halpin and Happ (49,50). The system to be modeled consists of one bulldozer, four trucks and two man-machine loaders. The bulldozer stockpiles material for the loaders. Two piles of material must be stocked prior to the initiation of any load operation. The time for the bulldozer to stockpile material is Erlang distributed and consists of the sum of two exponential variables each with a mean of 4. (This corresponds to an Erlang variable with a mean of 8 and a variance of 32). In addition to this material, a loader and an unloaded truck must be available before the loading operation can begin. Loading time is exponentially distributed with a mean time of 14 minutes for server 1 and 16 minutes for server 2.

After a truck is loaded, it is hauled, then dumped and must be returned before the truck is available for further loading. Hauling time is normally distributed. When loaded the average hauling time is 22 minutes. When unloaded, the average time is 18 minutes. In both cases the standard deviation is 3 minutes. Dumping time is uniformly distributed between 2 and 8 minutes. Following a loading operation, the loader rests for a 5 minute period of time before he is available to begin loading again. A schematic diagram of the system is shown in Figure 6-14. The system is to be analyzed for 8 hours and all operations in progress at the end of 8 hours should be completed before terminating the operations for a run.

Table 6-4. Run and Cumulative Statistics for Banking System, Example 7.

Run Values

Run	Average Time for Node 7	Average Number in Q-node			Average Utilization for Server(s)		
		4	5	11	7	8	10
1	4.38	2.19	2.14	2.33	1.00	1.00	1.67
2	4.09	2.16	2.39	1.36	1.00	1.00	1.60
3	4.43	2.26	2.32	2.02	0.99	0.98	1.71
4	4.19	2.15	2.24	1.77	1.00	1.00	1.72
5	4.49	2.30	2.29	2.09	1.00	1.00	1.69

Cumulative Values

Run	Average Time for Node 7	Average Number in Q-node			Average Utilization for Server(s)		
		4	5	11	7	8	10
1	4.38	2.19	2.14	2.33	1.00	1.00	1.67
2	4.23	2.17	2.26	1.85	1.00	1.00	1.64
3	4.30	2.20	2.28	1.90	1.00	1.00	1.66
4	4.27	2.19	2.27	1.87	1.00	1.00	1.67
5	4.32	2.21	2.28	1.91	1.00	1.00	1.68

Q-GERT Model.

The network to analyze this problem is given in Figure 6-15.

The nodes from 2 to 5 represent the bulldozing operations. The time to perform a bulldozing operation is Erlang distributed with parameters specified in parameter set 1. Only when two loads are delivered by the bulldozer will a load be available. This combining of loads is done at node 4, and each transaction stored in Q-node 5 represents two loads. Since it does not matter which mark time is associated with the two loads (interval statistics are not collected and attributes are not used), a choice criterion is not required, and hence, is not indicated. The transactions in Q-node 5 are ranked on a FIFO basis.

Nodes 5 through 8 and node 15 represent the loading operation. Q-node 6 represents the queue of trucks. Initially, there are 4 trucks waiting for loads. Since no new trucks are added to the system, the number in the queue can never exceed 4. Q-node 7 represents the queue of human loaders, and initially there are 2 manual loaders in the system. S-node 15 selects transactions from Q-nodes on an assembly basis (ASM) and, thus, requires inputs from Q-nodes 5, 6 and 7 in order for a loading (service) to be initiated. Since no loads are initially at node 5, the servers are initially idle. (Recall servers are set busy if its preceding Q-node has a transaction in it. The ASM rule requires all preceding Q-nodes to have a transaction in order for its server to be busy initially.) If both loaders are idle when a loading operation is being scheduled, S-node 15 selects the server with the *l*ongest *i*dle *t*ime (LIT). The service by either loader is represented by the branches from node 15 to node 8 and each has an exponential service time.

An interesting aspect of this model is the representation of the manual loaders as servers performing either service activity 1 or 2 and as transactions queueing up at Q-node 7. The reason for this dual representation is to allow for a resting time for the men involved in the service activity. The branch from node 8 to Q-node 7 represents this time. Since service cannot begin until there exists a transaction in Q-nodes 5,6 and 7, the service activity will have an enforced idle period due to this resting time. Q-node 7 is ranked on a FIFO basis so that there is a correspondence between the loaders in Q-node 7 and the server who has been idle the longest.

The hauling operation is represented by the activity from node 8 to node 9. The time to haul is *NO*rmally distributed. The truck dumping operation is represented by the activity from node 9 to node 10 and is *UN*iformly distributed. The transportation time for the truck to return

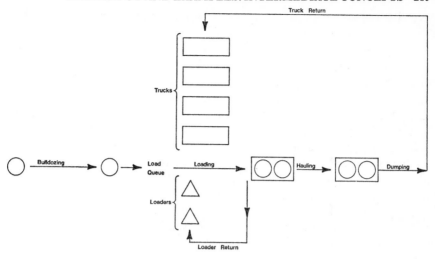

Figure 6-14   A truck hauling situation, Example 8.

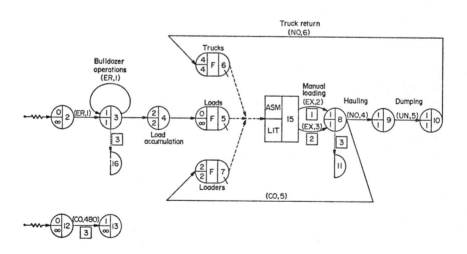

Figure 6-15   Q-GERT model of a truck hauling system, Example 8.

to the queue of trucks is *NO*rmally distributed and is represented by the branch from node 10 to node 6.

A disjoint timing network is used to stop the arrival process at time 480 and is represented by nodes 12 and 13. The branch from node 12 to node 13 represents an 8 hour day, that is, 480 minutes. This activity is coded as activity number 3. It is used to halt the bulldozer operations at node 3 (replaced by node 16) and hauling operations at node 8 (replaced by node 11), after 8 hours have passed. Since no new arrivals after time 480 will occur and since the loaders are not scheduled to return to the loader queue, only the activities involving truck operations will be completed. When the trucks return to their queue, no further activities will be scheduled and the run will be terminated.

In this network, no attributes are assigned to transactions and no statistics collection is indicated for the nodes and transactions in the network. Even under these circumstances, extensive statistical information is generated by the Q-GERT Analysis Program. The type of information obtained is listed below:

1. Number of trucks idle (Number of transactions in Q-node 6)

```
GEN,PRITSKER,HAULING-8,7,8,1977,0,0,0,,1,(15)1*
SOU,2*                        START NODE FOR BULLDOZING OPERATIONS
ACT,2,3,ER,1*                 FIRST BULLDOZER ACTIVITY
PAR,1,4,0,100,2*              PARAMETER VALUES FOR LOAD GENERATION
REG,3,1,1*                    GENERATION OF LOAD TRANSACTIONS
ACT,3,3,ER,1*                 SUBSEQUENT BULLDOZER ACTIVITIES
ACT,3,4*                      INFORMATION TRANSFER
REG,16*                       REPLACEMENT NODE TO STOP TRANSACTION GENERATION
REG,4,2,2*                    ACCUMULATION OF TWO LOADS FOR HAULING
ACT,4,5*                      INFORMATION TRANSFER
QUE,5/LOAD-Q,(10)15*          QUEUE FOR LOADS READY FOR LOADING
QUE,6/TRUCK-Q,4,4,(10)15*     QUEUE OF TRUCKS
QUE,7/LOADER-Q,2,2,(10)15*    QUEUE OF LOADERS
SEL,15,ASM,LIT,(7)5,6,7*      ASSEMBLY OF LOADS, TRUCKS, AND LOADERS
ACT,15,8,EX,2,1/LOADER-1*     LOADING ACTIVITY
PAR,2,14,0,100*               PARAMETER VALUES FOR LOADING TIME
ACT,15,8,EX,3,2/LOADER-2*     LOADING ACTIVITY
PAR,3,16,0,100*               PARAMETER VALUES FOR LOADING TIME
REG,8,1,1*                    COMPLETION OF LOADING
ACT,8,9,NO,4,,1*              HAULING ACTIVITY
PAR,4,22,0,100,3*             PARAMETER VALUES FOR HAULING TIME
ACT,8,7,CO,5*                 BREAK TIME FOR LOADER
REG,11*                       REPLACEMENT NODE TO STOP LOADING
REG,9,1,1*                    END OF HAULING
ACT,9,10,UN,5*                DUMPING ACTIVITY
PAR,5,,2,8*                   PARAMETER VALUES FOR DUMPING TIME
REG,10,1,1*                   END OF DUMPING
ACT,10,6,NO,6*                TRUCK TRAVEL TIME
PAR,6,18,0,100,3*             PARAMETER VALUES FOR TRUCK TRAVEL TIME
SOU,12*                       START OF TIMING SUBNETWORK
ACT,12,13,CO,480,3*           ONE DAY INFORMATION TRANSFER
REG,13*                       END OF DAY NODE
MOD,3,3,16,8,11*              NODE MODIFICATION SPECIFICATION
FIN*
```

Figure 6-16   Data input for a truck hauling system, Example 8.

2. Number of manual loaders waiting for loads (Number of transactions in Q-node 7)
3. Number of 2-unit loads waiting for service (Number of transactions in Q-node 5)
4. Busy time for loaders (Busy time of service activities 1 and 2)

Of course, other statistics could be collected by recording statistics at some of the nodes. The data input for this example is given in Figure 6-16.

Summary of Results

A summary of the statistical outputs obtained from the Q-GERT Analysis Program is given in Table 6-5. This summary is only for illustrative purposes and no detailed description is provided.

Table 6-5. Summary of Output Statistics for One Run of 513 Minutes of Truck Hauling System, Example 8.

	Average	Maximum
Number of loads waiting	1.00	3
Number of trucks idle	0.67	4
Number of loaders waiting	0.81	2

	Loader 1	Loader 2
Average utilization	0.47	0.40
Longest consecutive idle period	38.07	56.17
Longest consecutive busy period	50.59	51.47

To illustrate the working of the modifications used in Example 8, a trace of activities from time 470 to the end of the run is given in Figure 6-17. At time 480, activity 3 is completed. When activity 3 is completed, node 3 is replaced by node 16 and node 8 is replaced by node 11. Since nodes 16 and 11 have no output branches, no activities will be scheduled when either node 3 or node 8 is released. On the trace, node 3 is released at time 480.77. No activity is scheduled from node 3 as it has been replaced in the network by node 11. At times 498.33 and 506.42, node 8 is released and no activities are scheduled from node 8. A truck returns to Q-node 6 at time 512.89 and all activities for the run have been completed. Since no activities are on-going at this time, the run is terminated. A message that the run was terminated for this reason is printed.

***	3		470.33	0	0	7
3	3	470.33	480.77	0	0	7
3	4	470.33	470.33	0	0	10
***	4		470.33	0	0	10
4	5	470.33	470.33	0	0	10
***	5		470.33	0	0	10
***	10		471.24	0	0	6
10	6	471.24	492.00	0	0	6
***	7		472.52	0	0	2
***	9		479.50	0	0	1
9	10	479.50	482.19	0	0	1
***	13		480.00	3	0	8
***	3		480.77	0	0	7
***	10		482.19	0	0	1
10	0	482.19	494.82	0	0	1
***	6		487.32	0	0	11
15	8	487.32	506.42	1	0	11
***	9		491.56	0	0	5
9	10	491.56	494.25	0	0	5
***	6		492.00	0	0	6
15	8	492.00	498.33	2	0	6
***	10		494.25	0	0	5
10	6	494.25	512.89	0	0	5
***	6		494.82	0	0	1
***	8		498.33	2	0	6
***	8		506.42	1	0	11
***	6		512.89	0	0	5

ON RUN   1 SIMULATION ENDED DUE TO COMPLETION OF ALL ACTIVITIES

Figure 6-17   Trace of activities from time 470 to time 513, Example 8.

EXAMPLE 9. MODELING OF QUARRY OPERATIONS

Problem Statement

In this example, quarry operations are modeled. In the quarry, trucks deliver ore from three shovels to a single, primary crusher. The distances from each shovel to the crusher vary. In addition, trucks are assigned to specific shovels, so that a truck will always return to its assigned shovel after dumping a load at the crusher. There are two different truck sizes in use, twenty-ton and fifty-ton. The size of the truck affects its loading and dumping times at the shovel and the crusher. To each shovel is assigned two twenty-ton and one fifty-ton truck. The shovel queues are all ranked on a first-in, first-out basis. The crusher queue is ranked on truck size, largest trucks first. A schematic diagram of the quarry operations is shown in Figure 6-18. It is desired to analyze this system over 480 time units to determine the utilization of the shovels and crusher and information on the truck queue lengths at these service stations.

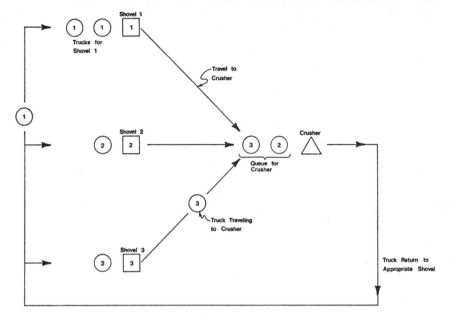

Figure 6-18   Schematic diagram of quarry operations, Example 9.

Q-GERT Model.

A Q-GERT network model of these quarry operations is presented in Figure 6-19. For explanation simplicity, all activity times are either constant times or are taken from an exponential distribution (EX).

Nodes 4 and 6 are source nodes. The twenty-ton trucks are initialized at node 4, and the fifty-ton trucks at node 6. The values for attributes 1 and 2 in each set are assigned at these source nodes. The first attribute contains the shovel identification number that the truck serves. These values are assigned with the incremental distribution, starting at a value of 1. Attribute 2 is used to represent truck size. A value of 20 is assigned at node 4 and 50 at node 6. Branching from nodes 4 and 6 is Condition-Take All and is based on the value of attribute 1. When attribute 1 is greater than 2, no further transactions are generated at the source nodes. In this manner, nodes 4 and 6 are released three times. The two branches from node 4 to node 18 cause two twenty-ton trucks to be generated every time node 4 is released. Thus, six transactions

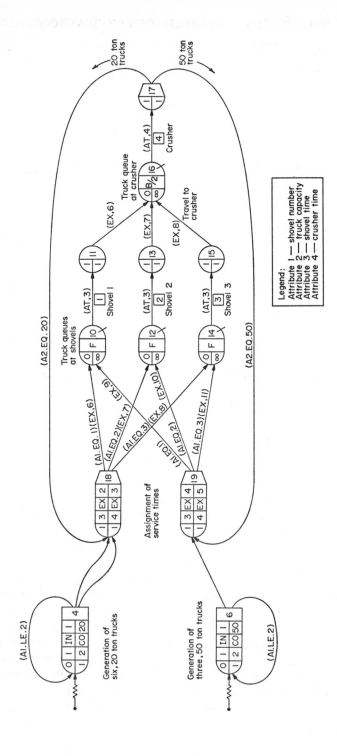

Figure 6-19 Q-GERT network of quarry operations, Example 9.

representing twenty-ton trucks are created. For node 6, three fifty-ton trucks are created.

The transactions representing the twenty-ton trucks are routed through node 18 where assignments are made to attributes 3 and 4. Attribute 3 is assigned the loading time at the shovel which is exponentially distributed with a mean of 5.0. Attribute 4 is assigned the dumping time at the crusher which is exponentially distributed with a mean of 2.0. Similarly, transactions representing fifty-ton trucks are assigned exponential loading and dumping times at node 19 with means of 10.0 and 4.0, respectively.

Next, the transactions are routed using condition-take first branching, to the appropriate shovel number by testing attribute 1. This matches the truck with its prescribed shovel. The duration times for the twenty-ton truck travel activities are exponentially distributed with means of 1.0, 2.5 and 1.75 to go to shovels 1, 2 and 3, respectively. For the fifty-ton trucks, travel times are also exponentially distributed with means of 1.2, 2.7 and 1.95 to go to shovels 1, 2 and 3, respectively. Thus, the system is initialized with all trucks unloaded, and they all must travel to their appropriate shovels before any loading can begin.

Nodes 10, 12 and 14 represent the shovel queues. The service times for the shoveling activities are all taken from the third attribute in the transaction being processed. The activities emanating from nodes 11, 13 and 15 represent truck travel to the crusher.

The crusher queue is represented by Q-node 16. This queue is ranked on attribute 2, big-value-first. The crusher service time is obtained from attribute 4 of the transaction being processed. Each time a truck finishes service, it branches from node 17. This branching is conditional-take first, based on the truck size carried in attribute 2. Node 17 directs the trucks to their proper assignment nodes where new service times are assigned to attributes 3 and 4. The simulation of trucks through the network continues until the end of simulation time of 480 is reached.

The input for the quarry model is given in Figure 6-20. On the GEN card, event and nodal traces are requested for run 1. The TRAce card indicates that traces for nodes 16 and 17 are desired.

Summary of Results

Since no statistic nodes were included in the Q-GERT model, statistics are only obtained for the average number in each Q-node and for average server utilization. A summary of results over 20 simulation runs is shown in Figure 6-21. Each run was made for 480 time units. The average over the 20 runs of the average number of trucks in Q-node 10 is

```
GEN,PRITSKER,QUARRY-9,6,15,1977,0,0,0,480.,20,F,0.0,4,1,,1*
TRACE,16,17*                      NODAL TRACE FOR NODES 16 AND 17
SOU,4,0,1,A*                      GENERATE SIX TRUCKS OF 20 TON SIZE
VAS,4,1,IN,1,2,CO,20*             ASSIGN SHOVEL NUMBERS AND TRUCK SIZE
SOU,6,0,1,A*                      GENERATE THREE TRUCKS OF 50 TON SIZE
VAS,6,1,IN,1,2,CO,50*             ASSIGN SHOVEL NUMBERS AND TRUCK SIZE
QUE,10/SHOVEL1Q,0,(8).25,.05*     QUEUE FOR SHOVEL 1
REG,11,1,1*                       END OF SHOVELING ACTIVITY
QUE,12/SHOVEL2Q,(8).25,.05*       QUEUE FOR SHOVEL 2
REG,13,1,1*                       END OF SHOVELING ACTIVITY
QUE,14/SHOVEL3Q,(8).25,.05*       QUEUE FOR SHOVEL 3
REG,15,1,1*                       END OF SHOVELING ACTIVITY
QUE,16/CRUSHERQ,(6)B/2,(8)1.0,.25* QUEUE FOR CRUSHER
REG,17,1,1,F*                     END OF CRUSHING ACTIVITY
REG,18,1,1,F*                     ASSIGN SERVICE TIMES FOR 20 TON TRUCKS
VAS,18,3,EX,2,4,EX,3*             SPECIFICATIONS FOR SERVICE TIMES
REG,19,1,1,F*                     ASSIGN SERVICE TIMES FOR 50 TON TRUCKS
VAS,19,3,EX,4,4,EX,5*             SPECIFICATIONS FOR SERVICE TIMES
PAR,2,5.0,1.0,10.0*               PARAMETER VALUES FOR SHOVEL (20 TON TRUCKS)
PAR,3,2.0,0.2,5.0*                PARAMETER VALUES FOR CRUSHER (20 TON TRUCKS)
PAR,4,10.,1.5,20.0*              PARAMETER VALUES FOR SHOVEL (50 TON TRUCKS)
PAR,5,4.0,0.5,10.0*               PARAMETER VALUES FOR CRUSHER (50 TON TRUCKS)
PAR,6,1.0,0.5,3.0*                PARAMETER VALUES FOR TRAVEL TO SHOVEL 1
PAR,7,2.5,1.0,4.0*                PARAMETER VALUES FOR TRAVEL TO SHOVEL 2
PAR,8,1.75,.75,3.5*               PARAMETER VALUES FOR TRAVEL TO SHOVEL 3
PAR,9,1.2,.6,3.2*                 PARAMETER VALUES FOR TRAVEL TO SHOVEL 1
PAR,10,2.7,1.1,4.2*               PARAMETER VALUES FOR TRAVEL TO SHOVEL 2
PAR,11,1.95,.85,3.7*              PARAMETER VALUES FOR TRAVEL TO SHOVEL 3
ACT,4,4,(9)A1.LE.2*               INFORMATION TRANSFER REGARDING 20 TON TRUCKS
ACT,4,18,(9)A1.GT.0*              INFORMATION TRANSFER REGARDING 20 TON TRUCKS
ACT,4,18,(9)A1.GT.0*              INFORMATION TRANSFER REGARDING 50 TON TRUCKS
ACT,6,6,(9)A1.LE.2*               INFORMATION TRANSFER REGARDING 50 TON TRUCKS
ACT,6,19,(9)A1.GT.0*              INFORMATION TRANSFER REGARDING 50 TON TRUCKS
ACT,18,10,EX,6,(9)A1.EQ.1*        TRAVEL ACTIVITY TO SHOVEL 1
ACT,18,12,EX,7,(9)A1.EQ.2*        TRAVEL ACTIVITY TO SHOVEL 2
ACT,18,14,EX,8,(9)A1.EQ.3*        TRAVEL ACTIVITY TO SHOVEL 3
ACT,19,10,EX,9,(9)A1.EQ.1*        TRAVEL ACTIVITY TO SHOVEL 1
ACT,19,12,EX,10,(9)A1.EQ.2*       TRAVEL ACTIVITY TO SHOVEL 2
ACT,19,14,EX,11,(9)A1.EQ.3*       TRAVEL ACTIVITY TO SHOVEL 3
ACT,10,11,AT,3,1/SHOVEL-1*        SHOVEL 1 SERVICE TIME
ACT,12,13,AT,3,2/SHOVEL-2*        SHOVEL 2 SERVICE TIME
ACT,14,15,AT,3,3/SHOVEL-3*        SHOVEL 3 SERVICE TIME
ACT,11,16,EX,6*                   TRAVEL TIME TO CRUSHER
ACT,13,16,EX,7*                   TRAVEL TIME TO CRUSHER
ACT,15,16,EX,8*                   TRAVEL TIME TO CRUSHER
ACT,16,17,AT,4,4/CRUSHER*         CRUSHER SERVICE TIME
ACT,17,18,(8)1,A2.EQ.20*          SEPARATE    TRANSACTIONS BY TRUCK SIZE
ACT,17,19,(8)2,A2.EQ.50*          SEPARATE    TRANSACTIONS BY TRUCK SIZE
FIN*
```

Figure 6-20   Q-GERT listing of input cards for quarry operations, Example 9.

0.59. A histogram of the average number in Q-node 10 on each run is presented in Figure 6-22. From Figure 6-22, it can be seen that the average number in Q-node 10 is between 0.40 and 0.45 on one run, between 0.45 and 0.50 on 3 runs, and between 0.50 and 0.55 on 5 runs. Thus, in 9 of the 20 runs representing 45 percent of the runs, the average number in the queue is less than 0.55.

The summary statistics in Figure 6-21 present estimates of the standard deviation of the sample mean and the minimum and maximum of the average number in each queue obtained over the 20 runs. Similar

GERT SIMULATION PROJECT QUARRY-9   BY PRITSKER
DATE 6/ 15/ 1977

FINAL RESULTS FOR   20 SIMULATIONS

NODE	LABEL	**AVERAGE NUMBER IN Q-NODE**					**AVERAGE WAITING TIME**			**NUMBER IN Q-NODE**
		AVE.	STD.DEV.	SD OF AVE	MIN.	MAX.	AVE.	STD.DEV.	SD OF AVE	MAX.
10	SHOVEL1Q	.5915	.1307	.0292	.4333	.9231	4.7691	1.2623	.2823	2.0000
12	SHOVEL2Q	.5202	.0949	.0212	.3785	.7467	4.6120	.7742	.1731	2.0000
14	SHOVEL3Q	.5239	.0823	.0184	.4037	.7427	4.3976	.6089	.1361	2.0000
16	CRUSHERQ	3.1066	.3988	.0892	1.8702	3.6163	8.9950	1.4613	.3267	8.0000

SERVER	LABEL	NO. PARALLEL SERVERS	**AVERAGE SERVER UTILIZATION**						**EXTREME VALUES**	
			AVE.	STD.DEV.	SD OF AVE	MIN.	MAX.	NO. OF OBS.	MAX. IDLE (TIME OR SERVERS)	MAX. BUSY
1	SHOVEL-1	1	.7631	.3490	.0110	.6763	.8710	20.	20.6793	146.6256
2	SHOVEL-2	1	.7185	.3501	.0112	.6357	.8345	20.	28.3708	140.3049
3	SHOVEL-3	1	.7179	.3468	.0105	.6002	.8172	20.	21.2142	96.2319
4	CRUSHER	1	.9100	.3299	.0067	.8256	.9477	20.	10.5309	229.2099

Figure 6-21   Final results for 20 runs of quarry operations, Example 9.

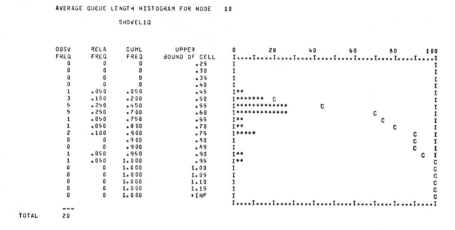

Figure 6-22   Histogram of average number of trucks in the queue of shovel 1, Example 9.

quantities are given for each server. From the output, it can be seen that the crushing operation is utilized 91 percent of the time and may be a bottleneck. Any future analysis or redesign should concentrate on improving the performance of the crushing operation.

To display the operation of the model, portions of the event trace and the nodal traces are given in Figure 6-23. A detailed analysis can be made of the transactions as they flow through the network or as they arrive and depart from specific nodes using the Q-GERT trace capability.

EXERCISES

6-1 Model and analyze a single-server queueing system where service is exponentially distributed with a mean service time of 1 hour and there are two types of arrivals. Arrival type 1 is an item of high priority and waits only for the processing of other high priority items. The time interval between arrivals of high priority items is exponentially distributed with a mean time between arrivals of 4 hours. The time between arrivals of low priority items is also exponentially distributed, but has a mean time between arrivals of 2 hours. Obtain statistics over 10 runs of length 1000 hours each on server utilization and the time spent in the system for high and low priority items. Assume that

START NODE	END NODE	START TIME	END TIME	ACTIVITY NUMBER	MARK TIME	TRANS. NUMBER	ATTRIBUTES			
RUN NO. 1										
13	16	119.68	120.58	0	0	8	2.00	20.00	1.00	.99
***	16		120.68	0	0	8	2.00	20.00	1.00	.99
12	12	120.71	120.71	2	0	6	2.00	50.00	2.03	.50
***	13		122.73	3	0	6	2.00	50.00	2.03	.50
15	15	121.27	121.27	0	0	4	3.00	50.00	6.35	10.00
***	16		123.33	2	0	6	2.00	50.00	2.03	10.00
13	13	122.73	122.73	0	0	6	2.00	50.00	2.03	.50
***	16		126.73	0	0	4	3.00	50.00	6.35	.50
16	16	123.41	123.33	4	0	5	1.00	50.00	1.50	10.00
17	17	123.41	123.41	4	0	4	3.00	50.00	6.35	4.24
***	19		133.41	0	0	5	1.00	50.00	1.50	10.00
19	19	123.41	123.41	0	0	5	1.00	50.00	1.50	4.24
***	10		123.41	0	0	5	1.00	50.00	1.96	5.60
10	11	125.53	125.53	1	0	5	1.00	50.00	1.96	5.60
***	15		127.49	1	0	6	2.00	50.00	2.03	5.60
11	11	127.49	126.73	1	0	5	1.00	50.00	1.96	.50
***	16		127.49	0	0	5	1.00	50.00	1.96	5.60
16	16	133.41	127.99	0	0	4	3.00	50.00	6.35	5.60
17	17	133.41	127.99	4	0	6	2.00	50.00	2.03	10.00
***	17		133.41	0	0	4	3.00	50.00	6.35	.50
19	19	133.41	133.91	0	0	4	3.00	50.00	6.35	10.00
***	19		133.41	0	0	6	3.00	50.00	1.53	10.00
16	14	133.91	133.41	4	0	5	2.00	50.00	2.03	.50
17	17	133.91	135.61	4	0	6	1.00	50.00	1.96	.50
***	19		133.91	0	0	6	2.00	50.00	2.03	5.60
19	19	133.91	139.51	0	0	6	2.00	50.00	6.82	3.77
***	12		135.49	0	0	6	2.00	50.00	6.82	3.77

NODAL TRACE FOR NODE, 16 **
RUN NO. 1

START NODE	END NODE	START TIME	END TIME	ACTIVITY NUMBER	MARK TIME	TRANS.	ATTRIBUTES			
15	16	3.61	4.56	0	0	9	3.00	20.00	2.86	.98
***										
16	16	4.56	4.56	0	0	9	3.00	20.00	2.85	.98
15	17	4.61	5.54	4	0	9	3.00	20.00	2.86	.98
			5.60	0	0	1	3.00	20.00	1.00	2.40
***										
16	16	5.60	5.60	4	0	1	3.00	20.00	1.00	2.40
11	16		8.00	0	0	1	3.00	20.00	1.00	2.05
11	16	10.50	11.66	0	0	2	1.00	20.00	10.00	2.05
13	16	11.00	15.00	0	0	7	2.00	20.00	10.00	5.00
11	16	11.50	12.00	0	0	3	1.00	20.00	10.00	3.21
***	1b		11.66	0	0	2	1.00	20.00	10.00	2.05

NODAL TRACE FOR NODE, 17 **
RUN NO. 1

START NODE	END NODE	START TIME	END TIME	ACTIVITY NUMBER	MARK TIME	TRANS.	ATTRIBUTES			
16	17	4.56	5.54	4	0	9	3.00	20.00	2.86	.98
***	17		5.54	4	0	9	3.00	20.00	2.86	.98
17	18	5.54	5.54	0	0	9	3.00	20.00	2.86	.98
16	17	5.60	8.00	4	0	1	3.00	20.00	1.00	2.40
***	17		8.00	4	0	1	3.00	20.00	1.00	2.40

Figure 6-23 Portions of event and nodal traces, Example 9.

service on low priority items is not interrupted to process high priority items.

6-2 Jobs arrive at a job shop with an interarrival time that is exponentially distributed with a mean time between arrivals of 1.25 hours. The time to process a job is uniformly distributed in the interval 0.75 to 1.25 hours. The time to process a job is estimated before the job is performed. Analyze the processing of jobs in the order of shortest processing time first for 500 transactions. Obtain statistics describing the average time the jobs are in the shop, the variation in the time the jobs are in the shop, and the utilization of the server. Assume that the *actual* processing times for the jobs are equal to the estimates of the processing times. Repeat the analysis with jobs with the longest processing time performed first, and then with the jobs processed in order of their arrival time. Compare the results.

6-3 Repeat Exercise 6-2 for a situation in which the actual processing time is equal to the estimated processing time plus a sample drawn from a normal distribution with a mean of zero and a standard deviation of 0.2

6-4 Modify the bank teller example to model a credit inquiry on selected non-drive-in bank customers. A credit inquiry is performed by the bank manager on new customers. Ten percent of the non-drive-in customers are in this category. The bank manager obtains the necessary information on the customer and initiates the inquiry which takes between 2 and 5 minutes, uniformly distributed. The time for a credit inquiry is exponentially distributed with a mean of 5 minutes during which time the customer waits in a separate room. The manager processes other customers during the time the credit inquiry is being performed, and there is no limit to the number of simultaneous credit inquiries that can be done. When the credit inquiry is completed, the customer for which the credit inquiry was made is served again by the manager and is given preference over customers who have not seen the manager. The manager completes any information gathering task before he issues the credit inquiry which takes 1 minute. Five percent of the credit inquiries result in a negative response and the customer is not routed to the tellers. The time to give a negative response is exponential with a mean of 10 minutes.

6-5 Embellish Exercise 6-4 so that the manager requires two inquiries for each customer with each inquiry having a 0.05 negative response probability.

6-6   Model and analyze the admitting process of a hospital as described below. The following three types of patients are processed by the admitting function:

Type 1. Those patients who are admitted and have previously completed their pre-admission forms and tests;

Type 2. Those patients who seek admission but have not completed pre-admission; and

Type 3. Those who are only coming in for pre-admission testing and information gathering.

Service times in the admitting office vary according to patient type as given below.

Patient Types and Service Times

Patient Type	Relative Frequency	Mean Time to Admit
1	0.90 before 10:00 A.M.	15 minutes
	0.50 after 10:00 A.M.	
2	0.10 always	40 minutes
3	0 before 10:00 A.M.	30 minutes
	0.40 after 10 A.M.	

Note: All of the above times are normally distributed
with $\sigma = 0.1\mu$ (min. = 0.0).

On arrival to admitting, a person waits in line if the two admitting officers are busy. When idle, an admitting officer always selects a patient who is to be admitted before those who are only to be pre-admitted. In addition, Type 1 patients are given highest priority. After filling out various forms in the admitting office, Type 1 patients are taken to their floors by an orderly while Type 2 and 3 patients walk to the laboratory for blood and urine tests. Three orderlies are available to escort patients to the nursing units. Patients are *not* allowed to go to their floor by themselves as a matter of policy. If all orderlies are busy, patients wait in the lobby. Once a patient has been escorted to a floor, they are considered beyond the admitting process. It takes the orderly 3 time units to return to the admitting room. Those patients who must go to the lab are always ambulatory, and as a result require no escorts. After arriving in the lab, they wait in line at the registration desk. After registration, they go to the lab waiting room until they are called on by a lab technician. After the samples are drawn, they walk back to the admitting office if they are to be admitted or leave if only pre-admission has been scheduled. Upon return to admitting, they are processed as normal Type 1 patients. The admitting office is open from 7:00 A.M. until 5:00 P.M. However, no pre-admissions (Type 3) are scheduled until 10:00 A.M. because of the heavy morning workload in the lab. At 4:00 P.M., incoming admissions are sent to the outpatient desk for processing. However, Type 2 patients returning from the lab are accepted until 5:00 P.M. which is the time both admitting officers go home and the office is closed. Analyze the above system for 200 days. It is of interest to determine the time in the system, that is, the time from arrival until on a floor (Type 1 and 2) or exit from the lab (Type 3). Also, determine the time between arrivals to the laboratory. Assume all patient queues are infinite and FIFO ranked except where noted. Activity times are specified below.

Activity Times (all times in minutes)

Explanation	Distribution: Parameters
time between arrivals to admitting office, t_1	exponential: mean = 15
travel time between admitting and floor, t_2	uniform: min = 3, max = 8
travel time between admitting and lab or lab and admitting, t_3	uniform: min = 2, max = 5
service time at lab registration desk, t_4	Erlang-3: mean = 4.5, k = 3
time spent drawing lab specimen, t_5	Erlang-2: mean = 5, k = 2
time for orderly to return from floor to admitting desk, t_6	constant: 3

6-7 A certain repair shop consists of a work station where incoming units are repaired and an inspection station where the repaired units are either released from the shop or recycled. The work station has three parallel servers, and the inspection station has one inspector. Units entering this system have interarrival times which are exponentially distributed with a mean of 10 time units. The repair time for a unit is Erlang distributed with mean 24 and variance 288. The "shortest processing time" priority dispatching rule is used at the work station: the unit with the smallest repair time is served first. Repaired units queue up for inspection on a FIFO basis. The inspection of a unit requires 6 time units; the unit is then rejected with probability p^n, where $p = .10$ and n is the number of times the unit has already been repaired. A unit is discarded after it is rejected three times. Rejected units queue up at the work station to be repaired again.

The initial conditions are:

1. The servers are idle;
2. The first new arrival will occur at time 0; and
3. The inspector is idle.

CHAPTER 7

ADVANCED Q-GERT CONCEPTS: PROGRAM INSERTS

In prior chapters, the modeling of systems using Q-GERT involved the use of Q-GERT symbols and procedures. The Q-GERT symbol set was designed to allow the modeling of a wide class of problems without requiring any programming background or use by the modeler. Many problems can be resolved using the features of Q-GERT previously presented. However, as a Q-GERT modeler encounters more complex systems, a need may develop for user written program inserts that model specialized situations. This chapter describes the procedures for a user of Q-GERT to insert FORTRAN subprograms into a Q-GERT network model. Subprograms are included in Q-GERT to assist the user in writing such programming inserts. In this chapter, these subprograms are defined and their use is illustrated. In addition, the internal Q-GERT variables that define the status of nodes, activities and transactions are provided.

MODELING STRATEGY

As a modeling procedure, it is recommended that a model be built without programming inserts. This "first cut" model may require aggregation at a high level. By approaching a problem in this manner, a segregation of network modeling aspects and any detailed programming aspects involved in model building can be made. This simple procedure can significantly decrease the design and development problems inherent in any large computer programming effort. By making the programming effort subservient to the network modeling task, a clear definition of the requirements and functions that need to be programmed usually results. In fact, the structure imposed by Q-GERT which specifies where programming inserts may be made can be a tremendous help in building models of complex situations. As is the case with most methodologies that impose structure, it is at the cost of flexibility. Q-GERT has the structure to allow for the orderly development of a model and yet provides sufficient flexibility to enable the building of models that have the fidelity necessary to produce a solution to the problem being studied.

LOCATION OF PROGRAMMING INSERTS IN Q-GERT MODELS

Q-GERT provides the definitions for a set of network constructs (nodes, branches, and information transfers) and the rules for combining these constructs into a network model. Q-GERT also prescribes the locations where a modeler may insert user written functions. Two locations are provided for making such programming inserts. These are:
1. At the start time of an activity; and
2. At a node release time.
In the former case, the user function replaces the function type specification that normally is associated with the time to traverse the activity. In the latter case, the user function specification replaces the function type specification that normally specifies the mechanism by which a value is assigned to a specific attribute of a transaction passing through the node. Hence, in the first case, the user function is called from a branch and, in the second case, it is called from a node. The parameter identifier in these situations is a user function number. The code letters UF are used to indicate that a user function is to be employed at a branch or node. The notation (UF,IFN) indicates that user function number IFN is to be employed. For example, the network segment shown below indicates that user function number 2 is to be called every

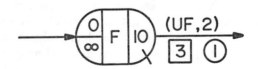

time service activity 3 is started. In user function 2, the time required to perform service activity 3 must be specified. The user may also code in function number 2 other decision elements such as the halting of ongoing activities, the reassignment of attribute values, and the replacement (modification) of nodes in the network. The primary use of user function 2, however, is the specification of a time to perform the service on the transaction passing through activity 3.

The symbolism for prescribing the use of a user function at a node is shown below. At node 5, user function 3 is used to compute a value that

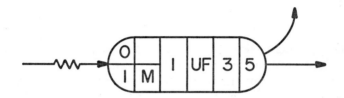

will be assigned to attribute 1 of the transaction flowing through node 5. User function 3 is a programming insert through which the modeler can adapt the network model to meet specific conditions that might occur when a transaction passes through a node. The purpose of the user function number is similar to that of the parameter set number in that it differentiates calls to the user written function UF. The specifications for the user written subroutine US are identical to UF.

An Example

The one server, single queue example will be used to demonstrate the procedures involved when programming user functions. In this example, the time between arrivals of transactions to the system is modeled by activity 1 which is the branch that sends transactions from node 5 back to node 5. Let the function type specification for this branch be UF with function number 1, that is, (UF,1). This specifies that the time between arrivals is to be calculated by the user-written FORTRAN code which corresponds to user function number 1. Let the service time for activity 3 be prescribed as a value to be calculated in user function number 2. With this specification, just prior to the start of service of a transaction, the Q-GERT program calls the user function, UF, with an argument value of 2. The modeler must then write function UF to compute a value for the service time of activity 3. The network model for this example is shown below.

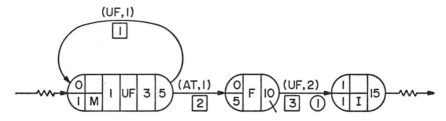

A user function is also used to assign a value to attribute 1 at source node 5. Here, user function number 3 is specified. The value of attribute 1 will be used to define the time to traverse activity 2, that is, the delay time from when a transaction arrives at the system at node 5 until it reaches the queue represented by node 10.

By the use of these three user functions, a Q-GERT modeler can make activity times dependent on system status. For this example, activity 1, the time between arrivals, can be made a function of the current simulation time. Activity 2, the delay of transactions, can be made dependent on the number of transactions in Q-node 10, and activity 3, the time for service, can be made dependent on the current remaining queue capacity.

GENERAL FORM FOR CODING FUNCTION UF(IFN)

The function subprogram UF(IFN) is called by Q-GERT whenever the function type UF is prescribed. The argument IFN is the user function number prescribed by the modeler. For example, if an activity is described by (UF,2) then the function number IFN is 2. IFN is used in the function subprogram UF to differentiate from among the many possible calls to UF at different locations in the network model. In this way, function UF can be written to contain all the FORTRAN programming inserts that are required to model the special features of a Q-GERT model. To state this in another way, IFN specifies a section of code in function UF which has been written to accomplish the special type of modeling required by user function number IFN.

The layout of function UF for the example of the previous section is shown in Figure 7-1.

FUNCTION UF(IFN)
Common and Dimension Cards
GO TO (1,2,3), IFN
1 Calculate a value for the time associated with activity 1.
  RETURN
2 Calculate a service time for activity 3.
  RETURN
3 Calculate a value for assignment to attribute 1 of each transaction
  passing through node 5.
  RETURN
  END

Figure 7-1 General Format for Function UF.

Figure 7-1 is not a FORTRAN listing but a representation of the typical form for writing function UF. Normally, the first executable statement in UF is a computed GO TO statement based on the value of the function number passed to UF as an argument. In this way, separate sections of UF are used to model different aspects of the system. When IFN equals 1, the code starting at statement 1 would be executed and used to calculate a value for the time associated with activity 1. Thus, by specifying function number 1 for the branch representing activity 1, Q-GERT calls UF with an argument of 1 when activity 1 is to be started. It is the modeler's responsibility to translate the argument to the proper statement location in function UF. Similarly, IFN values of 2 and 3 would cause the code starting at statements 2 and 3 to be executed, respectively.

The model development and analysis up to this point has been related to the construction of the network and the location of programming inserts. No FORTRAN coding has been required. This illustrates the approach we suggested earlier of conceptualizing the problem in network form and then performing the detailed coding.

User Function Requirements for the Example

The characteristics that will be modeled using the user function for the one server, single queue example are:
1. The time between arrivals as represented by activity 1 is 3.5 time units when the simulation time is between 10 and 50 time units. Otherwise, the time between arrivals should be 3.0 time units.

2. The service time as represented by activity 3 should be 2.8 time units as long as the number of transactions waiting for the server is less than 2. If 2 or more transactions are waiting for the server at the Q-node, the service time should be 2.5 time units.
3. The time delay for a transaction to go from its arrival point to the queue of the server as represented by activity 2 is to be modeled as a function of the number in the queue, that is, related to the distance to the end of the queue. A table relating queue status to the time for activity 2 is shown below. This table specifies that the time for activity 2 is the product of 0.1 and the number of spaces still available in the queue. Note that a capacity of 5 transactions was specified for Q-node 10. A functional relation for the values in the table can be written as 0.1∗ (capacity of the queue − current number in the queue).

Queue Status	Time for Activity 2
Empty	.5
1	.4
2	.3
3	.2
4	.1
5	0

User Function Coding for the Example

In order to write the FORTRAN code for function UF, it is necessary to have access to internal Q-GERT variables. Specifically, we require the variable names for the current simulation time, the current number of transactions at a Q-node and the capacity of a Q-node. The Q-GERT names for these three variables are listed below.

Variable Name	Definition
TNOW	Current value of simulation time.
NREL(NODE)	Current number of transactions in Q-node NODE.
NREL2(NODE)	The maximum number of transactions allowed at Q-node NODE (capacity).

At the end of this section, a selected list of Q-GERT variable definitions is presented.

Returning to our example, the coding required to prescribe the time between arrivals involves two statements. The first statement must be statement number 1 since the computed GO TO statement transfers to statement number 1 when the function number (IFN) is set at 1. At statement 1, we will prescribe the time between arrivals to be 3 time units, as this is the normal case. This is accomplished by setting the function value UF to 3. That is, the value to be returned is identified by the function name as required by standard FORTRAN procedures. Following statement 1, we test to see if the current simulation time is between 10 and 50 time units, and if it is, the value of UF is changed to 3.5. This completes the code required to model user function number 1. A RETURN to Q-GERT would then be made. The FORTRAN code for these statements is shown below.

```
1 UF = 3.0
  IF(TNOW.GT.10.0.AND.TNOW.LT.50.0) UF = 3.5
  RETURN
```

Now consider specifying the service time associated with activity 3. The code for this section of function UF is similar to that written above. However, the code would start at statement 2 since function number 2 is specified for service activity 3. Normally, the service time is 2.8 time units, and at statement 2, UF is set equal to 2.8. The next statement tests the number of transactions in Q-node 10 and, if it is greater than or equal to 2, the value assigned to UF is changed to 2.5. The variable that defines the number of transactions in Q-node 10 is NREL(10). The code for prescribing the service time for activity 3 is shown below.

```
2 UF = 2.8
  IF(NREL(10).GE.2) UF = 2.5
  RETURN
```

Note that the modeler knows that function number 2 involves setting the service time as a function of the status of Q-node 10, and the use of NREL(10) is based on this knowledge.

The FORTRAN coding to assign a value for attribute 1 at node 5 starts at statement 3. The capacity of Q-node 10 to hold transactions is stored as the variable NREL2(10). The remaining capacity is the capacity minus the current number of transactions, that is, NREL2(10) –NREL(10). According to FORTRAN convention, variables whose names start with I, J, K, L, M, and N are integer valued. To obtain a floating point or "real" value for these variables, the FORTRAN function FLOAT is used. Performing this operation and multiplying by 0.1 yields the desired statement that specifies the value to be assigned to attribute 1 at node 5. This is shown below.

$$3 \quad UF = 0.1 * FLOAT \ (NREL2(10)-NREL(10))$$
$$RETURN$$

Since the capacity of Q-node 10 is known to the modeler, he could have used the value 5 in place of NREL2(10) in the above statement. Which approach to use is strictly a preference of the modeler. Statement 3 given above allows the capacity of the queue to be changed on input without changing the user function, and, hence, might be preferred by some modelers.

Combining the three segments of function UF results in the code shown in Figure 7-2. In this figure, the labeled COMMON block that contains the Q-GERT variables TNOW, NREL and NREL2 is included.

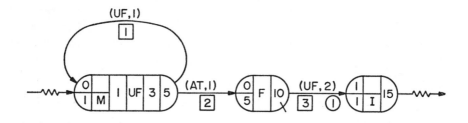

```
      FUNCTION UF (IFN)
      COMMON /QVAR/ NDE,NFTBU(100),NREL(100),NRELP(100),NREL2(100),NRUN,
     1NRUNS,NTC(100),PARAM(100,4),TBEG,TNOW
      GO TO (1,2,3), IFN
C*** SET INTERARRIVAL TIME
    1 UF = 3.0
      IF(TNOW.GT.10.0.AND.TNOW.LT.50.0) UF = 3.5
      RETURN
C*** SET SERVICE TIME FOR ACTIVITY 3
    2 UF = 2.8
      IF(NREL(10).GE.2) UF = 2.5
      RETURN
C*** SET ATTRIBUTE 1 OF TRANSACTION PASSING THROUGH NODE 5 EQUAL TO
C*** THE TIME TO TRAVERSE ACTIVITY 2
    3 UF = 0.1 * FLOAT(NREL2(10)-NREL(10))
      RETURN
      END
```

Figure 7-2   Coding example of function UF.

This example has demonstrated how a modeler can include specific conditions regarding a system by employing function UF. It has also illustrated the two locations at which a modeler can insert FORTRAN code. The segregation of function UF according to function number helps to simplify the programming requirements placed upon the modeler. The writing of subroutine US (ISN, DTIM) is similar to function UF (IFN) where ISN is the user subroutine number and DTIM is the value to be set in the subroutine.

In the remainder of this chapter, information is provided on: 1) definitions of Q-GERT variable names; 2) procedures for accessing the Q-GERT subprograms for sampling from different density functions; and 3) subprograms capable of performing complex Q-GERT functions such as nodal modifications, activity halting, event scheduling, and attribute assignment. Throughout the chapter any reference to function UF also applies to subroutine US.

DEFINITIONS OF Q-GERT VARIABLES

Table 7-1 provides a list of the Q-GERT variables* that can be used directly in function UF if the labeled COMMON block QVAR, shown below, is included in function UF.

COMMON/QVAR/NDE, NFTBU(100), NREL(100), NRELP(100), NREL2(100), NRUN, 1 NRUNS, NTC(100), PARAM(100,4), TBEG, TNOW

Each of the variables defined in Table 7-1 will now be discussed.

NDE

The variable NDE is the number of attributes associated with a transaction including the mark time attribute. The mark time is stored as the NDEth attribute of a transaction. The value of NDE is one more than the number of attributes specified on input.

NFTBU

The vector NFTBU is used to store the node number at which statistics collection, value assignments and branching occur when a node is released. Initially, NFTBU(NODE) = NODE which specifies that branching is to occur from NODE when NODE is released. When a network modification occurs such that a new node, say NEWNO, is to replace

*QVAR is shown for the 100 node version of the Q-GERT Analysis Program.

Table 7-1.   Selected List of Q-GERT Variable Definitions.

Variable Name*	Definition
NDE	Number of attributes associated with a transaction. NDE counts the mark time as an attribute.
NFTBU(NODE)	Node number at which statistics collection, value assignments and branching occurs when NODE is released.
NREL(NODE)	For Q-node, current number in queue. For S-node, queue selection code (numeric). Otherwise, number of remaining requirements for nodal release.
NRELP(NODE)	For Q-node, initial number in Q-node. For S-node, numeric queue selection code (see Table 5-2). Otherwise, number of requirements for first release of NODE.
NREL2(NODE)	For Q-node, maximum capacity of queue. For S-node, numeric server selection code (see Table 5-3). Otherwise, number of subsequent requirements to release NODE.
NRUN	Current run number, that is, NRUN = 3 signifies that the third simulation of the network is being performed.
NRUNS	Total number of runs requested.
NTC(NODE)	The number of transactions that have passed through node NODE since time TBEG. If NODE has been replaced by another node, NTC(NODE) is not increased.
PARAM(I,J)	Jth value of parameter set I (see Figure 3-2).
TBEG	Time at which data collection is to begin (TBEG is input on GEN card).
TNOW	Current simulation time.

* In the list of variables, the argument NODE denotes the current node number which is normally known to the user through his knowledge of the location of the call to UF.

NODE in the network, Q-GERT effects the following change: NFTBU (NODE) = NEWNO. Specifically, if node 3 is to replace node 2 in the network, then NFTBU(2) = 3. When node 2 is released, the transaction is transferred to node NFTBU(2), that is, node 3.

NREL, NRELP, NREL2

The vectors NREL, NRELP, and NREL2 are associated with the values assigned to the input or left hand side of a node. A graphical representation for regular nodes, Q-nodes, and S-nodes is shown below.

To conserve computer storage, the same arrays are used to reference different quantities as required by regular nodes, Q-nodes, and S-nodes. At the beginning of each analysis run, it is required to have the input values for NRELP and NREL2 assigned to each node. Thus, any change made to these values by the user during a run must be reset at the end of the run. This can be done by using subroutine UO described later in this chapter.

The NREL array is used to maintain current information concerning the number of remaining incoming transactions required to release a node or the current number of transactions at a Q-node. In the former case, every incoming transaction to node NODE causes NREL(NODE) to be decreased by 1. When NREL(NODE) reaches a value of zero, node number NODE is released. At that time, NREL(NODE) is reset to NREL2(NODE). At the beginning of each analysis run, NREL(NODE) is reset to NRELP(NODE) for each node in the network.

For Q-nodes, NREL maintains the current number of transactions at the Q-node. Each time a transaction arrives at the Q-node and the server associated with the Q-node is busy, NREL is increased by 1. Every time a service activity draws a transaction from a Q-node, NREL is decreased by 1. Statistics are automatically kept on NREL to obtain the average number at the Q-node during a run. At the beginning of an analysis run, NREL is set equal to NRELP so that the initial number of transactions at a Q-node is prescribed for each run.

NRUN, NRUNS

The variable NRUN specifies the current analysis run being performed, and NRUNS is the total number of runs to be made. If ten analysis runs are to be made then NRUNS = 10, and NRUN takes on the values 1,

2, ..., 10. Examples of the use of NRUN are:
1. If NRUN equals 1, initialize user variables.
2. NRUN can be used as an argument to specify different queue or server selection rules to be used on different runs. To accomplish this, a user array containing the selection rules would be prescribed by the modeler. At the beginning of each run, the NRELP and NREL2 values associated with a selector node could be set equal to the appropriate value. For example, if the user defined an array NRULE that contained the server selection rule to be used at node 5, then setting NREL2(5) = NRULE(NRUN) would specify a different server selection rule at node 5 for each analysis run.

NTC

The variable NTC(NODE) defines the number of transactions that have passed through NODE. NTC(NODE) is reset to zero at time TBEG. If NODE has been replaced in the network by a nodal modification, NTC(NODE) is not incremented when a transaction releases the node (since the transaction is not passing through the node). NTC(NODE) is used internally in Q-GERT for: 1) computing statistics on nodes; 2) providing a value for the incremental (IN) assignment function; and 3) indicating whether a node has been released. Such information is required for conditional branching. Because NTC(NODE) is used for multiple purposes, care is required in its use. Specifically, note that NTC(·) is reset to zero at time TBEG. Further, if a node is modified before a transaction passes through it, the NTC(NODE) value will not change from zero. Since conditional branching is based on the value of NTC(NODE), the combined use of TBEG and nodal modifications could affect routing decisions.

The value of NTC can be used by a modeler to specify the routing of a transaction based on user defined conditions. Suppose node number 12 is *not* part of the network model. In this case, NTC(12) is not used by Q-GERT. The modeler then can use NTC(12) as a switching device by changing its value from 0 to 1 in UF when specified conditions are met. Q-GERT can then use this information through normal conditional branching procedures by specifying the conditions: N12.R or N12.NR. This clearly is an advanced concept and requires the modeler to be familiar with the operation of the Q-GERT program. At the start of each run, the vector NTC is initialized to zero by the Q-GERT program. All nonzero values of NTC are printed as part of the run summary report.

PARAM

The two-dimensional array PARAM is used to store the parameter values associated with a parameter set. PARAM(I,J) stores the Jth parameter value for parameter set I. The parameter values are read on input from PAR cards. For some distributions, the parameter values are stored directly. For the following distributions, the parameter values are converted to facilitate the sampling procedure:
1. lognormal;
2. beta;
3. gamma;
4. beta fitted to three values; and
5. triangular.
Later in this chapter, the Q-GERT subprograms available for changing the parameter values are described.

The array PARAM is dimensioned to have 100 rows and 4 columns. For rows of PARAM that are not specified by parameter set numbers, the user may use the PARAM array for storing model specific information. Since values can be read into the PARAM array through the use of the PAR input cards, this can be a convenient procedure for inserting model specific information into the network model.

TNOW

The analysis of a Q-GERT network is performed by simulating the flow of transactions through the network and maintaining a list of events that are associated with the ending of activities for the transactions. The time at which events occur is updated by the Q-GERT Analysis Program and is specified by the variable TNOW. TNOW is always the current simulation time. When a user function is specified at a node, there can be no ambiguity with regard to the current simulation time as time does not change at a node. TNOW is both the release time of the node and the time at which branching occurs from the node. When a user function is specified for a branch, TNOW is the time at which branching is occurring. The time specified for performing the activity represented by the branch is added to TNOW to obtain the time at which the activity represented by the branch should be completed. This end of activity time is then placed on the calendar of events in proper chronological order. In no way does this scheduling of an event change the value of TNOW which remains as the time the branch was selected for routing the transaction. TNOW is only advanced to the time of the next event when no further operations are required at the current time. *The user should not reset the value of TNOW.*

TBEG

The variable, TBEG, is the time from which data is to be maintained on statistics nodes, queues and servers. TBEG is specified on data input on the GEN card. At time TBEG, the Q-GERT Analysis Program clears the statistical storage arrays associated with all statistics and sink nodes, Q-nodes and servers.

This completes the discussion of the selected list of Q-GERT variables. Whenever a Q-GERT variable is used in function UF, the labeled COMMON block QVAR must be included in function UF.

NUMERIC CODES ASSOCIATED WITH FUNCTION TYPES, QUEUE SELECTION RULES AND SERVER SELECTION RULES

Table 7-2 presents the numeric codes used in the Q-GERT program that correspond to the alphabetic descriptors for function types, queue selection rules and server selection rules. The Q-GERT program translates the alphabetic information that is specified on input to the numeric codes shown in Table 7-2. When accessing these values in function UF through the use of NREL, NRELP or NREL2, it is the numeric value that should be considered. The use of numeric codes in the Q-GERT program is predicated on the computational efficiency inherent in dealing with numeric values.

FUNCTIONS AVAILABLE FOR OBTAINING SAMPLES FROM PROBABILITY DISTRIBUTIONS

Table 7-3 presents the functions that are included in Q-GERT for obtaining samples from probability distributions. The modeler may use these functions in UF to directly obtain samples. For example, to obtain a sample from a normal distribution with parameters as specified by parameter set number 2, the following statement would be used in function UF:

SAMP = NO(2)

With this statement, SAMP is a sample from a normal distribution with

Table 7-2. Codes for Distribution Types, Queue Selection and Server Selection

Distribution Types	Queue Selection	Server Selection
1 COnstant	1 POR	1 POR
2 NOrmal	2 CYC	2 CYC
3 UNiform	3 RAN	3 RAN
4 ERlang	4 LAV	4 LBT
5 LOgnormal	5 SAV	5 SBT
6 POisson	6 LWF	6 LIT
7 BEta	7 SWF	7 SIT
8 GAmma	8 LNQ	8 RFS
9 Beta PERT	9 SNQ	
10 Not Used	10 LNB	
11 TRiangular	11 SNB	
12 ATtribute value	12 LRC	
13 INcremental	13 SRC	
14 User Function	–14 ASM	

a mean and standard deviation as specified by parameter set 2 (the first and fourth parameters of the parameter set). The function NO(2) returns a value with a "real" representation. Thus, if the sample is to be tripled, the statement TSAMP = 3.*NO(2) could be used. If the three in the above statement was specified without the decimal point, that is, an integer representation, a mixed mode multiplication would result.

The samples obtained from any of the functions listed in Table 7-3 will always be between the minimum and maximum values specified by the modeler. The minimum and maximum are contained in the parameter set as the second and third values, respectively. Any value that is below the minimum value causes the sample to be set at the minimum value. Similarly, any value greater than the maximum value causes the sample to be set at the maximum value (see Truncated Versus Mixed Distributions Section, Chapter 6).

The names selected for the functions that obtain samples from probability distributions correspond to the input codes for distribution types. User defined variable names must be different from these function names.

Function DRAND(ISTRM)

Function DRAND(ISTRM) is the subprogram in Q-GERT for obtaining a pseudorandom number. A pseudorandom number is a number be-

Table 7-3. Probability Distribution Functions for Use in UF.

Function Name and Arguments*	Description
BE(J)	Beta distribution using parameter set J.
DPROB(CP,VAL, NVAL,ISTRM)	Discrete probability distribution where CP is a vector of cumulative probabilities for values stored in the vector VAL. NVAL is the number of values in the distribution and ISTRM is the random number stream to be used.
DRAND(ISTRM)	Pseudorandom number generator using stream ISTRM.
ER(J)	Erlang distribution using parameter set J.
EX(J)	Exponential distribution using parameter set J.
GA(J)	Gamma distribution using parameter set J.
LO(J)	Lognormal distribution using parameter set J.
NO(J)	Normal distribution using parameter set J.
PO(J)	Poisson distribution using parameter set J.
TR(J)	Triangular distribution using parameter set J.
UN(J)	Uniform distribution using parameter set J.

* All functions return real values. REAL FUNCTIONs are used for LO and NO. A real representation of an integer is returned from FUNCTION PO.

tween 0 and 1 which has the properties that every value in the range is equally likely and there is no correlation among values.*

Function DRAND is the only machine dependent subprogram included in the Q-GERT Analysis Program. The author recommends using a random number generator that is either familiar to the user or which is in common use at the user's computer facility. In Appendix 3, a version of DRAND that has been used on CDC computer systems is provided. The listing of this routine provides the format with which DRAND should be built for inclusion in the Q-GERT Analysis Program.

Within function UF, DRAND can be used to select among a set of alternatives. For example, suppose it is desired to set the value X: to 1, 30 percent of the time; to 2, 50 percent of the time; and to 3, 20 percent of the time. To accomplish this, we would use a random number. Since 30 percent of the random numbers are less than 0.3 (recall all values are equally likely in the range (0,1)), we associate the value of X = 1 for ran-

* Because they are generated on digital computers by deterministic methods, there is a great deal of controversy over the definition of pseudorandom numbers. From the philosophical basis upon which Q-GERT is built, Lehmer's definition of a pseudorandom sequence is appealing, " ... a vague notion embodying the idea of a sequence in which every term is unpredictable to the uninitiated and whose digits pass a certain number of tests ... depending somewhat on the uses to which the sequence is to be put." (71)

dom numbers less than 0.3. Similarly, we set X = 2 if the random number is between 0.3 and 0.8, and X = 3 if the random number is between 0.8 and 1.0. The code to accomplish this is shown below.

$$RN = DRAND(1)$$
$$X = 3.0$$
$$IF(RN.LE.0.8)X = 2.0$$
$$IF(RN.LE.0.3)X = 1.0$$

The local variable RN is set equal to the random number and is then used in the tests to obtain the desired value for X. Since function DRAND returns a new random number every time it is called, the use of RN is required. In general, care is required when DRAND is used directly in test statements.

The argument to DRAND identifies the random number stream to be employed in generating the random number. Ten streams are available in the Q-GERT Analysis Program. The different streams are made available to allow the Q-GERT user to have a greater degree of control over the experimental conditions for which the program is run. As discussed in Chapter 6, each stream can be initialized to the same starting value for each run through data input on the SEE card.

Function DPROB(CPROB,VALUE,NVAL,ISTRM)

Function DPROB obtains samples from a probability mass function that is defined by the vectors CPROB and VALUE. CPROB(I) is the cumulative probability associated with VALUE(I). That is, the probability of obtaining a sample less than or equal to VALUE(I) is CPROB(I). The number of possible values in the probability mass function is defined by the variable NVAL. ISTRM is the random number stream to be used when obtaining a sample from the vector VALUE.

When function DPROB is used in function UF, the user must define the vectors CPROB and VALUE. Typically, this can be accomplished in a DATA statement in function UF. A user initialization routine, UI, to be described later can also be used for defining CPROB and VALUE.

As an example of the use of DPROB, consider the probability mass function shown below.

I	PROB(I)	CP(I)	VAL(I)
1	.10	.10	10
2	.05	.15	15
3	.20	.35	25
4	.30	.65	50
5	.20	.85	75
6	.15	1.00	100

To obtain a sample from the above distribution, the following statement would be used

$$SAMP = DPROB(CP,VAL,6,2)$$

In this statement, CP is the cumulative probability distribution, VAL contains the potential sample values corresponding to the cumulative distribution. NVAL is set to 6 since there are 6 values in the probability mass function. Random number stream 2 is prescribed for obtaining the sample. With the use of the above statement, 10 percent of the values of SAMP will be equal to 10, 5 percent will be equal to 15, 20 percent will be equal to 25 and so on.

PARAMETER CHANGES REQUIRED WHEN USING LOGNORMAL, BETA, GAMMA, BETA PERT OR TRIANGULAR DISTRIBUTIONS DIRECTLY IN FUNCTION UF

The values of parameters stored in the parameter sets for sampling from the lognormal, beta, gamma, beta-PERT and triangular distributions are different from the parameter specifications listed in the standard Q-GERT input fields. The standard input values are automatically modified by Q-GERT. When the functions are called in UF, it is the modeler's responsibility to ensure the correct parameter values are used when obtaining samples from the above distributions. To accomplish the change of parameters, the following subroutines are provided.

Subroutine CPLO(JP)	Changes values of parameter set number JP to values required for sampling from a lognormal distribution.
Subroutine CPBE(JP)	Changes values of parameter set number JP to values required for sampling from a beta distribution.
Subroutine CPGA(JP)	Changes values of parameter set number JP to values required for sampling from a gamma distribution.
Subroutine CPBP(JP)	Changes values of parameter set JP specified for beta PERT to sample from a beta distribution.
Subroutine CPTR(JP)	Changes values of parameter set number JP to values required for sampling from a triangular distribution.

One method for changing parameter values is to insert an activity at the beginning of the network whose purpose is to change the parameters. This procedure is shown below.

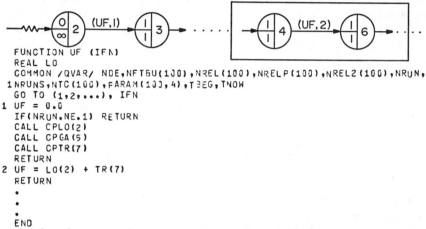

```
FUNCTION UF (IFN)
REAL LO
COMMON /QVAR/ NDE,NFTBU(100),NREL(100),NRELP(100),NREL2(100),NRUN,
1NRUNS,NTC(100),PARAM(100,4),TBEG,TNOW
   GO TO (1,2,...), IFN
1  UF = 0.0
   IF(NRUN.NE.1) RETURN
   CALL CPLO(2)
   CALL CPGA(5)
   CALL CPTR(7)
   RETURN
2  UF = LO(2) + TR(7)
   RETURN
   .
   .
   .
END
```

In the above, parameter sets 2, 5 and 7 will be altered to provide values for sampling from the lognormal, gamma and triangular distributions, respectively. The values are only to be altered once. The Q-GERT variable, NRUN, is the run number. Only when NRUN equals 1 should the subroutines that change the parameter values be called. The Q-GERT labeled COMMON block QVAR is included since it contains NRUN.

Note that a value should be assigned to UF as required by FORTRAN FUNCTION convention. With the above code, the activity time from node 4 to node 6 is the sum of samples from the lognormal and triangular distributions.

Another method for changing the parameter values is to use subroutine UI which is described in the next section.

SUBROUTINE UI

Before each analysis run for a network, the Q-GERT Analysis Program calls subroutine UI to allow the modeler to initialize user defined variables and to create special initial conditions. As an example, UI could have been used instead of the activity between node 2 and node 3 in the example given in the previous section. A test on the run number is still required as UI is called at the beginning of every run.

A version of subroutine UI with only a RETURN statement is included as part of the Q-GERT Analysis Program. Subroutine UI is called after the Q-GERT data cards have been processed. Any data cards to be read in UI should follow the BEG* or FIN* card.

SUBROUTINE UO

After each analysis run for a network, the Q-GERT Analysis Program calls subroutine UO to provide the modeler an opportunity to perform any end-of-run computations or to output user specified information. A version of subroutine UO with only a RETURN statement is included as part of the Q-GERT Analysis Program.

SPECIAL SUBPROGRAMS FOR USE WHEN CODING UF

Since Q-GERT is a FORTRAN program, the number of special functions that can be provided for assisting the user in the coding of UF is open ended. Table 7-4 presents an alphabetic list and description of the subprograms included with the Q-GERT package. Some of the subprograms perform the function of retrieving a value for a Q-GERT variable. These are included for user convenience. In the following sections, a discussion of the use of these subprograms is given.

SUBPROGRAMS ASSOCIATED WITH TRANSACTIONS

The subprograms relating to transactions deal mainly with the acquisition of or setting of attribute values for a specific transaction. The transaction at a node or the transaction being routed from a node is referred to as the current transaction. The subprograms are designed to acquire or set the attribute values of the current transaction. Also discussed in this section is the inserting (putting) of a transaction into the network using subroutine PTIN.

Function GATRB(J)

To access the third attribute of the transaction currently being processed, the following statement is used:

AT3 = GATRB(3)

This statement assigns the value of attribute 3 to the variable AT3. In function UF, AT3 can be used for testing the third attribute of the current transaction.

Table 7-4. Definition of Subprograms Available for Use in UF

Subprogram	Use and Definition of Arguments*
Function CAPQ(NODE)	Returns CAPQ as the capacity (maximum number of transactions allowed) of Q-node NODE.
Function GATRB(J)	Returns GATRB as the value of the Jth attribute of the transaction currently being processed.
Subroutine GETAT(ATT)	Returns the vector ATT($\cdot$). ATT(J) contains the value of the Jth attribute associated with the transaction currently being processed. The user must dimension ATT in UF.
Subroutine HALTA(NODE, NACT, REMTI,ATT)	Halts activity NACT scheduled from node NODE if it is ongoing when HALTA is invoked. Sets REMTI to the remaining time until completion and ATT($\cdot$) to the attributes of the transaction associated with the activity.
Function ISTUS(NODE, NSERV)	Returns ISTUS as the status of the service activity NSERV whose Q-node or S-node is NODE. The value of ISTUS is assigned as follows: +N number of busy servers 0 server is idle <0 server is blocked.
Function NACTY(IDUM)	Returns NACTY as the activity number associated with the activity just completed or started.
Subroutine NODMOD(NOUT, NIN)	Causes a modification to occur that replaces node NOUT with node NIN.
Function NOFQ(IDUM)	Returns NOFQ as the number of the Q-node associated with the service activity just completed. IDUM is a dummy argument and is not used.
Subroutine PATRB(ATTR,J)	Assigns the value ATTR to attribute J of the current transaction.
Subroutine PTIN(NODE,TIME, TIMEM,ATT)	Puts transaction in the network at node NODE at time TNOW+TIME. The mark time of the transaction is TIMEM and the attributes of the transaction are given by ATT(I), I=1,...,(NDE–1). ATT must be dimensioned in UF.

* For subnetwork node numbers (discussed in Chapter 10), use the conversion function NODCV(N,I) to retrieve an internal node number for subnetwork node N-I. For example, the node number for subnetwork node 3-4 is retrieved by the statement NODE = NODCV(3,4). This is required for subnetwork nodes wherever the variable NODE is used as an argument.

Table 7-4 (continued).

Subprogram	Use and Definition of Arguments**
Subroutine PUTAT(ATT)	Assigns the values contained in ATT to the attributes of the current transaction. The user must dimension ATT in UF.
Function RCAPQ(NODE)	Returns RCAPQ as the remaining capacity of Q-node NODE.
Function REMST(NSERV)	Returns REMST as the service time remaining on service activity NSERV. If NSERV is idle, a value of zero is returned. If there are parallel service activities, REMST is set to the smallest remaining service time.
Subroutine SNACT(ICA, NACT,REMTI)	For the next activity to be completed, SNACT returns the next activity number as NACT and the remaining time until completion as REMTI. If ICA is set to 1 by the user, SNACT also cancels the completion of the activity. If ICA is set to 0, only the values of NACT and REMTI are set.
Subroutine STAGO(NSERV, NODE,TIME,ICATT,ATT)	Causes server NSERV to stop processing a transaction and sends transaction stopped to node NODE with a time delay of TIME. If ICATT is set to 1, the attributes of the transaction are changed to the vector ATT. The status of server NSERV is then updated according to the condition of the Q-nodes preceding it. If NODE=0, the transaction is lost to the system. If server NSERV is idle, no action is taken.
Subroutine STSER(NSERV)	Stops service by server NSERV, deletes transaction from system and updates status of NSERV.

** For subnetwork activity numbers (discussed in Chapter 10), use the conversion function NATCV(N,I) to retrieve an internal activity number for subnetwork activity N-I. For example, the activity number for subnetwork activity 5-6 is retrieved by the statement NACT=NATCV(5,6). This is required for subnetwork activities wherever the variable NACT or NSERV is used as an argument.

Table 7-4 (continued).

Subprogram	Use and Definition of Arguments
Function TINIQ(NODE)	Computes the time integrated number in Q-node NODE from time TBEG to time TNOW. To compute the average number in Q-node NODE divide by (TNOW–TBEG).
Subroutine STARTA(NODE, NACT)	Causes activity NACT emanating from node NODE to be started, that is, the subroutine schedules an end of activity event for activity NACT.
Function TISS(NODE,NSERV)	Computes the time integrated status of server(s) NSERV from time TBEG to time TNOW. NODE is the start node of the activity representing NSERV. NODE can be either a Q-node or an S-node. To compute the average utilization divide by (TNOW–TBEG).
Function TMARK(IDUM)	Returns TMARK as the time the current transaction was last marked.
Function XNINQ(NODE)	Returns XNINQ as number of transactions currently in Q-node NODE.
Subroutine XTEND(NACT, TIME)	Causes the time of completion for activity NACT to be extended by the value of TIME. If NACT is not ongoing, the requested extension is ignored. Note: NACT can be a service activity.
Function AVEWT (NODE)	Computes the average waiting time of all transactions passing through Q-node NODE from time TBEG. Assumes the waiting time for each transaction currently in the Q-node is the entire waiting time of the transaction.
Subroutine PACTY	Prints a list of on-going activities when called.

Subroutine GETAT (ATT)

If it is desired to access all attribute values, then subroutine GETAT(ATT) is called. The argument, ATT, to subroutine GETAT is a vector which must be dimensioned to the number of attributes per transaction. If there are three attributes specified for each transaction then the statement

CALL GETAT(ATT)

assigns attribute 1 to ATT(1), attribute 2 to ATT(2) and attribute 3 to ATT(3).

Subroutine PATRB(ATTR,J)

To set or reset the Jth attribute, a call is made to subroutine PATRB (ATTR,J). The variable ATTR is defined to contain the new value of attribute J. Thus the statement

CALL PATRB(10.,3)

sets attribute 3 equal to 10 for the current transaction.

Subroutine PUTAT(ATT)

To change all attribute values for a transaction, a call is made to subroutine PUTAT(ATT). In this instance, the modeler defines a vector ATT with the values to be assigned to the current transaction. If there are two attributes per transaction, the following statements will assign: attribute 1, a value of 10; and attribute 2, a value of 20.

ATT(1) = 10.
ATT(2) = 20.
CALL PUTAT(ATT)

The mark time of the transaction is not changed by a call to PUTAT. In the above, ATT must be specified as a dimensioned variable in function UF.

Function TMARK(IDUM)

The function TMARK(IDUM) returns the mark time of the current transaction. IDUM is a dummy argument that is not used in function TMARK. It is included due to the requirement of ANSI FORTRAN that every function have at least one argument.

Subroutine PTIN(NODE,TIME,TIMEM,ATT)

To generate a transaction and put it in the network, subroutine PTIN(NODE,TIME,TIMEM,ATT) is called. TIMEM is the mark time for the transaction and ATT is a vector containing the attributes of the transaction. The transaction is scheduled to arrive at node NODE at TNOW+TIME. The statements

    ATT(1) = 20.
    ATT(2) = 3.
    CALL PTIN(10,2.,TNOW,ATT)

insert a transaction at node 10 of the network at time TNOW+2. The mark time of the transaction is TNOW and its two attributes are 20. and 3.

SUBPROGRAMS ASSOCIATED WITH Q-NODES

Five functions are provided that relate to Q-GERT variables associated with Q-nodes: CAPQ(NODE); RCAPQ(NODE): XNINQ(NODE); NOFQ(IDUM); and TINIQ(NODE). The first three functions are included to assist the modeler by providing descriptive names for quantities associated with Q-nodes. In addition, by using the functions described above, real valued representations of the quantities are obtained and the labeled COMMON block QVAR need not be included in function UF. Clearly, the inclusion of these functions in Q-GERT is only for the convenience of the modeler.

Function CAPQ(NODE)

Function CAPQ(NODE) returns the capacity of Q-node NODE. The statement

MAX10 = CAPQ(10)

sets the variable MAX10 equal to the maximum number of transactions allowed at Q-node 10. Recall that the Q-GERT variable NREL2(NODE) is used to store the capacity of Q-node NODE. Thus, the statement

MAX10 = NREL2(10)

performs the same function as the previous statement.

Function RCAPQ(NODE)

Function RCAPQ(NODE) returns the value of the remaining capacity of Q-node NODE. This is the quantity, NREL2(NODE) – NREL (NODE).

Function XNINQ(NODE)

The function XNINQ(NODE) returns the value of the current number of transactions in Q-node NODE. This is the value of NREL(NODE).

Function NOFQ(IDUM)

This function returns the number of the Q-node or S-node associated with the service activity that just completed processing the current transaction. The argument of function NOFQ is a dummy argument and is only included to meet ANSI FORTRAN requirements.

Function TINIQ(NODE)

The function TINIQ(NODE) makes available to the user the time integrated number in Q-node NODE from time TBEG to time TNOW on the current run. Thus, TINIQ provides the following quantity:

$$\int_{TBEG}^{TNOW} NREL(NODE)\ dt$$

The average number in Q-node NODE would then be obtained from the statement: ANIQ = TINIQ(NODE)/(TNOW−TBEG). When statistics are collected for an entire run, TBEG is 0.

USER DEFINED NODAL MODIFICATIONS:
SUBROUTINE NODMOD(NOUT,NIN)

To allow the modeler to make nodal modifications based on the status of the system, subroutine NODMOD(NOUT,NIN) is included in the Q-GERT program. Thus, if it is desired to replace node 5 by node 7 when user function 3 is activated, the following statement would be included in function UF:

3 CALL NODMOD(5,7)

This statement accomplishes the desired nodal replacement. Basically, subroutine NODMOD(NOUT,NIN) changes the value of the Q-GERT variable, NFTBU, in the following fashion:

NFTBU(NOUT) = NIN

With this change, node NIN will be branched from when node NOUT is released. Also, statistic collection and value assignments as specified at node NIN will be made. At the beginning of each run, NFTBU is reset by Q-GERT with the following statement NFTBU(NODE) = NODE.

SUBPROGRAMS ASSOCIATED WITH ACTIVITIES

Three subroutines, STARTA(NODE,NACT), HALTA(NODE,NACT, REMTI,ATT) and XTEND(NACT,TIME) are provided for starting an activity, halting an activity and for extending the duration of an on-going activity. One subroutine, SNACT, can be used to obtain the time until the next activity completion occurs, and, if desired, the stopping of that next activity. The function, NACTY(IDUM), provides the user a means to obtain the number of the activity that released a node.

Subroutine STARTA(NODE,NACT)

Subroutine STARTA(NODE,NACT) causes activity number NACT to be started. The variable NODE defines the start node number of activity NACT. When subroutine STARTA is called from function UF, an end of activity event for activity NACT is scheduled. It is presumed that the attributes of the transaction currently being processed are to be duplicated and associated with the transaction passing through activity NACT. If new attributes are to be defined, subroutine PTIN should be used. Subroutine STARTA only applies to nonservice activities as it is assumed that the activity can be started whenever STARTA is called. This requires that transactions can be processed in parallel by activity NACT without limit.

Subroutine HALTA(NODE,NACT,REMTI,ATT)

Subroutine HALTA causes activity number NACT whose start node is NODE to be stopped. The time remaining to process the transaction currently associated with activity NACT is returned as the value of REMTI. If NACT is not ongoing then REMTI is set to a negative value. The attributes of the transaction associated with NACT are returned in the vector ATT($\cdot$).

Subroutine HALTA can be used to stop parallel activities incident to a node when the node is released. For example, consider the Q-GERT subnetwork given on the next page. In function UF, when node 10 is released, all ongoing activities incident to node 10 are stopped. If desired, the value of RT, the remaining time, can be used to assess any savings caused by stopping ongoing activities.

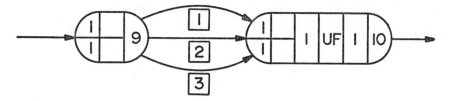

```
        FUNCTION UF
        DIMENSION TATT(3)
        NOACT=NACTY(IDUM)
        DO 10 I=1,3
        IF (NOACT.EQ.I) GO TO 10
        CALL HALTA(9,I,RT,TATT)
    10  CONTINUE
        UF=0.0
        RETURN
        END
```

Subroutine XTEND(NACT,TIME)

Subroutine XTEND(NACT,TIME) is used to extend the completion time for activity NACT by TIME time units. Subroutine XTEND removes activity NACT from the calendar of future events, recomputes a new activity completion time and puts the event back on the event calendar in the proper chronological order. The value of TIME can be negative; however, caution is required in using subroutine XTEND to shorten the time to perform an activity. In no case may the completion time of the activity be less than the current time, TNOW. If subroutine XTEND is called and activity NACT is not ongoing, the requested extension is ignored. Subroutine XTEND may be used to extend the time required to perform a service activity.

The statement CALL XTEND(10,50.) imposes an extra 50 time unit delay on the transaction being processed through activity 10. If no transaction was being processed by activity 10, no action is taken.

Subroutine SNACT(ICA,NACT,REMTI)

Subroutine SNACT is used to obtain information about the next activity to be completed. That is, the activity listed first on the event calendar. When SNACT is called, it determines the activity number, NACT, of the next activity to be completed and the remaining time to complete the activity, REMTI. When no activities are scheduled for completion, SNACT sets NACT to zero. If SNACT was called at TNOW, then activity NACT is scheduled to be completed at TNOW+REMTI. The argument ICA is set by the user and is an indicator that the next activity is to be cancelled. If ICA=1, the completion of NACT is cancelled. If ICA=0, NACT is not cancelled and only the values of NACT and REMTI are returned to the user. Subroutine SNACT provides the user a means for deleting all pending activity completions when a node is released by repetitively cancelling the next activity completion. SNACT also provides the user with a means for determining the time at which the next scheduled change to the system is to occur.

As an example of the use of subroutine SNACT, consider the situation in which a project has been cancelled, and it is necessary to stop all ongoing activities. This can be accomplished with the following two statements:

```
7  CALL SNACT(1,NUMAC,REMTI)
   IF (NUMAC .NE. 0) GO TO 7
```

With these statments, SNACT is called to cancel the next activity completion until a zero is assigned to NUMAC.

Function NACTY(IDUM)

This function, when called from a user function employed at a node, returns the number of the activity that caused the node to be released. When called from a branch, it returns the activity number associated with the branch. The argument of function NACTY is a dummy argument and is only included to meet ANSI FORTRAN requirements.

SUBPROGRAMS ASSOCIATED WITH SERVICE ACTIVITIES

The following five subprograms are available for ascertaining and changing the status of service activities: ISTUS(NODE,NSERV); TISS(NODE,NSERV); REMST(NSERV); STSER(NSERV); and STAGO(NSERV,NEWN,TIME,ICATT,ATT).

Function ISTUS(NODE,NSERV)

The status of a service activity can be obtained by using function ISTUS(NODE,NSERV) where NODE is the Q-node or S-node that precedes the service activity and NSERV is the service activity number. To obtain the status of server number 3 that has Q-node 10 preceding it, the following statement would be made:

ISS = ISTUS(10,3)

The value assigned to the variable ISS for this statement would be zero if server 3 is idle, would be n if n parallel servers are busy, and would be negative if the server is currently in a blocked status.

Function TISS(NODE,NSERV)

The function TISS(NODE,NSERV) makes available to the user the time integrated status of service activity NSERV, from time TBEG to time TNOW. Thus, TISS provides the following quantity:

$$\int_{TBEG}^{TNOW} \max[0; ISTUS(NODE,NSERV)]dt$$

NODE must be a Q-node or an S-node and NSERV must be a service activity. The average utilization of server NSERV would be obtained from the statement: AUS=TISS(NODE,NSERV)/(TNOW−TBEG).

Function REMST(NSERV)

To obtain the amount of remaining service time for a service activity, function REMST(NSERV) is used. This function returns the amount of time left before server number NSERV completes his next service. The remaining service time is equal to the scheduled end of activity time minus current time (TNOW). If server number NSERV represents parallel service activities and parallel activities are ongoing, then function REMST sets the remaining service time to the smallest value of the remaining service time of all ongoing activities for service activity

NSERV. If service activity NSERV is not ongoing, a value of zero is returned as the remaining service time. Thus, the time to complete service on a transaction being processed by server 1 is obtained from the statement: TTCS=REMST(1).

Subroutine STSER(NSERV)

To stop the service provided by server NSERV, subroutine STSER(NSERV) is called. Each call to this routine stops one service activity being performed by server number NSERV. If multiple service activities are in progress for server NSERV then the transaction whose service is nearest completion is stopped. In addition, the transaction being served is deleted from the system. The status of server number NSERV is updated so that if items are waiting in the queue of NSERV, the server is made busy. If no items are waiting, the server is made idle.

Suppose it is desired to stop service on a transaction being processed by server 2 whose Q-node is 1 if the remaining service time on the transaction is less than 15 time units. The following statements achieve this objective:

```
IF (ISTUS(1,2) .EQ. 0) RETURN
IF (REMST(2) .LT. 15.0) CALL STSER(2)
```

Subroutine STAGO(NSERV,NEWN,TIME,ICATT,ATT)

If it is desired to stop service and route the transaction on which service was stopped to another node, subroutine STAGO(NSERV, NEWN, TIME,ICATT,ATT) is called. This subroutine performs a similar function to subroutine STSER with the addition that the transaction on which service is stopped is routed to node NEWN with a time delay of TIME. By setting the argument ICATT to 1, the attributes of the rerouted transaction are changed to ATT. The mark time of the transaction is not changed. If ICATT is zero, no change is made to the attributes of the transaction.

When subroutine STAGO is called, the status of server NSERV is updated according to the condition of the Q-nodes preceding it. If multiple service activities are in progress for server NSERV then the transaction whose service is nearest completion is stopped. If a zero value is assigned to the variable NEWN, the second argument of the subroutine, then the transaction on which service was stopped is lost to the system, Thus, the statement CALL STAGO (3,0,0.0,0,ATT)is equivalent to the statement CALL STSER(3).

To stop service on the transaction being processed by server 2 and to route the transaction to node 18 in 10 time units, the following statement would be employed:

CALL STAGO(2, 18, 10., 0, ATT)

If all the transaction's attributes were to be changed then ATT should be defined appropriately, and a code of 1 given as the fourth argument. However, if only one attribute value is to be changed or it is desired to mark the transaction with the current time, then a convenient procedure is to perform the attribute change operations at node 18 or to route the transaction to a node that precedes node 18 that performs the necessary marking and attribute change operations.

DUMMY SUBPROGRAMS

A dummy subprogram is one that includes only RETURN and END statements. Dummy subprograms included in Q-GERT are:
1. Function UF; and Subroutine US;
2. Subroutine UI; and
3. Subroutine UO.

Such routines are required as calls to them are issued by the Q-GERT program to provide communication points with the user. Thus, a user need not rewrite these subprograms if they are not used in his model. Should they be included, however, it is the user's responsibility to insure that his subprograms are loaded and not the dummy routines.

RESTRICTION ON USE OF USER SUBPROGRAMS THAT CAN START ACTIVITIES

FORTRAN IV does not permit recursive calls to subprograms. Care must be taken so that the code written in function UF does not result in a call to UF. This can occur when subroutine PTIN, STARTA, STSER or STAGO are used. These subroutines would be called in UF within a specific function number. If an activity is started based on such a call and, if the activity started had the distribution type UF, then function UF would be called again with a new function number. This second call to UF would be a recursive call and is not allowed in standard FORTRAN IV. To avoid recursive calls, subroutine US should be used.

The Q-GERT error code 87 normally results when such a recursive call is made. Error code 87 specifies that sufficient storage space is not available for end-of-activity events. This error results because the activity requested to be scheduled is continually scheduled due to the loss of "return" information by the FORTRAN program. As an example, consider the following rather involved situation where a user function is called to stop service on a transaction being processed by activity 3. In UF, subroutine STSER(NACT) would be used with NACT=3. If the function type UF is prescribed for activity 3 then when STSER is called, the Q-GERT Analysis Program would examine the Q-node associated with activity 3. If a transaction was waiting, it would schedule an end-of-service event for activity 3. To do this requires the use of function UF to obtain the service time. Hence, the recursive call and an error type 87. If US is prescribed for activity 3, no error occurs.

This chapter has presented procedures for including FORTRAN inserts into Q-GERT models. With such procedures, Q-GERT becomes a highly flexible modeling and simulation tool. The next chapter presents three examples of the use of these FORTRAN inserts.

EXERCISES

7-1. Develop Q-GERT network segments and the code for function UF to model the following:
  a) At node 10, route a transaction to node 15 if the number of transactions in Q-node 20 is greater than or equal to 5. Otherwise, route the transaction to node 20.
  b) If node 10 has been released seven times when a transaction is passing through node 5, assign a value of 3 to attribute 2 of the transaction passing through node 5. Otherwise, assign a value of zero to attribute 2.
  c) At node 16, determine if node 50 has been modified. If it has been modified, route any incoming transaction to node 50. Otherwise, route transactions to node 51.

7-2. For the one server, single queue situation, develop the Q-GERT model and user code when the service time is a sample from the probability mass function as shown below.

Probability	Service Time (min.)
.2	4
.3	6
.1	7
.4	10

The interarrival times are exponentially distributed with a mean of 7.75 minutes.

7-3. Modify Exercise 7-2 so that the queue of the server is limited to five transactions and the mean of the interarrival time distribution is dependent on the number of balkers per unit time from the Q-node. If the number of balkers per unit time exceeds 1 at the time of an arrival, the mean interarrival time is increased to 8.0 minutes. Otherwise, it remains at 7.75 minutes [Hint: Consider the use of the Q-GERT variable NTC.]

7-4. For the one server, single queue situation, it has been determined that the service time remaining on a transaction being processed is altered at the time of an arrival of another transaction. If the new arrival causes more than five transactions to be in the queue, the service time remaining is decreased by one tenth of a minute for each waiting customer greater than five, including the new arrival. In no case, however, can the remaining service time be decreased by more than 50 percent and the remaining service time can only be decreased once, that is, if two transactions arrive during the servicing of a transaction, only the first arrival causes a decrease in the remaining service time. Assume that interarrival times are exponentially distributed with a mean of 2 time units and service time is exponentially distributed with a mean of 1.7 time units.

7-5. Develop the FORTRAN code required to maintain statistics on the number of transactions in a single server queueing situation. At the end of the simulation, print out the average number of transactions in the system and the maximum number of transactions ever in the system.

7-6. Develop a network model and program inserts for the single server queueing situation to compute the average waiting time of a transaction at a Q-node. At the end of a run, print out the average waiting time in the queue for a transaction, the number of transactions that waited at the queue, the average waiting time of those transactions that waited, and the maximum waiting time for a transaction. (Note: For more advanced statistics collection, see Chapter 9 for user collected statistics procedures.)

7-7. Develop a section of a Q-GERT network that involves a transaction going from Q-node 10 to node 20 through nodes 12 and 14. It is desired to restrict the time required for the transaction to go from node 10 to node 20 to be greater than 25 time units. Note that the restriction is from the time the transaction is taken out of the queue and starts service in the service activity (or activities) following Q-node 10.

7-8 For the single server queueing situation, it is desired to process all transactions residing at the queue prior to completing the simulation run at time 480. No arrivals are permitted after time 480. Develop the Q-GERT network and program inserts to accomplish this processing of all transactions residing at a queue at the end of a run.

Chapter 8

MODELS ILLUSTRATING ADVANCED CONCEPTS

In this chapter, three examples will be presented that involve programming inserts. The examples demonstrate how program inserts are included in function UF to augment the modeling capabilities of the standard Q-GERT symbol set. The use of subroutines UI and UO are also illustrated. Procedures for employing Q-GERT variables and Q-GERT subprograms within the user written subprograms are illustrated. The examples were selected to provide diverse illustrations of the use of user functions within the Q-GERT modeling structure.

Example 10 involves the analysis of a PERT type network to obtain a measure of the criticality of each activity of the network. The use of function NACTY to obtain the number of an activity that causes the release of a node and function GATRB to get an attribute value are illustrated.

Example 11 involves the analysis of a one server, single queue system in which the service activity can breakdown. This example illustrates how Q-GERT functions are used for: computing remaining service time, REMST; stopping service, STSER; and putting a transaction in the network, PTIN. Also, the functions for retrieving the value of an attribute of a transaction, GATRB, and its mark time, TMARK, are used.

The third example of this chapter, Example 12, presents a model of an inventory situation where customers' requests are backordered. The Q-GERT subprograms for starting an activity, STARTA; stopping service, STSER; assigning a new attribute value to a transaction, PATRB;

and accessing an attribute of a transaction, GATRB, are illustrated in this example. Also, the functions for obtaining the time integrated status of a server, TISS, and the time integrated number of items in a queue, TINIQ, are used.

The examples presented in this chapter have intentionally been kept small. In this way, the procedures for writing the program inserts in function UF can be explained without undue complexity. Although practical applications may require larger networks than the ones presented in this chapter, the coding requirements for function UF will normally not be more extensive nor more difficult than those presented herein.

EXAMPLE 10. OBTAINING ACTIVITY CRITICALITY INDICES

In a project network, the sequence of activities whose durations, when added together, produce the total time for the project is called the critical path for the project. If any activity on the critical path is lengthened, the entire project is extended. In PERT, the critical path is determined by using the expected value of each activity's duration. The path or sequence of activities whose sum of expected times is the longest is then defined as the critical path. It can be shown that the expected project duration as computed by the expected times of the activities on the critical path will always be optimistic; that is, the estimate will always be smaller than the theoretical expected value.* If a project is balanced in the sense that there are many paths which have approximately the same expected duration, then the PERT computed estimate can have a large bias.

Problem Statement

Example 6 of Chapter 4 illustrated how the Q-GERT Analysis Program could be used to obtain unbiased estimates of the expected duration of a project. In this example, the Q-GERT Analysis Program will be used to obtain estimates of the probability or relative frequency that an activity is on a critical path. This probability is referred to as the criticality index for the activity (134). The network presented in Example 6 will be used to illustrate the computation of criticality indices for the activities of the network. Four hundred runs of the network will be made to obtain estimates of the criticality indices.

* Several authors have developed improved estimates which, although they are optimistic, are less optimistic than the standard one employed in PERT (31,43,67).

Model Development

The PERT network representation of the project for which criticality indices are desired is shown in Figure 8-1. Before discussing the Q-GERT model, a brief description of the procedure for determining if an activity is on a critical path will be given. Consider that one run of the network has been made and that node 6 has been reached. The activity that caused node 6 to be released must be on the critical path as it caused the project to be completed. Thus, the *last* activity completed that is incident to node 6 (either activity 6, 8 or 9) is on the critical path. If when node 6 is released, the activity number causing this releasing is retained along with the start node for the activity, it will be possible to specify one activity on the critical path and also to trace back in the network to a prior node that is also on the critical path. Suppose activity 6 caused node 6 to be released. Then, on this run, activity 6 would be critical and node 3 would be on the critical path.

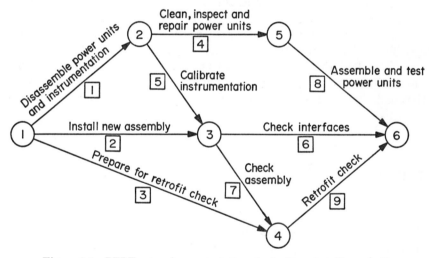

Figure 8-1 PERT network representation of retrofit project, Example 10.

Next, it would be necessary to trace back from node 3 to determine the activity that caused it to be released. Suppose it was activity 2. In this case, activity 2 would be critical on this run and its start node, node 1, would be on the critical path. Since node 1 is a source node, we need not trace back any further and the activities on the critical path for this run would be activities 2 and 6.

The procedure for tracing back through the network requires the storing of information as to which activity caused each node to be released. The start node of the activity is also stored as a potential node on the critical path. Thus, as the activities are performed and nodes are released, data is stored regarding potential critical activities and critical nodes. When the sink node is reached, the trace back through the network identifies the actual critical activities and critical nodes for the run of the network.

To accomplish the storing of potential critical nodes and critical activities, a user function will be prescribed for each non-source node of the network. The user function number at a node will be the node number, that is, user function 2 will be assigned at node 2. The program insert for each user function will involve the recording of the last activity completed and the start node for that activity. The number of the last activity completed can be obtained by using function NACTY. The start node of the last activity completed will be assigned to attribute 1 of the transaction. At the source node, the source node number will be assigned to attribute 1. By using the *last* criterion choice specification at a node, the attributes of the transaction that released the node will be maintained. The user function at the node can then record the value of attribute 1. This value will be the start node number of the activity that was critical to the node. Also in the user function, the current node number will be placed in attribute 1 so that when branching occurs from the node, attribute 1 will contain the start node number for the branches selected.

Q-GERT Model

The Q-GERT network model for this example is shown in Figure 8-2. The source node for the network is node 1. A value of 1 is assigned to attribute 1 using the specification (CO,1). Similarly at other nodes, the user function number and node number correspond. In user function I, a value of I for attribute 1 is prescribed.

For each node, the number of releases is set equal to the number of incoming branches. The choice criterion is specified as L so that the attributes of the last transaction arriving at the node are maintained. Statistics are to be kept on the first release times of the node. Node 6 is the sink node for the network and, when it is released, one run of the project is completed.

The programmed insert contained in function UF is shown in Figure

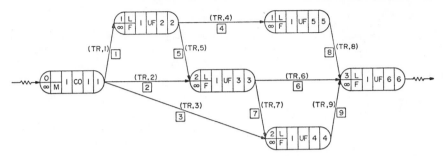

Figure 8-2 Q-GERT model for computing critically indices, Example 10.

8-3. User functions are prescribed for each node of the network with the user function number equal to the node number, IN. The array NACN(IN) is used to store the *number of the activity* critical to *node* IN. The array NNCN(IN) is used to store the *number of the node* critical to node IN.

```
FUNCTION UF(IN)
COMMON /UCOM1/ NACN(6),NNCN(6)
NACN(IN)=NACTY(IDUM)
NNCN(IN)=GATRB(1)
UF=IN
RETURN
END
```

Figure 8-3 Function UF to maintain critical activities and nodes, Example 10.

When a node is released, function UF is called and the activity number of the last activity completed is obtained from function NACTY. The statement NACN(IN) = NACTY(IDUM) stores this activity number as the activity critical to node IN. Since the attributes associated with the last arriving transaction are maintained, the statement NNCN(IN) = GATRB(1) causes function GATRB to obtain attribute 1 and store the value in NNCN(IN) as the node that is critical to node IN. The last statement assigns the value of IN to UF. This statement causes attribute 1 of transactions that leave node IN to have an attribute 1 value equal to the node number. This completes the description of function UF.

When a run is completed, the Q-GERT Analysis Program calls subroutine UO. The FORTRAN listing of subroutine UO for Example 10 is shown in Figure 8-4. First, the last critical node is established as the sink node for the network by the statement LCN = 6. At statement 100, the last critical activity, LCA, is the activity that is critical to the last critical node. The number of times this activity has been on a critical path is indexed by 1 by the statement NUMC(LCA) = NUMC(LCA) + 1. The start node of this last critical activity is established by the statement LCN = NNCN(LCN). Note that the argument for the array NNCN is LCN as critical nodes were stored with reference to subsequent nodes. Next, a test to see if the source node for the network has been reached. This will be the case if LCN is 1. If LCN is not 1, a transfer is made to statement 100 to continue the trace back process through the network. If LCN is 1, a test is made to see if all runs have been made by testing the number of runs to be made, NRUNS, against the current run number, NRUN. If all runs have not been made, a return is made to perform another run. If all runs have been made, the criticality index for each activity is computed as the number of times an activity has been on the critical path divided by the number of runs made. The activity number and its criticality index are then printed out for each activity.

```
      SUBROUTINE UO
      COMMON /QVAR/ NDE,NFT3U(100),NREL(100),NRELP(100),NREL2(100),
     1 NRUN,NRUNS,NTC(100),PARAM(100,4),TBEG,TNOW
      DIMENSION NUMC(9)
      COMMON /UCOM1/ NACN(6),NNCN(6)
      DATA NUMC/9*0/
      LCN=6
  100 LCA=NACN(LCN)
      NUMC(LCA)=NUMC(LCA)+1
      LCN=NNCN(LCN)
      IF(LCN.NE.1) GO TO 100
      IF(NRUNS.GT.NRUN) RETURN
      XRUNS=NRUNS
      DO 200 I=1,9
      YCRIT=NUMC(I)
      YCRIT=YCRIT/XRUNS
      WRITE(6,300) I,YCRIT
  200 CONTINUE
  300 FORMAT(27X,35H THE CRITICALITY INDEX FOR ACTIVITY,I4,3H IS,F10.6)
      RETURN
      END
```

Figure 8-4   Subroutine UO, Example 10.

The data input for this example is shown in Figure 8-5. The data input is identical to that presented for Example 6 with the addition of the value assignment data cards (VAS) for each node of the network.

```
GEN,PRITSKER,PERTCRIT-10,3,15,1977,4,1,1,,400,(14)1*
SOU,1*
VAS,1,1,CO,1*
STA,2/NODE-2,(7)0.0,0.5*
VAS,2,1,UF,2*
STA,3/NODE-3,2,(7)3.,0.5*
VAS,3,1,UF,3*
STA,4/NODE-4,2,(7)10.,0.5*
VAS,4,1,UF,4*
STA,5/NODE-5,(7)12.,0.5*
VAS,5,1,UF,5*
SIN,6/PROJCOMP,3,(7)15.,0.5*
VAS,6,1,UF,6*
PAR,1,3,1,5*
PAR,2,6,3,9*
PAR,3,13,10,19*
PAR,4,9,3,12*
PAR,5,3,1,8*
PAR,6,9,8,16*
PAR,7,7,4,13*
PAR,8,6,3,9*
PAR,9,3,1,8*
ACT,1,2,TR,1,1*          DISASSEMBLE POWER UNITS
ACT,1,3,TR,2,2*          INSTALL NEW ASSEMBLY
ACT,1,4,TR,3,3*          PREPARE FOR RETROFIT
ACT,2,5,TR,4,4*          CLEAN, INSPECT, AND REPAIR POWER UNITS
ACT,2,3,TR,5,5*          CALIBRATE INSTRUMENTATION
ACT,3,6,TR,6,6*          CHECK INTERFACES
ACT,3,4,TR,7,7*          CHECK ASSEMBLY
ACT,4,6,TR,9,9*          RETROFIT CHECK
ACT,5,6,TR,8,8*          ASSEMBLE AND TEST POWER UNITS
FIN*
```

Figure 8-5 Data input for obtaining criticality indices for retrofit project, Example 10.

Summary of Results

The output of the criticality indices for each activity of the network is shown in Figure 8-6. The criticality index for activity 1 is 0.6075 which means that 60.75 percent of the time it was on the critical path. Based on this output, each activity can possibly be on the critical path. To decrease the project duration, the activities with the highest criticality indices should be examined for possible improvement. Improvement in these activities will not necessarily decrease project duration as there is a (1 – criticality index) chance that the activity will not be on the critical path. The other outputs for this example are identical to those presented and discussed in Example 6.

```
THE CRITICALITY INDEX FOR ACTIVITY    1 IS    .607500
THE CRITICALITY INDEX FOR ACTIVITY    2 IS    .197500
THE CRITICALITY INDEX FOR ACTIVITY    3 IS    .195000
THE CRITICALITY INDEX FOR ACTIVITY    4 IS    .120000
THE CRITICALITY INDEX FOR ACTIVITY    5 IS    .487500
THE CRITICALITY INDEX FOR ACTIVITY    6 IS    .275000
THE CRITICALITY INDEX FOR ACTIVITY    7 IS    .410000
THE CRITICALITY INDEX FOR ACTIVITY    8 IS    .120000
THE CRITICALITY INDEX FOR ACTIVITY    9 IS    .605000
```

Figure 8-6   Criticality indices for activities in a retrofit project, Example 10.

EXAMPLE 11. A JOB SHOP ENVIRONMENT WITH MACHINE BREAKDOWNS

Problem Statement

A schematic diagram of job processing and machine breakdown for a machine tool is given in Figure 8-7. Jobs arrive to a machine tool on the average of one per hour. The distribution of these interarrival times is exponential. During normal operation, the jobs are processed on a first-in, first-out basis. The time to process a job is normally distributed with a mean of 1/2 hour and a standard deviation of 1/10 of an hour. Processing times are never less than 1/4 of an hour nor greater than 2 hours. In addition to the processing time, there is a set up time that is uniformly distributed between 0.2 and 0.5 of an hour. Jobs that have been processed by the machine tool are routed to a different section of the shop and are considered to have left the machine tool area.

The machine tool experiences breakdowns during which time it can no longer process jobs. The time between breakdowns is gamma distributed with a mean of 20 hours and a standard deviation of 2 hours. When a breakdown occurs, the job being processed is removed from the machine tool and, after a 0.1 hour delay, is placed at the head of the queue of jobs waiting to be processed. The service time for the job preempted by the machine breakdown is the remaining service time plus an additional setup time which is again uniformly distributed.

When the machine tool breaks down, a repair process is initiated which is accomplished in three phases. Each phase is exponentially distributed with a mean of 3/4 of an hour. Since the repair time is the sum of independent and identically distributed exponential random variables, the repair time is Erlang distributed.

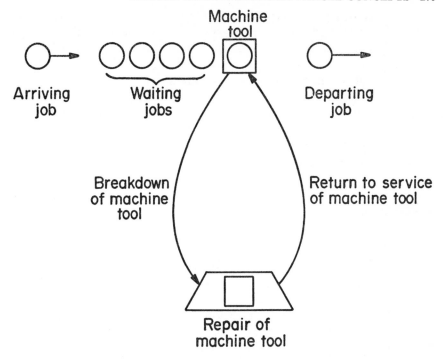

Figure 8-7 Schematic diagram of the processing of jobs by a machine tool that has breakdowns, Example 11.

The machine tool is to be analyzed by building a Q-GERT model to obtain information on the utilization of the machine tool and the time required to process a job.

Model Development

This machine tool problem is basically an elaboration of the one server, single queue system. New features to be included are a setup time and a down time for the server. The setup time can be modeled by making a value assignment to attribute 1 of a normally distributed sample and then adding a sample from a uniform distribution to it. The processing time for the machine tool will then be taken from attribute 1.

The addition of machine breakdowns is more complicated. A procedure is required that causes the server to not process jobs when it is being repaired. One procedure for modeling this is to consider repair time as a different type of job for the machine tool. When a breakdown occurs, this "different" type of job would be put at the head of the queue waiting for processing by the machine tool. If the machine tool is processing a regular job, service on the job must be stopped, the remaining service time for the job calculated, and the job routed back to the queue to wait for the machine to be repaired. In this example, two attributes will be used. Attribute 1 will be to store either the service time for a job, the service time remaining for an interrupted job or the repair time to fix the machine tool. Attribute 2 will be a transaction identifier where a 0 implies a regular job, a 1 implies a preempted job, and a 2 implies a repair transaction.

Q-GERT Model

The Q-GERT network model for the machine tool with breakdowns is shown in Figure 8-8. Nodes 5, 10 and 15 portray the one server, single queue system. At node 5, the processing time for a regular job is stored in attribute 1 through a value assignment specification. First, a sample from a normal distribution is placed in attribute 1. Then a sample from a uniform distribution is added to attribute 1. Attribute 2 is assigned a value of 0 to indicate that it is a regular job. Transactions are ranked at Q-node 10 on the basis of big value of attribute 2 first. This will rank the jobs in the queue in the order of repair transactions, job transactions that have been preempted and regular jobs. The time to perform activity 3 is specified as (AT,1) so that the service time is taken from attribute 1 of the transaction being served. For job transactions, attribute 1

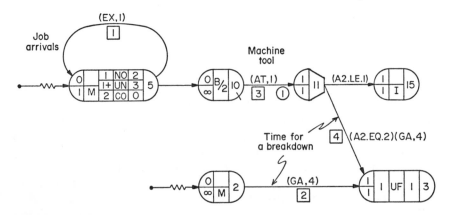

Figure 8-8   Q-GERT model of machine tool processing with breakdowns, Example 11.

is the service time plus the setup time. For repair transactions, it is the repair time.

At node 11, conditional-take first branching is performed so that completed jobs are routed to node 15 and repair transactions are routed to node 3. The condition specifies that transactions be routed to node 15 whenever attribute 2 is less than or equal to 1. This routes regular jobs and preempted jobs to node 15. When attribute 2 equals 2, transactions are routed to node 3. The time to reach node 3 is gamma distributed and represents the time between breakdowns of the machine tool. The first breakdown is modeled by the branch from node 2 to node 3. At node 3, user function 1 is specified and it is here where the specialized coding is required to insert a repair transaction into the model and to preempt and reroute a job transaction that is being processed.

Function UF for this example is shown in Figure 8-9. When function UF is called for function number 1, a repair transaction is created and inserted into the network at Q-node 10. Since only one user function number is employed in this example, there is no need for a computed GO TO statement. The first two statements in UF define the attributes of the repair transaction. Attribute 1 is the repair time and is a sample from an Erlang distribution with parameter set number 5.

```
      FUNCTION UF(IFN)
      COMMON /UCOM1/ TOTRT
      COMMON /GVAR/ NDE,NFTBU(100),NREL(100),NRELP(100),NREL2(100),
     1 NRUN,NRUNS,NTC(100),PARAM(100,4),TBEG,TNOW
      DIMENSION RATT(2)
C****SET ATTRIBUTE 1 TO REPAIR TIME.  ACCUMULATE TOTAL REPAIR TIME.
      RATT(1)=ER(5)
      RATT(2)=2.0
      TOTRT=TOTRT+RATT(1)
C****INSERT REPAIR TRANSACTION INTO NETWORK AT Q-NODE 10
      CALL PTIN(10,0.0,TNOW,RATT)
      UF=0.0
C****CHECK STATUS OF SERVER
      IF(ISTUS(10,3).EQ.0) RETURN
C****PREEMPT JOB AND SEND TO Q-NODE 10 WITH NEW ATTRIBUTES
      RATT(1)=REMST(3)+UN(3)
      RATT(2)=1.0
      CALL STAGO(3,10,0.1,1,RATT)
      RETURN
      END
```

Figure 8-9 FORTRAN listing of function UF, Example 11.

Attribute 2 is set equal to 2 to specify that this transaction is a repair transaction. For statistical purposes, the total repair time is maintained in the variable TOTRT. TOTRT is initialized to zero in subroutine UI. The transaction whose attributes are defined by the vector RATT are then inserted in the network at node 10 with a zero time delay by a call to subroutine PTIN. Since Q-node 10 is ranked on big values of attribute 2 (B/2) and attribute 2 was set to 2, this transaction is placed at the head of the queue of transactions residing at Q-node 10. If the machine tool is idle, the repair transaction will seize the machine tool server and the user need not include code to accomplish this. (Note: it is assumed that an idle machine can fail.) If the status of server 3 is idle (0), a return from function UF is made. If the server is not idle, the job being processed must be stopped.

Before stopping the job, its remaining service time is computed. If this is not done first, the remaining processing time will be lost. A new processing time is computed as the sum of the remaining service time plus an additional setup time. The remaining service time is obtained through the use of function REMST for server number 3. Added to this time is a sample from a uniform distribution with parameter set number 3. The sum of these two times is stored in RATT(1) and it will be used as attribute 1 of the transaction that is preempted. Attribute 2 is specified as 1 to indicate that this is a job transaction that was preempted (it will, therefore, have priority over new jobs in Q-node 10). The vector RATT is a temporary storage array defined by the user for transferring attributes of a transaction being routed. Processing of the transaction can now be stopped and it can be routed to Q-node 10 using the statement CALL STAGO(3,10,0.1,1,RATT). This statement stops service activity 3 and routes the preempted transaction to node 10 in 0.1 hours with new attributes as defined by RATT. Thus, when a repair transaction is required, a current job will be preempted and placed at the top of the queue of jobs to be processed. The server will not be available for the duration of the repair. At the end of the repair, the next machine failure is scheduled by selecting the branch from node 11 to node 3.

Figure 8-10 shows the FORTRAN listings for subroutines UI and UO. For this example, UI is employed to initialize the total repair time, TOTRT, to zero. Subroutine UO is used to compute average utilization and average out-of-commission time for the machine tool. During its operation, the status of the machine tool can be: working on a job, idle, and being repaired. From the Q-GERT standpoint, the machine is either idle or busy. When it is busy, it is processing a job transaction or a repair transaction. To obtain the average time the machine was busy processing jobs, special coding must be included in subroutine UO. The first statement in subroutine UO computes the total time the machine tool was busy processing jobs, TOTUT. This total utilization time is the time integrated status of the server minus the total repair time. Function TISS is used to obtain the total time integrated status of the server.

```
      SUBROUTINE UI
      COMMON /UCOM1/ TOTRT
      TOTRT=0.0
      RETURN
      END


      SUBROUTINE UO
      COMMON /UCOM1/ TOTRT
      COMMON /QVAR/ NDE,NFTBU(100),NREL(100),NRELP(100),NREL2(100),
     1 NRUN,NRUNS,NTC(100),PARAM(100,4),TBEG,TNOW
      TOTUT=TISS(10,3)-TOTRT
      AUTIL=TOTUT/TNOW
      AOUTC=TOTRT/TNOW
      WRITE(6,100) AUTIL,AOUTC,TNOW
100   FORMAT(5X,≠AVERAGE UTILIZATION = ≠,F6.3/5X,≠AVERAGE OUT-OF-COMMISS
     1ION = ≠,F6.3/5X,≠SIMULATION TIME = ≠,F10.3)
      RETURN
      END
```

Figure 8-10   FORTRAN listings of subroutines UI and UO, Example 11.

The average utilization is the total time obtained from TISS divided by
the time to complete the run. Since subroutine UO is called at the end
of the run, TNOW is the run time. The percentage of time the machine
is out of commission, AOUTC, is the ratio of the total repair time to the
total run time. The statement for AOUTC illustrates this computation.
The last executable statement in UO is to printout the average utilization, the average out of commission time and the total time for the run.
This completes the description of subroutine UO. The data input for
this example is shown in Figure 8-11.


```
GEN,PRITSKER,MACH-TOOL-11,3,4,1977,1,0,0,6000.,5,(14)2*
SOU,5,0,1*                           ARRIVAL OF JOB NODE
VAS,5,1,NO,2,1+,UN,3,2,CO,0*         ASSIGNMENT OF ATTRIBUTES TO JOBS
QUE,10/M-TOOL-Q,(6)B/2*              MACH. ONE TOOL QUEUE
REG,11,1,1,F*                        CONDITIONAL BRANCHING NODE
STA,15/JOB-TIME,1,1,,I,5.,,5.*       END OF JOB NODE
SOU,2*                               SOURCE NODE FOR FIRST BREAKDOWN
REG,3,1,1*                           NODE FOR USER FUNCTION PROCESSING OF BREAKDOWNS
VAS,3,1,UF,1*                        USER FUNCTION ASSIGNMENT
PAR,1,60.*                           INTERARRIVAL TIME PARAMETERS
PAR,2,30.,15.,,120.,,6.*             PROCESSING TIME PARAMETERS
PAR,3,,12.,30.*                      SETUP TIME PARAMETERS
PAR,4,1200.,,,120.*                  TIME BETWEEN BREAKDOWN PARAMETERS
PAR,5,80.,,,3*                       REPAIR TIME PARAMETERS
ACT,5,5,EX,1,1*                      SCHEDULE NEXT JOB ARRIVAL
ACT,5,10*                            TRANSFER JOB TO QUEUE
ACT,10,11,AT,1,3/MACHTOOL,1*         MACHINE TOOL PROCESSING
ACT,11,15,(8)1,A2.LE.1*              TRANSFER JOB FROM MACHINE TOOL
ACT,11,3,GA,4,4,,2,A2.EQ.2*          SCHEDULE NEXT BREAKDOWN
ACT,2,3,GA,4,2*                      SCHEDULE FIRST BREAKDOWN
FIN*
```

Figure 8-11   Q-GERT data input for machine tool processing, Example 11.

Summary of Results

Table 8-1 presents results from five runs each with a 6000 time unit duration for the machine tool process. In Table 8-1, the fraction of time the machine was busy working on a job, the fraction of time the machine was being repaired and the fraction of time the machine was idle because no job was to be processed are presented. From the table it is seen that the machine tool is working on jobs approximately 78 percent of the time. The other 22 percent of the time is spent in either an idle or repair state. If additional jobs were not anticipated, it might not be necessary to investigate methods for reducing the fraction of time the machine is being repaired. However, if capacity expansion was envisioned, a reduction in repair time would be one way to increase machine capacity. Clearly, a cost structure would be required in order to make a detailed assessment.

Table 8-1   Machine Utilization Fractions, Example 11.

Run Number	Fraction of Time Machine Is Busy	Fraction of Time Machine Is Being Repaired	Fraction of Time Machine Is Idle
1	0.701	0.147	0.152
2	0.790	0.176	0.034
3	0.846	0.107	0.047
4	0.726	0.164	0.110
5	0.850	0.132	0.018
Average	0.783	0.145	0.072

Figure 8-12 presents the final summary report for the five simulation runs performed for this example. From this report, it is seen that the average time a job is in the system is over 548 time units. The variability associated with the time a job is in the system is extremely high and is an indication that due dates, if they exist, may not be being met. Further examination into the processing time and the cause for its variability should be made. One cause for the long time in the system is the amount of queueing being done by the job. From the output report it is seen that on the average 8.54 jobs were in the queue. Further, on one of the simulation runs, the average number of jobs in the queue was as high as 12.46 and at one time during the five simulation runs as many as 22 jobs were waiting to be processed. Since jobs wait for other jobs to be

GERT SIMULATION PROJECT MACH-TCOL-11 BY PRITSKER
DATE 3/ 4/ 1977

FINAL RESULTS FOR   5 SIMULATIONS

AVERAGE NODE STATISTICS

NODE	LABEL	PROBABILITY	AVE.	STD.DEV.	SD OF AVE	NO OF OBS.	MIN.	MAX.	STAT TYPE
15	JOB-TIME	1.0000	548.0963	250.8925	112.2026	5.	178.8157	777.9919	I

AVERAGE NUMBER IN Q-NODE

NODE	LABEL	AVE.	STD.DEV.	SD OF AVE	MIN.	MAX.
10	M-TOOL-Q	8.5419	4.4873	2.0068	1.7624	12.4600

NUMBER IN Q-NODE

MAX.
22.0000

AVERAGE WAITING TIME

AVE.	STD.DEV.	SD OF AVE
448.3703	219.1544	98.0088

AVERAGE SERVER UTILIZATION

SERVER	LABEL	NO. PARALLEL SERVERS	AVE.	STD.DEV.	SD OF AVE	NO. OF OBS.	MIN.	MAX.
3	MACHTOOL	1	.9277	.0566	.0253	5.	.8481	.9819

EXTREME VALUES

MAX. IDLE (TIME OR SERVERS)	MAX. BUSY
221.9244	5475.4311

Figure 8-12   Summary report for machine tool with breakdowns, Example 11.

processed and for the machine to be repaired, a certain amount of queueing should be expected.

The last section of the Q-GERT summary report provides information on server utilization. This line of statistics relates to the time the machine tool is busy processing a job and the time that the machine tool is being repaired. The output indicates that on the average the machine tool was busy or being repaired over 92 percent of the time. Also indicated is the longest time that the machine was in an idle state which was approximately 222 time units. The longest time period the machine was either working or being repaired was 5475 time units. If the machine operator was also responsible for repairing the machine, this long maximum busy time could be disastrous. Further analysis of the results would require more details concerning the operation of the machine tool and cost factors involved.

EXAMPLE 12. AN INVENTORY CONTROL SYSTEM

Problem Statement

A large discount house is planning to install a system to control the inventory of a particular radio. The number of radios demanded per week is Poisson distributed with a mean of 2, that is, the time between demands is exponentially distributed with a mean of 0.5 weeks. The procurement lead time (the time from the placement of an order for radios until the receipt of the radios) is lognormally distributed and requires one week on the average with a standard deviation of 0.5 weeks. Each radio sells for $75 and costs the store $40. An inventory carrying charge of $.004/dollar-week is assessed by store management. If a customer demands a radio when it is not in stock, the customer demand is backordered. The store has determined that each such backorder involves a cost of $10 in processing the customer backorder and notifying the customer of the availability of the radio. When the store places an order for radios from its distributor, it is estimated that a cost of $25 is involved. Store policy is to review the inventory position (radios on-hand plus radios on-order minus backorders) after every transaction and to place an order for more radios when the inventory position is equal to 3 radios. When this occurs, the store orders 10 radios. The initial number of radios in stock at the store is 13. A schematic diagram of the inventory situation described above is presented in Figure 8-13.

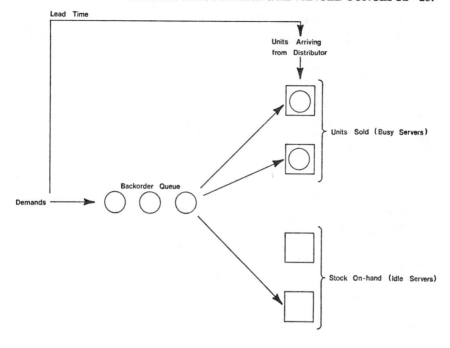

Figure 8-13 Schematic diagram of inventory situation, Example 12.

The objective of the Q-GERT analysis of the inventory situation is to obtain the average values per week for the following quantities: 1) profit; 2) sales; 3) inventory on-hand, and 4) backorders.

Model Development

Modeling inventory situations with Q-GERT is not a straightforward process. This example is included to illustrate one way of modeling inventory situations and to demonstrate the use of the Q-GERT support subprograms.

Each demand for a radio represents a customer. Each radio in stock can be thought of as a server that satisfies the demand for a radio. If no units are in stock, then all servers are busy and the customer demand must wait until more radios are placed in inventory (service). One procedure for modeling this is to set the number of servers equal to the number of radios in stock. When a demand occurs, the server (radio) is made busy indefinitely. When radios arrive from the distributor, servers (radios) can be made available by stopping service activities. The number of service activities stopped would be equal to the number of arriving radios. When no radios are in stock, all servers are busy and customer demands would be backordered. This would correspond to customer demands queueing up waiting for a service (radio). Each time a customer demand occurs, the inventory position would be decreased by 1 as the demand would either be satisfied or backordered, that is, radios on-hand would be decreased by 1 or the number of backorders would be increased by 1. A check on inventory position against the reorder point would then be made and, if the inventory position is equal to the reorder point, an order would be placed. The placing of an order involves the starting of an activity whose duration corresponds to the lead time. When the order arrives (when the activity representing the lead time is completed), a user function will be required to stop service for each of the arriving radios. This corresponds to placing the appropriate number of arriving radios in stock. By making servers available, backorders will be processed if any exist.

Q-GERT Model

The Q-GERT model of the inventory situation with backorders is shown in Figure 8-14. Surprisingly, the model looks similar to a single queue system with 13 servers. This result is due to the duality between queueing and inventory systems. At node 5, the next demand is created by the self-loop around node 5. The current demand is routed to Q-node 10 directly. At node 5, user function 1 is specified. In user function 1, the inventory position will be decreased and a determination made regarding the placing of an order for more radios to the distributor.

When a transaction arrives to Q-node 10, it will be placed in service immediately if less than 13 servers are busy. The thirteen servers as explained above represent the 13 radios that can be in stock. The number of radios in stock is equal to 13 minus the number of busy servers. The value of 13 is the sum of the order quantity and the reorder point (sometimes referred to as the stock control level). The time the server will be busy, that is, the time the radio is out of stock, is arbitrarily set to a large value by using the incremental function starting at 5000. A constant of 5000 could have been used. If a demand occurs when all 13 servers are busy, the demand waits at Q-node 10 and represents a backorder.

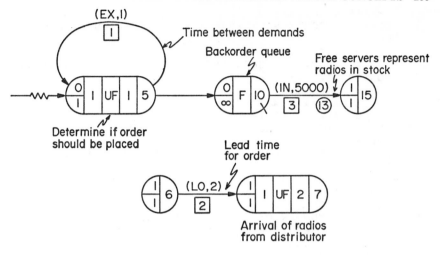

Figure 8-14 Q-GERT model of inventory situation with backorders, Example 12.

The disjoint network involving node 6 and 7 represents the process of ordering and receiving radios from the distributor. Activity 2 will be started by a call to subroutine STARTA included in user function 1. When activity 2 is completed, node 7 is released. This represents the arrival of radios which are used to satisfy backorders or are placed in stock in user function 2.

The user functions for this example are shown in Figure 8-15. For user function 1, a demand has occurred. The inventory position is decreased by 1 and the number of sales increased by 1. Next, the inventory position, POS, is checked against the reorder point, RP. If the inventory position is greater than the reorder point, no further action is required and a return from the user function is made after UF is set to zero, as required by FORTRAN conventions.

When the inventory position is less than or equal to the reorder point, an order is placed. Activity 2 which emanates from node 6 is started by a call to subroutine STARTA. This models the lead time required to obtain radios from the distributor. Inventory position is then increased by the order quantity. As above, UF is set to zero.

User function 2 is invoked when a transaction arrives at node 7. In user function 2, service is stopped on NQUANT servers. This represents the arrival of NQUANT radios which permits that number of demands to be satisfied once again.

In Figure 8-16, the FORTRAN listing, the initial conditions and

```
      FUNCTION UF(IFN)
      COMMON /UCOM1/ SALES,ORDERS,POS,NQUANT,QUANT,RP
      UF=0.0
      GO TO (1,2), IFN
C****ANOTHER DEMAND.  DECREASE INVENTORY POSITION BY ONE.
    1 POS=POS-1.
      SALES=SALES+1.
C****CHECK POSITION AGAINST REORDER POINT
      IF(POS.GT.RP) GO TO 5
C****PLACE ORDER FOR SCL-POS
      ORDERS=ORDERS+1.
C****CAUSE ORDER TO ARRIVE BY STARTING ACTIVITY 2.
      CALL STARTA(6,2)
C****RESET INVENTORY POSITION
      POS=POS+QUANT
    5 RETURN
C**** INCREASE NUMBER OF SERVERS FREE BY NQUANT.
C****EACH FREE SERVER REPRESENTS A UNIT IN STOCK.
    2 DO 10 I=1,NQUANT
      CALL STSER(3)
   10 CONTINUE
      RETURN
      END
```

Figure 8-15   Listing of function UF for inventory situation with backorders, Example 12.

values for POS, QUANT and RP are set. For convenience, integer and real variables for the order quantity are included.

```
SUBROUTINE UI
COMMON /UCOM1/ SALES,ORDERS,POS,NQUANT,QUANT,RP
SALES=0.
ORDERS=0.
POS=13.
NQUANT=10
QUANT=10.
RP=3.
RETURN
END
```

Figure 8-16   Listing of subroutine UI, Example 12.

In Figure 8-17, the FORTRAN listing of subroutine UO is given. UO is written to obtain the average statistics specified by the problem statement. The price and cost values associated with the inventory situation are established through a DATA statement in subroutine UO. First, the number of sales made is computed. The current number of backorders at the end of the run is subtracted from the number of sales to obtain

```
      SUBROUTINE UO
      COMMON /GVAR/ NOE,NFTBU(100),NREL(100),NRELP(100),NREL2(100),
     1 NRUN,NRUNS,NTC(100),PARAM(100,4),TBEG,TNOW
      COMMON /UCOM1/ SALES,ORDERS,POS,NQUANT,QUANT,RP
      DATA PPS,CPU,CPB,CPI,CPO/75.,40.,10.,.004,25./
C****PPS=PRICE/SALE, CPU=COST/UNIT, CPB=COST/BACKORDER
C****CPI=INVENTORY CARRYING CHARGE/$-WEEK, CPO=COST/ORDER
      XSALES=SALES-XNINQ(10)
      WRITE(6,99) PPS,CPU,CPB,CPI,CPO
      WRITE(6,100) QUANT,RP,XSALES,ORDERS,TNOW
      TIIN=(QUANT+RP)*TNOW-TISS(10,3)
      TIBO=TINIQ(10)
      AIIN=TIIN/TNOW
      ABO=TIBO/TNOW
      PROFIT=XSALES*PPS-(XSALES*CPU+CPB*TIBO+CPI*CPU*TIIN+CPO*ORDERS)
      AVEPFT=PROFIT/TNOW
      WRITE(6,101) AIIN,ABO,AVEPFT,PROFIT
   99 FORMAT(5X,*PRICE/SALE = $*,F7.2/5X,*COST/UNIT = $*,F7.2/5X,
     1*COST/BACKORDER = $*,F7.2/5X,*INVENTORY CARRYING CHARGE/$-WEEK = $
     2*,F8.3/5X,*COST/ORDER = $*,F7.2)
  100 FORMAT(//5X,*ORDER QUANTITY = *,F5.0/5X,*REORDER POINT = *,
     1F5.0/5X,*NUMBER OF SALES = *,F5.0/5X,*NUMBER OF ORDERS = *,F5.0/
     25X,*SIMULATION TIME = *,F8.2)
  101 FORMAT(//5X,*AVERAGE INVENTORY = *,F8.3/5X,*AVERAGE NUMBER OF BACK
     1ORDERS = *,F8.3/5X,*AVERAGE PROFIT = $*,F7.2/5X,*TOTAL PROFIT = $*
     2,F10.2)
      RETURN
      END
```

Figure 8-17   Listing of subroutine UO, Example 12.

the actual number of sales made during the run. The revenue and cost coefficients are then printed. Next, the number of sales, the number of orders, the order quantity, the reorder point and the run length are printed. The time integrated number of units (radios) in inventory is then computed by subtracting the time integrated status of the servers from the total area of a rectangle whose dimensions are 13 and the total time for the simulation. The equation for the area is (QUANT+RP) *TNOW. Since TISS represents the total time servers were busy, the difference TIIN represents the total inventory-on-hand for the run. Recall when a server is busy, the radio corresponding to that server is not in stock. The time integrated number of backorders is then computed using the Q-GERT function TINIQ, the time integrated number in the queue. The average inventory and average backorders are calculated. Total profit can then be obtained by subtracting purchasing costs, backorder costs, inventory carrying costs and ordering costs from sales revenue. The average profit is then computed and the desired values are printed out. This completes the description of the code required to model the inventory situation involving backorders.

The data input required for Example 12 is shown in Figure 8-18.

```
GEN,PRITSKER,INVENTORY-12,8,30,1977,0,0,0,52.,1,(14)1*
SOU,5,0,1*                    ARRIVAL OF A DEMAND
VAS,5,1,UF,1*                 CHECK INV-POS IN UF1
ACT,5,5,EX,1,1*               TIME BETWEEN DEMANDS
PAR,1,.1*                     INTER-DEMAND TIME PARAMETERS
ACT,5,10*                     TRANSFER OF DEMAND
QUE,10/BACKORDQ*              BACKORDER QUEUE
ACT,10,15,IN,5000,3/INV-COMP,13*  DELETING A RADIO FROM STOCK
REG,15,1,1*                   END OF ACTIVITY 3
REG,6,1,1*                    START NODE FOR ORDER ACTIVITY
ACT,6,7,LO,2,2*               LEAD TIME FOR ORDER
PAR,2,1.,,,,.5*               LEAD TIME PARAMETERS
REG,7,1,1*                    NODE AT WHICH ORDER IS RECEIVED
VAS,7,1,UF,2*                 USER FUNCTION CALL FOR ORDER RECEIPT
FIN*
```

Figure 8-18 Data input for inventory situation with backorders, Example 12.

Summary of Results

The information printed in subroutine UO is shown in Figure 8-19. The first part of this figure provides information regarding the cost information for the inventory analysis. Next, the conditions under which the run was made are printed along with outputs regarding the number of sales and orders placed. For a reorder point of 3 and order quantity of

```
PRICE/SALE = $  75.00
COST/UNIT = $  40.00
COST/BACKORDER = $  10.00
INVENTORY CARRYING CHARGE/$-WEEK = $       .004
COST/ORDER = $  25.00


ORDER QUANTITY =     10
REORDER POINT =      3
NUMBER OF SALES =    518
NUMBER OF ORDERS =    51
SIMULATION TIME =    52.00


AVERAGE INVENTORY =     2.185
AVERAGE NUMBER OF BACKORDERS =    2.310
AVERAGE PROFIT = $ 300.69
TOTAL PROFIT = $  15635.67
```

Figure 8-19 Summary of results from subroutine UO for inventory system, Example 12.

10, 518 radios were sold and 51 orders to the warehouse distributor were made in the 52 weeks of operation.

The third section of the output shows that the average inventory on hand was 2.185 units. This corresponds to the number of idle servers during the 52 weeks. The average number of backorders was 2.310. For the decision rules employed in this run, the average profit per week was $300.69 which corresponds to a total profit of $15,635.67 for 52 weeks. This total profit figure does not take into account indirect costs associated with running the business such as administrative and marketing expense. It is presumed in this example that these factors remain constant with regard to the decision variables under consideration. The next step in the analysis would be to change the decision rules to allow a comparison to be made based on the profit obtained for each set of decision rules.

EXERCISES

8-1.   Change the parameters associated with the activity times in Example 10 and attempt to make the criticality index for each activity of the network equally probable. Note that this does not mean to make each criticality index 0.5 since there are more than two activities ongoing simultaneously. (Hint: This problem relates to assembly line balancing and could be referred to as criticality index balancing.)

8-2.   For Example 10, assess project performance if the time to perform the activity whose criticality index is largest is reduced by 10 percent? 20 percent? 30 percent?

8-3.   Discuss how you could use the concept of a criticality index and the Q-GERT Analysis Program for allocating funds for improving project performance.

8-4.   In Example 11, add the feature that if there are more than three jobs to be processed by the machine tool when it breaks down, all jobs except the last three to arrive are routed to a subcontractor. The job in progress is also routed to the subcontractor.

8-5.   For Example 11, redevelop the model to include the possibility that the repairman process breaks down and a delay of three hours is incurred in order to get a spare part for the repair process. The time between repair process breakdowns is exponentially distributed with a mean of 100 hours. If the repair breakdown occurs when the repair process is not active, no action is taken.

8-6. Convert the inventory situation modeled in Example 12 to one involving lost sales instead of backorders.

8-7. Convert the inventory situation depicted in Example 12 to one involving periodic reviews of the inventory position. The periodic review is to occur every two weeks.

8-8. Change the inventory situation presented in Example 12 to allow the time between demands for radios to be a function of the number of backorders incurred per unit time. If the number of backorders per unit time is greater than 1, the average demand for radios decreases by 10 percent. If the average number of backorders per week is less than 0.5, the average demand for radios increases by 20 percent.

8-9. Cargo arrives at an air terminal in unit loads at the rate of two unit loads per minute. At the freight terminal there is no fixed schedule, and planes take off as soon as they can be loaded to capacity. Two types of planes are available for transporting cargo. There are three planes with a capacity of 80 unit loads and two planes that have a capacity of 140 unit loads. The round trip time for any plane is normally distributed with a mean of 3 hours, a standard deviation of 1 hour, and minimum and maximum times of 2 and 4 hours, respectively. The loading policy of the terminal manager is to employ smaller planes whenever possible. Only when 140 unit loads are available will a plane of type 2 be employed. Develop a Q-GERT network to model this system to estimate the waiting time of unit loads and the utilization of the two types of planes over a 100 hour period. Assume at first that the loading time of planes is negligible. Embellish the model to include a one minute per unit loading time. (Hint: There are several ways to model this situation. Branching based on the release of a non-existent node could prove helpful.)

8-10. In a private branch exchange telephone switching system, two types of telephone lines must be available to make an outgoing call: 1) a line for talking (voice communication) which is referred to as a G1 line; and 2) a line for dialing (for digit transmission) which will be referred to as a G2 line. Since the dialing operation takes much less time than a conversation, the company has installed 10 G1 lines and one G2 line. From past data, it has been determined that the time between outgoing calls is exponentially distributed with a mean of 1 minute (minimum of 0 and maximum of 60 minutes). If all G1 lines are busy at the time of a call, the caller hangs up and tries to call again in T minutes where T is normally distributed with a mean of 15, standard deviation of 2, minimum of 0 and maximum of 60. If a G1 line is available, the caller waits for a G2 line if necessary. The G1 line is held while waiting for a G2 line. When a line of each type is available, the customer dials and the dialing time is exponentially distributed with a mean of 0.2 minutes, minimum 0.1 and maximum 0.5. After dialing, the G2 line is released and the G1 line is held for the duration of the conversation. Conversation time is exponentially distributed with a mean of 10 minutes, minimum of 3 minutes and a maximum of 30 minutes. Develop the Q-GERT network model of this situation to obtain statistics on the following quantities: time to complete dialing; time to complete conversation; total time to complete a call; utilization of G1 and G2 lines; rate at which callers were not able to complete their call.

8-11. Clients to a psychiatric ward arrive at the rate of two per day. Each client is given a test and the test scores are uniformly distributed between 30 and 44. When the ward is full, clients are not admitted if their score is greater than 41. The ward has space for 28 clients. A client is discharged from the ward when his test score exceeds 48. A client's test score is estimated to change daily in a uniform manner in the range -0.2 to 1.2. When a potential client arrives and the ward is full, a current client will be bumped from the ward if he (she) is within two days of being released. Initially, there are 18 clients on the ward and their test scores are 30 to 47. Develop a Q-GERT network model to obtain statistics on the utilization of the ward, the number of clients that are bumped, the number of clients that are turned away and the length of stay of clients on the ward.

Chapter 9

USER-COLLECTED STATISTICS, WAITING TIMES AND AUXILIARY ATTRIBUTE ARRAYS

Advanced procedures for modeling complex systems have been described. With such features, complex Q-GERT networks can be constructed. To support the design and use of such networks, user-collected statistical procedures and auxiliary attribute array features have been incorporated into the Q-GERT Analysis Program.

The first section of this chapter describes methods by which a Q-GERT user can collect statistical quantities within a user function. Arrays are provided for storing statistical information. The user accesses the arrays by using subprograms provided in the Q-GERT Analysis Program. Subprograms are available to: 1) initialize the arrays; 2) collect values of variables during a run; and 3) calculate and print statistical quantities. Two examples of the use of these subprograms are given in this chapter. In the first example, the procedure for collecting data for periodic intervals of time is illustrated. The second example illustrates the collecting of cost related performance measures during an analysis of a project.

In the second part of this chapter, a discussion of methods for calculating waiting times of transactions at a Q-node is given. Three methods are provided that allow the user to collect as much information on waiting times as is required for problem resolution. One of the methods employs user-collected statistics procedures.

The last section of this chapter describes subprograms included in the Q-GERT Analysis Program that are used for maintaining sets of auxiliary attributes of transactions. These subprograms can be used to augment the attribute storage arrays of Q-GERT. The subprograms were not described in Chapter 7 as they would be used only for network models in which transactions had an excessive number of attributes or on large network models.

USER-COLLECTED STATISTICS

Routines are available in the Q-GERT Analysis Program that allow the user to collect data on any system variable. The data collected may be based either on the observation of variables or on the time-persistent behavior of variables. In addition, data can be organized into cells in order to obtain histograms that portray the relative frequency with which a variable is within a range of values. Table 9-1 gives a list of subroutines available in Q-GERT for user-collected statistics. The following sections provide a discussion of the routines and their use. These routines are normally called in subroutines UI and UO and in function UF.

Collection of Statistics Based on Observations

Statistics based on the observation of variables are collected, reported and initialized through three subroutines: COL; COLP; and COLC. These subroutines are designed to be called from user-written routines.

Subroutine COL(XX,ICLCT) is used to collect the sample value of a variable. The variables are given numeric codes that are communicated to subroutine COL by it second argument (ICLCT). The value of the sample is passed to COL by its first argument, XX, and must be a REAL variable. As an example of the use of subroutine COL, consider the case in which the user desires to observe, every five time units, the number of transactions in Q-node 4. This variable is identified by a numeric code, to identify, for example, that it is the third variable for which COL is being called. To obtain values every 5 time units, a sampling node is used which is released every 5 time units by a self loop activity. The node has a reference to UF in its value assignment section. In UF, the analyst retrieves the number in Q-node 4 by using function XNINQ, that is, writing the statement YY=XNINQ(4). The particular sample of the number in the queue at these periodic times would then be added to all previous samples by the following statement:

CALL COL(YY,3)

Table 9-1. Subroutines for User-Collected Statistics.

Subroutine Name	Description*
SUBROUTINE COL (XX, ICLCT)	Collects sums and sums of squares of values XX for variable number ICLCT.
SUBROUTINE COLP (ICLCT)	If ICLCT=0, print statistics for all variables. If ICLCT>0, print statistics for variable number ICLCT.
SUBROUTINE COLC (ICLCT)	If ICLCT=0, clear the entire statistical storage array UOBV($\cdot,\cdot$). If ICLCT>0, clear row ICLCT of UOBV.
SUBROUTINE TIM (XX, ISTAT)	Integrates the values XX over time for variable number ISTAT.
SUBROUTINE TIMP (ISTAT)	If ISTAT=0, print statistics for all variables. If ISTAT>0, print statistics for variable number ISTAT.
SUBROUTINE TIMC (ISTAT)	If ISTAT=0, clear statistical storage array UTPV($\cdot,\cdot$). If ISTAT>0, clear row ISTAT of UTPV.
SUBROUTINE HIS (XX, IHIST)	Increments the number of times the value XX has fallen in a specified range for variable number IHIST.
SUBROUTINE HISP (IHIST)	If IHIST=0, print a histogram for all variables. If IHIST>0, print a histogram for variable number IHIST.
SUBROUTINE HISC (IHIST)	If IHIST=0, reset all values regarding histograms to zero. If IHIST>0, reset the values for variable IHIST with regard to histograms to zero.
SUBROUTINE CLEAR	Initialize statistical storage arrays UOBV and UTPV and reset the histogram storage area to zero.

* When using these subroutines, the variables ICLCT, ISTAT and IHIST are assigned numeric codes by the user to distinguish among different variables on which statistics collection is to be performed.

Five quantities are stored in an internal array of the Q-GERT program for each ICLCT variable. The name of this array is UOBV(ICLCT,J), J=1,5. In general, row ICLCT is used for values of variables with code ICLCT (in this case, ICLCT=3). The statement CALL COL(YY,3) causes YY to be added to the sum of other values and is stored in UOBV(3,1). The square of YY is added to the sum of squares of other values and is stored in UOBV(3,2). In addition, when COL is called, the number of observations stored in UOBV(3,3) is increased by one, and the minimum and maximum values of YY are retained in UOBV(3,4) and UOBV(3,5), respectively.

The user can obtain output statistics based on the values collected by COL by calling subroutine COLP(ICLCT). If subroutine COLP is called with ICLCT=0, a report of all COL variables is generated. If ICLCT is greater than 0, a statistical report is printed for the ICLCTth variable. The report consists of estimates of the mean, standard deviation, standard deviation of the mean, the minimum and maximum values observed and the number of observations on which the statistics are based. The values stored in UOBV(.,.) are not altered when these statistics are reported. COLP is called with a zero argument automatically at the end of all runs to obtain a report on all COL statistics.

Subroutine COLC(ICLCT) is used to reset or clear the statistical storage array UOBV. If subroutine COLC is called with ICLCT equal to 0, all rows of UOBV are cleared. If ICLCT is greater than 0, only row ICLCT of UOBV is cleared. Q-GERT contains a call to COLC with ICLCT=0 prior to the start of run 1. If separate statistics are desired on each run, COLC should be called by the user in subroutine UI.

On input, the user prepares a COL card to specify alphanumeric labels to be associated with each ICLCT statistic. The fields for the COL card are:

Field	Description
1	Card type, COL
2	Numeric code, ICLCT. Following a slash (/), an 8 character alphanumeric label for variable number ICLCT. Default is 8 blanks.
3–15	Repeats of Field 2.

Further information on the COL card is given in Appendix 1. The use of COLC, COL and COLP is demonstrated in Example 13.

Collection of Statistics for Time-Persistent Variables

Statistics based on time-persistent variables are collected, reported, and initialized through three subroutines: TIM, TIMP, and TIMC. These subroutines are designed to be called from user-written routines.

Subroutine TIM(XX,ISTAT) is used to collect statistics based on time-persistent variables. The argument, XX, is a value for the variable of interest and is a REAL variable. ISTAT is the index for the ISTAT[th] time-persistent variable.

When TIM is used, the variable in question is assumed to have maintained a constant value over a time interval. This type of variable is referred to as a time-persistent variable. An example of a time-persistent variable would be the number of transactions being processed. The number of transactions has a constant value from the time of arrival of a transaction until the next arrival or next departure of a transaction. The length of the time interval dictates the weight assigned to the value of the variable in computing its average over the entire run. Subroutine TIM integrates the value of the variable over the time interval. The statement, CALL TIM(XISYS,2), collects the integrated value of the number in the system identified by code 2 by updating the following six quantities in the array, UTPV(2,J), J=1, . . . ,6: the sum of the time integrated values; the sum of the time integrated values squared; the time of the last change; the minimum value observed; the maximum value observed; and the value for the next time interval which is XISYS. Through input data or in subroutine UI, an initial value is assigned to XISYS. Changes to XISYS must be made prior to the call to subroutine TIM, and, hence, XISYS will be the number in the system for the next time period.

Subroutine TIMP(ISTAT) is used to print a statistical report on time-persistent variable statistics. If subroutine TIMP is called with ISTAT equal to 0, a report for all time-persistent statistical variables is generated. If ISTAT is greater than 0, a report is printed for the ISTAT[th] variable only. A statistical report is automatically prepared at the end of *all* runs if subroutine TIM is used.

Subroutine TIMC(ISTAT) is used to reset or clear the statistical storage array UTPV. If subroutine TIMC is called with ISTAT equal to 0, all the rows of UTPV are cleared. If ISTAT is greater than 0, only row ISTAT of UTPV is cleared. Q-GERT calls TIMC at the beginning of each run with an argument of 0. The variable UTCLR(ISTAT) is set equal to the time at which TIMC was last called with argument ISTAT or with an argument of zero.

By input on a TIM card, the user specifies, for each ISTAT value, a corresponding alphanumeric label and an initial value. The fields for the TIM card are:

Field	Description
1	Card type, TIM
2	Numeric code, ISTAT. Following a slash (/), an 8 character alphanumeric label for variable number ISTAT
3	Initial value
	Repeats of Fields 2 and 3

Further information on the TIM card is given in Appendix 1.

As an example of the use of subroutine TIM, consider the collection of statistics on the number of transactions in a queueing system. If XIS is defined as the variable representing the number of transactions in the system, then XIS increases by 1 at the time of an arrival and decreases by 1 at the time of departure. Identifying function number 1 with source nodes and function number 2 with sink nodes, the following user function code will maintain statistics on XIS.

```
        FUNCTION UF(IFN)
        COMMON/UCOMI/XIS
        GO TO (1,2),IFN
C*****  ARRIVAL OF A TRANSACTION. ADD 1 TO XIS
   1    XIS=XIS+1
        CALL TIM(XIS,1)
        UF=0.0
        RETURN
C*****  TRANSACTION DEPARTURE. SUBTRACT 1 FROM XIS
   2    XIS=XIS-1
        CALL TIM(XIS,1)
        UF=0.0
        RETURN
        END
```

Note that in the above code, the value of XIS is updated prior to the call to subroutine TIM.

The initialization of XIS and the time-persistent storage array are performed in subroutine UI as follows

```
        SUBROUTINE UI
        COMMON/UCOMI/XIS
C*****  CLEAR STATISTICS ARRAY
C*****  ASSUME SYSTEM STARTS WITH NO TRANSACTIONS
```

```
          CALL TIMC(1)
          XIS=0
          CALL TIM(XIS,1)
          RETURN
          END
```

The printing of statistics on XIS for each run is done in subroutine UO as follows:

```
          SUBROUTINE UO
          CALL TIMP(1)
          RETURN
          END
```

If it is desired to collect the average over runs of the number of transactions in the system, a call to subroutine COL in subroutine UO would be made as shown in the modified version of subroutine UO.

```
          SUBROUTINE UO
C*****    COMMON FOR TNOW AND UTPV AND UTCLR
          COMMON/UCOMI/XIS
C*****    UPDATE STORAGE ARRAY UTPV BY CALLING TIM
          CALL TIM(XIS,1)
C*****    PRINT RUN STATISTICS
          CALL TIMP(1)
C*****    COMPUTE AVERAGE FOR THIS RUN
C*****    UTCLR(1) IS TIME THAT TIMC WAS LAST CALLED
          AVE=UTPV(1,1)/(TNOW-UTCLR(1))
C*****    COLLECT AVE AS ONE OBSERVATION
          CALL COL(AVE,1)
          RETURN
          END
```

In this code, subroutine COL is called at the end of each run. There is no need to call COLC or COLP as clearing is only to be performed at the beginning of the first run and printing at the end of the last run. The Q-GERT Analysis Program provides these subroutine calls.

Histograms

Histograms are computed, reported and initialized through the three subroutines: HIS, HISP, and HISC. These subroutines are designed to be called from user-written routines.

Subroutine HIS is used to determine the relative frequency with which a variable falls within a set of prescribed limits. It is normally used for observed valued variables.* The number of cells, the upper limit of the first cell, and the width of each cell of the histogram are user data inputs for each histogram. If histogram 1 is for the variable TISYS, the statement CALL HIS(TISYS,1) would add one observation to the cell that covered the interval in which the TISYS value occurred.

Subroutine HISP(IHIST) is used to print the histograms for the variable desired. If subroutine HISP is called with IHIST equal to 0, histograms for all variables for which histogram information is collected is printed. If IHIST is greater than 0, a histogram for the IHIST[th] variable for which histograms are to be produced is generated. Histograms are automatically printed at the end of all runs.

Subroutine HISC(IHIST) is used to zero or clear the statistical storage array associated with histogram data. If subroutine HISC is called with IHIST equal to 0, the statistical storage array for all histograms is cleared. If IHIST is greater than 0, the statistical storage area for only the IHIST[th] variable is cleared.

On input, through the use of HIS cards, the user specifies for each IHIST value its corresponding label, the number of cells, the upper limit of the first cell, and the width of each cell. The fields for the HIS card are:

Field	Description
1	Card Type, HIS
2	Numeric code, IHIST. Following a slash(/), an 8 character alphanumeric label for histogram IHIST.
3	Number of interior cells (2 cells are always added)
4	Upper limit of the first cell
5	Width of each cell
	Repeats of Fields 2 through 5

Further information on the HIS card is given in Appendix 1.

---

* Subroutine HIS can be and has been used to plot one variable, NX, versus time by calling subroutine HIS, NX times with argument TNOW, that is

                    DO 10 I=1,NX
              10 CALL HIS(TNOW,1)

The calls to HIS are made from a node that is released periodically.

Clearing of All User Collected Statistical Storage Arrays

Subroutine CLEAR is used for clearing the entire user statistical storage area. A call to this subroutine will perform the same function as separate calls to HISC, TIMC and COLC each with an argument of 0. The most recent time at which subroutine CLEAR is called is maintained as the variable UTCLR(I) where I is a time-persistent variable code number.

The user statistical storage area is automatically cleared by Q-GERT at the beginning of each network analysis. Also, the storage array for statistics based on time-persistent variables is automatically cleared at the start of each run of each network simulation as these statistics are only meaningful for a single simulation run. If averages over a set of runs are desired for time-persistent variables, the analyst can use subroutine COL and HIS in subroutine UO as described previously.

EXAMPLE 13.   STATISTICAL COLLECTION OF DATA FOR SUBINTERVALS

This example involves the collection of data periodically during a run. A run will be divided into subintervals and statistical quantities of interest for each subinterval will be collected. The procedure for accomplishing this data collection is to build a disjoint network which causes function UF to be called periodically. In UF, the user-data collection subroutines are called. The disjoint network can be as simple as one node and a self-loop branch as shown below.

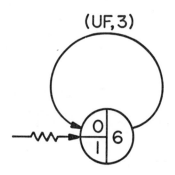

Node 6 is a source node and the activity from node 6 to node 6 is initiated at time 0. The time for this activity will be the subinterval time so that node 6 is released periodically. The user function call prescribed by the activity from node 6 to node 6 will be used to collect the desired data. Thus, for the one server, single queue system, UF could be employed to collect statistical information concerning the average queue size for the last interval and the average utilization of the server for the last interval. Each value obtained for a subinterval could then be combined to estimate the variability from subinterval to subinterval of these average quantities.

Q-GERT Model

The two disjoint networks for this example and the data input to describe the networks are given in Figure 9-1. No special features are involved in the Q-GERT network shown in Figure 9-1.

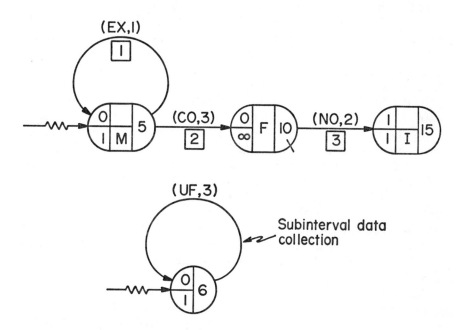

Figure 9-1 Q-GERT network for obtaining subinterval data, Example 13.

```
GEN,PRITSKER,SUBINT-13,8,1,1977,1,0,0,1000.,1*
SOU,5,0,1*                        ARRIVAL NODE
ACT,5,5,EX,1,1*                   SCHEDULE NEXT ARRIVAL
PAR,1,15.,0.,100.*                INTER ARRIVAL TIME PARAMETERS
ACT,5,10,CO,3,2*                  TRANSFER CUSTOMER TO QUEUE
QUE,10/SERVER-Q*                  QUEUE OF SERVER
ACT,10,15,NO,2,3/JEFF,1*          SERVICE ACTIVITY
PAR,2,10.,0.,200.,2.*             SERVICE TIME PARAMETERS
STA,15/TIMINSYS,1,1,,I,5.,2.*     CUSTOMER TIME IN SYSTEM
SOU,6,0,1*                        DATA COLLECTION FOR SUBINTERVALS
ACT,6,6,UF,3*                     SCHEDULE NEXT SUBINTERVAL DATA COLLECTION
COL,1/AVEQSIZE,2/AVE-UTIL*        USER COLLECT DATA CARD
HIS,1/AVEQSIZE,8,0.5,0.5*         USER HISTOGRAM DATA CARDS
HIS,2/AVE-UTIL,18,0.05,0.05*
FIN*
```

Figure 9-1   (Continued)

The user function to collect the subinterval data along with UI and UO are shown in Figure 9–2. The first statement in function UF sets UF equal to TBSI, the time between subintervals. When a return is made from UF to the Q-GERT Analysis Program, the value prescribed for UF is then used as the activity time.

Continuing with the description of function UF, the next statement specifies that if TNOW is greater than zero, bypass the initialization of the variables TLAST, QLAST and ULAST. Since the test on TNOW is required to avoid computing averages over a zero time interval, initialization is performed in UF rather than in UI. TLAST is the time of the last call to UF, that is, the time of the last data collection. QLAST is the time-integrated number in the queue up until the last data collection and ULAST is the time-integrated utilization of the server up to the last data collection. Time-integrated values rather than averages are used since the data for a subinterval is desired and maintaining averages would require additional computations. Since only two variables were involved, dimensioned variables were not used. (To generalize the scheme presented, a vector of last values would be used.)

At statement 10, QNOW, the time integrated number in the queue up to the current time, is obtained by using function TINIQ(10). The function TINIQ(NODE) was described in Chapter 7 and provides the time integrated number in the queue for Q-node NODE. The quantity (QNOW−QLAST) divided by the time interval is the average queue size, AQSIZE, for the time interval. The time interval TIMEI, equals TNOW−TLAST. (As long as constant time intervals are used, this quantity need not be computed and TBSI could have been used). The value of QLAST and TLAST are now updated to QNOW and TNOW. Subroutines COL and HIS are called with the average queue size which is defined as variable 1 for each of these data collection subroutines. The labels associated with variable number 1 along with the number of

```
      FUNCTION UF(IFN)
      COMMON /QVAR/ NDE,NFTBU(100),NREL(100),NRELP(100),NREL2(100),
     1 NRUN,NRUNS,NTC(100),PARAM(100,4),TBEG,TNOW
      DATA TBSI/100./
      UF=TBSI
C****IF TNOW .EQ. 0.0, RESET INITIAL VALUES
C****AND DO NOT COLLECT STATISTICS
      IF(TNOW.GT.0.0) GO TO 10
      TLAST=0.
      QLAST=0.
      ULAST=0.
      RETURN
C****COMPUTE AND CALCULATE AVE. NUMBER IN QUEUE
   10 QNOW=TINIQ(10)
      TIMEI=TNOW-TLAST
      AQSIZE=(QNOW-QLAST)/TIMEI
      QLAST=QNOW
      TLAST=TNOW
      CALL COL(AQSIZE,1)
      CALL HIS(AQSIZE,1)
C****COMPUTE AVERAGE SERVER UTILIZATION
      UNOW=TISS(10,3)
      AUTIL=(UNOW-ULAST)/TIMEI
      ULAST=UNOW
      CALL COL(AUTIL,2)
      CALL HIS(AUTIL,2)
      RETURN
      END


      SUBROUTINE UI
      CALL COLC(0)
      CALL HISC(0)
      RETURN
      END


      SUBROUTINE UO
      CALL COLP(0)
      CALL HISP(0)
      RETURN
      END
```

Figure 9-2 Listings of function UF and subroutines UI and UO for subinterval sampling, Example 13.

cells in the histogram, upper limit of the first cell, and width of each cell are specified through data input.

A similar procedure is used for obtaining data on server utilization. The variable UNOW represents server utilization up to the current time TNOW. This quantity is the total time the server has been busy from the beginning of the run. It is obtained through use of the function TISS(NODE,NSERV) where NODE is a Q-node or S-node number and NSERV is the server number. The average utilization of the server, AUTIL, is then computed by dividing UNOW−ULAST by TIMEI. The variable ULAST is then set to UNOW to provide a reference point for the next time UF is called. The average utilization is then passed to sub-routines COL and HIS. Average utilization of the server is identified by code number 2. This completes the description of function UF.

Subroutine UI is used to clear all storage arrays associated with the collection of statistics by the user. Since UI is called at the beginning of each run, a new subinterval set of observations will be obtained for each run. The statistics obtained for the subinterval data are printed out in subroutine UO by calls to COLP and HISP. Subroutine UO is included to illustrate the calls to subroutines COLP and HISP. Since only one run is being made for this example, calls to COLP and HISP will auto-matically be made when obtaining the summary reports. (Therefore, this code results in two sets of outputs.)

This example illustrates the use of user-collected statistical sub-programs and demonstrates the ease with which such programs can be used. Although this example was for the one server, single queue system, it could be used with any Q-GERT network.

Summary of Results

The user-collected data output is shown in Figure 9–3 for run number 1. The Q-GERT summary report for run number 1 is shown in Figure 9–4. A comparison of the user and first run outputs illustrates that the aver-age values are the same as is expected.

The user statistics, however, provide estimates of the standard devia-tion of the sample mean based on the 10 subinterval averages computed during the first run. The estimate of the standard deviations for average queue size is 0.3568 and for average server utilization is 0.0604. If it is assumed that the subintervals provide independent observations of the average values observed, then these estimates of the standard deviation of the sample mean can be used for setting confidence intervals and for making statistical tests. Figure 9-5 presents the histogram of the ten average server utilizations observed. Probability statements based on this histogram can be made directly.

Subinterval sampling provides an alternate procedure to the making of multiple runs (replications). The advantage of subinterval sampling is the lack of a transient period in subintervals after the first subinter-val. The disadvantage involves the assumption of independence be-tween subintervals. If the subinterval is long then the fact that the end-ing condition of one subinterval is the beginning condition of the next subinterval should not cause a significant amount of dependence over the entire subinterval (40,66).

```
**USER STATISTICS FOR VARIABLES BASED ON OBSERVATION AT TIME          1000.000 IN RUN     1**

                AVE        STD DEV      SD OF AVE      MINIMUM      MAXIMUM      OBS

AVEQSIZE      1.0276       1.1283        .3568         .0200        3.5021      10
AVE-UTIL       .7648        .1911        .0604         .4960        1.0000      10
```

Figure 9-3 User output statistics report for subinterval sampling, Example 13.

```
GERT SIMULATION PROJECT SUBINT-13     BY PRITSKER
         DATE 8/ 1/ 1977

**FINAL RESULTS FOR FIRST SIMULATION**

      TOTAL ELAPSED TIME =   1000.0000

      **NODE STATISTICS**

NODE    LABEL       AVE.      STD.DEV.     NO OF     STAT
                                          OBS.      TYPE
15    TIMINSYS    26.1668    13.8854       77.       I

**NUMBER IN Q-NODE**                                   ** WAITING TIME **
                                                          IN QUEUE

NODE    LABEL      AVE.      MIN.    MAX.    CURRENT     AVERAGE
                                            NUMBER
10    SERVER-Q    1.0276     0       5.      2          12.8451

**SERVER UTILIZATION**

SERVER   LABEL    NO. PARALLEL    AVE.      MAX. IDLE        MAX. BUSY
                    SERVERS              (TIME OR SERVERS)  (TIME OR SERVERS)
3        JEFF         1         .7648       25.9421           230.4884
```

Figure 9-4 First run summary report, subinterval sampling, Example 13.

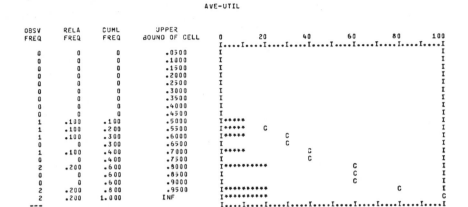

Figure 9-5 User-generated histogram for average server utilization, Example 13.

EXAMPLE 14. A MODEL OF COSTS ASSOCIATED WITH AN INDUSTRIAL SALES NEGOTIATION PROCESS*

A major oil company decided to build a new gasoline plant. Gasoline plants strip liquid hydrocarbons from natural gas, and the liquid is used as blending stock by oil refineries. The purchasing firm wanted to buy the new plant as a completely installed package. Systematically, the purchasing agent and his buyers began to inform a select number of prospective vendors of the proposed gasoline plant and to invite these vendors to negotiate for the job.

Q-Gert Model

Figure 9-6 is a Q-GERT network model which could have been used by one of the vendor firms. The activity numbers are referenced to Table 9-2 which contains a description of each activity along with the time distribution, cost estimates and probabilities for that activity. Fixed and variable costs are associated with the negotiation activities. A fixed cost is charged each time an activity occurs while a variable cost accumulates over the period of time required to complete the activity. Each activity will now be discussed with activity numbers given in brackets after the description.

* This example is taken from Moore and Clayton (87).

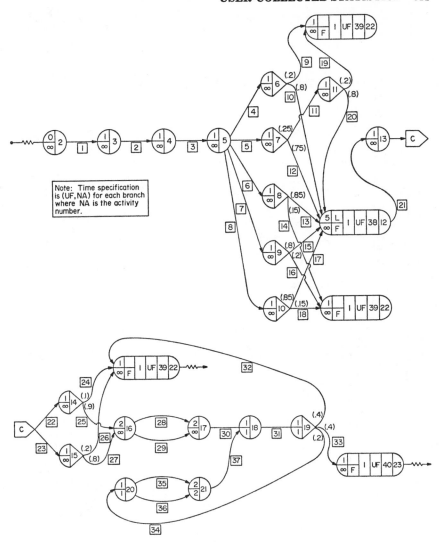

Figure 9-6 Q-GERT diagram of industrial sales negotiation model, Example 14.

The sales negotiation process involves the initial contact by company salesmen [1]. A report to the marketing vice president and to the president is then made [2,3]. For this company, a decision to perform preliminary analyses is standard for the large type of project being considered. As will be seen, an evaluation of this policy could be cost effective. Next, on the Q-GERT network, five parallel studies are performed beginning

Table 9-2. Activity Descriptions for Sales Negotiations Network, Example 14.

Activity No.	Activity Description	Distribution	Time in hours			Cost in dollars*		Proba-bility
			Mode	Min	Max	(a)	(b)	
1	Sales call by company salesman	Beta	2.00	1.25	4.0	0	11.	1.00
2	Sales report to marketing vice president	Beta	0.50	0.25	1.0	0	31.	1.00
3	Marketing vice president reports to president	Beta	0.25	0.25	0.50	0	51.	1.00
4	Preliminary engineering report	Beta	24.0	16.0	40.0	200.	20.	1.00
5	Preliminary production report	Constant	8.0	N/A	N/A	100.	12.	1.00
6	Preliminary financial report	Constant	16.0	N/A	N/A	50.	10.	1.00
7	Preliminary marketing report	Constant	8.0	N/A	N/A	50.	10.	1.00
8	Preliminary purchasing report	Beta	24.0	16.0	40.0	300.	17.	1.00
9	Negative engineering report examined	Constant	8.0	N/A	N/A	0	20.	0.20
10	Favorable engineering report examined	Constant	8.0	N/A	N/A	0	20.	0.80
11	Production subcontracting investigated	Beta	24.0	8.0	40.0	0	10.	0.25
12	Favorable production report examined	Constant	8.0	N/A	N/A	0	20.	0.75
13	Favorable financial report examined	Constant	10.0	N/A	N/A	60.	20.	0.85
14	Negative financial report examined	Constant	12.0	N/A	N/A	120.	20.	0.15
15	Favorable marketing report examined	Constant	12.0	N/A	N/A	61.	20.	0.80
16	Negative marketing report examined	Constant	16.0	N/A	N/A	248.	20.	0.20
17	Favorable purchasing report examined	Constant	2.0	N/A	N/A	61.	17.	0.85
18	Negative purchasing report examined	Constant	2.0	N/A	N/A	61.	17.	0.15
19	Unfavorable production subcontract examined	Constant	2.0	N/A	N/A	0	51.	0.20
20	Favorable production subcontract examined	Constant	8.0	N/A	N/A	0	20.	0.80
21	Corporate level planning conference	Constant	8.0	N/A	N/A	750.	0	1.00

Table 9-2. Activity Descriptions for Sales Negotiations Network, Example 14. (Continued)

Activity No.	Activity Description	Distribution	Time in hours			Cost in dollars*		Proba-bility
			Mode	Min	Max	(a)	(b)	
22	Sales call by marketing vice president and salesman	Constant	16.0	N/A	N/A	400.	31.	1.00
23	Engineering call by engineering vice president	Constant	16.0	N/A	N/A	400.	32.	1.00
24	Unfavorable sales call conference	Beta	3.0	1.0	18.0	0	73.	0.10
25	Favorable sales call no conference	Constant	0.0	N/A	N/A	0	0	0.90
26	Unfavorable engineering call conference	Beta	3.0	1.0	16.0	0	73.	0.20
27	Favorable engineering call no conference	Constant	0.0	N/A	N/A	0	0	0.80
28	Marketing negotiation plan formulation	Beta	24.0	8.0	40.0	200.	20.	1.00
29	Engineering design plan formulation	Beta	80.0	40.0	160.0	800.	26.	1.00
30	Corporate level strategy conference	Beta	2.0	1.0	8.0	0	73.	1.00
31	Negotiation conference with buying firm	Beta	6.0	2.0	16.0	400.	73.	1.00
32	No sale	Constant	0.0	N/A	N/A	0	0	0.40
33	Contract awarded	Constant	0.0	N/A	N/A	0	0	0.40
34	Modifications requested by buyer	Constant	0.0	N/A	N/A	0	0	0.20
35	Modification of marketing negotiation plan	Beta	12.0	4.0	20.0	200.	20.	1.00
36	Modification of engineering design plan	Beta	40.0	20.0	80.0	800.	26.	1.00
37	Corporate meeting to reconcile modifications	Beta	1.0	0.5	4.0	0	73.	1.00

*Column (a) is the fixed cost for the activity while column (b) is the variable cost for the activity assumed to be linear over time.

at node 5. These involve engineering [4], production [5], financial [6], marketing [7] and purchasing [8]. Except for the production report, the evaluation of the reports is performed at the nodes following the activities, as represented by activities 9 and 10 and 13 through 18. If any of the reports is negative, the project is not negotiated further and the network terminates at node 22. Node 22 is repeated three times in Figure 9–6 for graphical convenience. The evaluation of the production schedule is slightly more complicated in that the possibility for production subcontracting is investigated [11]. An unfavorable production subcontract could also occur [19] which would lead to termination of the negotiation process. When all five reports are favorable, node 12 is released. Node 12 is a statistics node and the time at which node 12 is released will be collected. A user function is employed at node 12 to collect cost data with regard to the costs of the sales negotiation process up to the time at which five favorable reports are obtained. Based on the five reports, corporate level planning conferences are held [21]. Further information is then sought of a marketing and engineering nature [22,23]. If either of these calls results in unfavorable information, the sales negotiation process is again terminated [24,26]. If positive information is obtained from the calls [25,27], marketing negotiation plans and engineering design plans are formulated [28,29]. Based on these plans, corporate level strategy is developed in a conference [30]. This strategy is implemented in a negotiation conference with the buying firm [31]. The results of the negotiation conference are: no sale [32]; contract awarded [33]; or further negotiations requested by the buyer involving plan modifications [34]. Marketing and engineering modifications are then performed [35,36]. A corporate level meeting to evaluate and reconcile the modifications is then held [37]. Following this, a return is made to node 18 of the Q-GERT network where another negotiation conference with the buying firm is held [31]. At node 23, a successful sale has been made. Total costs when a successful sale is made are collected at node 23. Total costs of the negotiation when a sale has not been made are collected at node 22.

The GERT network model for the sales negotiation process allows an analyst to include probabilistic outcomes as modeled by the probabilistic branching at nodes throughout the network. In addition, recycling of activities is permissible as illustrated by the loop of nodes 18, 19, 20 and 21.

Function UF is employed to obtain all activity times and total costs for the negotiation process at an intermediate node of the network (node 12) and at the nodes representing no sale [22] and sale [23]. Function UF is shown in Figure 9-7. Statement 1 is used for activities having a constant time and statement 2 is used for those activities whose time is beta distributed. Statement 3 is used to obtain user collected statistics at the three statistics nodes of the network. Statement 4 is used to stop any activities in progress when a lost sale occurs.

```
FUNCTION UF(IFN)
COMMON /QVAR/ NDE,NFTBU(100),NREL(100),NRELP(100),NREL2(100),
1 NRUN,NRUNS,NTC(100),PARAM(100,4),TBEG,TNOW
COMMON /UCOM1/ SETC(37),VARC(37),TOTALC
GO TO (2,2,2,2,1,1,1,2,1,1,2,1,1,1,1,1,1,1,1,1,1,1,1,2,1,2,1,
*2,2,2,2,1,1,1,2,2,2,3,4,3), IFN
1 UF=PARAM(IFN,1)
GO TO 100
2 UF=BE(IFN)
100 TOTALC=TOTALC+SETC(IFN)+VARC(IFN)*UF
RETURN
3 JJ=IFN-37
CALL COL(TOTALC,JJ)
CALL HIS(TOTALC,JJ)
UF=0.0
RETURN
4 CALL SNACT(1,NACT,TIREM)
IF(NACT.EQ.0) GO TO 3
TOTALC=TOTALC-VARC(NACT)*TIREM
GO TO 4
END
```

Figure 9-7 Function UF for sales negotiation model, Example 14.

When UF is called and a transfer is made to statement 1, the time for the activity is taken as the value of the first column of row IFN of the PARAM array. These constants are read into PARAM on input and illustrate the use of Q-GERT input to read constant values. A transfer is then made to statement 100 where the total costs are increased by the sum of the setup and the variable cost for the activity. The variable cost is the product of the cost per unit time and the activity time. The function number associated with statements 1 and 2 of UF are equivalent to the activity number of each branch on the network. Function numbers 38, 39 and 40 are used for user collected statistics. When an activity time is beta distributed, the computed GO TO statement in UF causes a transfer to statement 2 where a sample from a beta distribution is taken as the value for UF. Total cost for the project is then updated by the equation specified in statement 100.

For this example, a setup cost and a variable cost that is proportional to the time to perform the activity is used. Note that the cost for an activity is added to the total cost when the activity is started. By changing statement 100, different cost relations as a function of time could be modeled. Also, by judicious choice of function numbers, the long computed GO TO statement could be eliminated.

When a lost sale occurs, node 22 is released and user function 39 is activated. In UF, this causes a transfer to statement 4. Since a lost sale can be caused by one negative report or by an unfavorable call, other activities that are on-going should be stopped as soon as possible after the determination is made that the sale is lost. To stop other activities, the Q-GERT subroutine SNACT is used. By setting the first argument to one, SNACT stops the next scheduled activity and provides the activity number and the time remaining on the activity. The statement to accomplish this is CALL SNACT(1,NACT,TIREM) where the 1 indicates the next event is to be stopped, NACT is the activity number (which will be zero if no activity is scheduled to occur) and TIREM is the time that was remaining on the activity.

If NACT = 0, no activity is on-going, and a transfer to statement 3 in UF is made to collect the costs associated with the current run. If NACT is greater than zero, the costs that were added into the total cost variable, TOTALC, must be decreased because resources are reassigned before the activity was completed. The cost not expended on activity NACT is VARC(NACT)*TIREM and this quantity is subtracted from TOTALC. A transfer back to statement 4 is made to stop all activities on-going when the lost sale was detected.

At statement 3, the index JJ is computed as the function number minus 37. The 37 is the number of activities that have function numbers. Function number 38 was prescribed for node 12 and, hence, a JJ value of 1 corresponds to the collection of total cost values at node 12. A JJ value of 2 corresponds to the collection of total cost statistics at node 22 (function number 39), and a JJ value of 3 corresponds to the collection of total costs at node 23 (function number 40). This completes the description of function UF. This example provides the general organization for including other statistical measures in Q-GERT networks. At the end of all runs, Q-GERT prints the user collected statistical information.

The initialization of the total cost variable for each run of the network is performed in UI. In addition, the cost variables, SETC(I) and VARC(I), for each activity are read in subroutine UI. Also required is the changing of the parameter values when the user samples from the beta distribution directly as discussed in Chapter 7. The coding to perform these three tasks is shown in Figure 9–8. The first statement in subroutine UI initializes the total cost, TOTALC, to zero for each run of the network. Next, a check on the run number, NRUN, being equal to one is made. If NRUN is one, the setup costs and variable costs for each activity are read. Since these costs are not part of the standard Q-GERT program, it is good practice to print the values to obtain a written record of the values used. Since subroutine UI is called following the reading of the Q-GERT data cards, the data corresponding to the setup costs and variable costs would follow the FIN card of the Q-GERT input.

```
      SUBROUTINE UI
      COMMON /GVAR/ NDE,NFTBU(100),NREL(100),NRELP(100),NREL2(100),
     1 NRUN,NRUNS,NTC(100),PARAM(100,4),TBEG,TNOW
      COMMON /UCOM1/ SETC(37),VARC(37),TCTALC
C*** INITIALIZE TCTAL COST
      TOTALC=0.0
      IF(NRUN.GT.1) RETURN
C*** READ AND PRINT SETUP AND VARIALBE COSTS
      WRITE(6,101)
      DO 1 I=1,37
      READ(5,100) SETC(I),VARC(I)
      WRITE(6,102) SETC(I),VARC(I)
      GO TO (2,2,2,2,1,1,1,2,1,1,2,1,1,1,1,1,1,1,1,1,1,1,1,2,1,2,1,
     *2,2,2,2,1,1,1,2,2,2), I
C*** CHANGE VALUES OF PARAMETERS
C*** FOR BETA SAMPLING
    2 CALL CPBP(I)
    1 CONTINUE
      RETURN
  100 FORMAT(2F5.0)
  101 FORMAT(5X,≠SETUP≠,5X,≠VARIABLE≠/6X,≠COST≠,7X,≠COST≠/)
  102 FORMAT(F8.0,F12.0)
      END
```

Figure 9-8 Subroutine UI for sales negotiation model, Example 14.

For those activities for which sampling from the beta distribution is to be employed, a call is made to subroutine CPBE to change the parameters of the beta distribution. For this example, the parameter set number has been set equal to the activity number which is equal to the function number. This equivalence between activity number, function number and parameter set number is not required and is only done in this example for explanation convenience. In fact, fewer activity numbers could be employed by referring to all the activities that have zero time and zero costs associated with them by the same number. For expository purposes, using different activity numbers is better. This completes the discussion of subroutine UI. The data input for this example is shown in Figure 9–9.

Summary of Results

The Q-GERT model of the industrial sales negotiation process was analyzed for 500 runs. Summaries of the time and cost results are presented in Figures 9-10 and 9-11. The estimate of the probability of losing a sale, node 22, is 0.844. This indicates that over 84 percent of the negotiations end in failure.

```
GEN,PRITSKER,SALES-14,3,15,1977,1,2,1,,500,(14)1*
SOU,2*
REG,3*
REG,4*
REG,5*
REG,6,,,,P*
REG,7,,,,P*
REG,8,,,,P*
REG,9,,,,P*
REG,10,,,,P*
REG,11,,,,P*
STA,12/FAV-RPTS,5,(7)10.,2.*
REG,13*
REG,14,,,,P*
REG,15,,,,P*
REG,16,2*
REG,17,2*
REG,18,,1*
REG,19,,1,P*
REG,20,,1*
REG,21,2,2*
SIN,22/LOST-SAL,(7)10.,10.*
SIN,23/SUCCESS,(7)100.,20.*
VAS,12,1,LF,38*
VAS,22,1,UF,39*
VAS,23,1,UF,40*
ACT,2,3,UF,1,1*          SALES CALL BY COMPANY SALESMAN
ACT,3,4,UF,2,2*          SALES REPORT TO MARKETING VICE PRESIDENT
ACT,4,5,UF,3,3*          MARKETING VICE PRESIDENT REPORTS TO PRESIDENT
ACT,5,6,UF,4,4*          PRELIMINARY ENGINEERING REPORT
ACT,5,7,UF,5,5*          PRELIMINARY PRODUCTION REPORT
ACT,5,8,UF,6,6*          PRELIMINARY FINANCIAL REPORT
ACT,5,9,UF,7,7*          PRELIMINARY MARKETING REPORT
ACT,5,10,UF,8,8*         PRELIMINARY PURCHASING REPORT
ACT,6,22,UF,9,9,,.2*     NEGATIVE ENGINEERING REPORT EXAMINED
ACT,6,12,UF,10,10,,.8*   FAVORABLE ENGINEERING REPORT EXAMINED
ACT,7,11,UF,11,11,,.25*  PRODUCTION SUBCONTRACTING INVESTIGATED
ACT,7,12,UF,12,12,,.75*  FAVORABLE PRODUCTION REPORT EXAMINED
ACT,8,12,UF,13,13,,.85*  FAVORABLE FINANCIAL REPORT EXAMINED
ACT,8,22,UF,14,14,,.15*  NEGATIVE FINANCIAL REPORT EXAMINED
ACT,9,12,UF,15,15,,.8*   FAVORABLE MARKETING REPORT EXAMINED
ACT,9,22,UF,16,16,,.2*   NEGATIVE MARKETING REPORT EXAMINED
ACT,10,12,UF,17,17,,.85* FAVORABLE PURCHASING REPORT EXAMINED
ACT,10,22,UF,18,18,,.15* NEGATIVE PURCHASING REPORT EXAMINED
ACT,11,22,UF,19,19,,.2*  UNFAVORABLE PRODUCTION SUBCONTRACT EXAMINED
ACT,11,12,UF,20,20,,.8*  FAVORABLE PRODUCTION SUBCONTRACT EXAMINED
ACT,12,13,UF,21,21*      CORPORATE LEVEL PLANNING CONFERENCE
ACT,13,14,UF,22,22*      SALES CALL BY MARKETING V.P. AND SALESMAN
ACT,13,15,UF,23,23*      ENG. CALL BY ENG. V.P. AND PROJ. ENGINEER
ACT,14,22,UF,24,24,,.1*  UNFAVORABLE SALES CALL CONFERENCE
ACT,14,16,UF,25,25,,.9*  FAVORABLE SALES CALL NO CONFERENCE (DUMMY)
ACT,15,22,UF,26,26,,.2*  UNFAVORABLE ENGINEERING CALL CONFERENCE
ACT,15,16,UF,27,27,,.8*  FAVORABLE ENGINEERING CALL NO CONFERENCE (DUMMY)
ACT,16,17,UF,28,28*      MARKETING NEGOTIATION PLAN FORMULATION
ACT,16,17,UF,29,29*      ENGINEERING DESIGN PLAN FORMULATION
ACT,17,18,UF,30,30*      CORPORATE LEVEL STRATEGY CONFERENCE
ACT,18,19,UF,31,31*      NEGOTIATION CONFERENCE WITH BUYING FIRM
ACT,19,22,UF,32,32,,.4*  NO SALE (DUMMY)
ACT,19,23,UF,33,33,,.4*  CONTRACT AWARDED (DUMMY)
ACT,19,20,UF,34,34,,.2*  MODIFICATIONS REQUESTED BY BUYER (DUMMY)
```

Figure 9-9 Data input for sales negotiation model, Example 14.

```
ACT,20,21,UF,35,35*        MODIFICATION OF MARKETING NEGOTIATION PLAN
ACT,20,21,UF,36,36*        MODIFICATION OF ENGINEERING DESIGN PLAN
ACT,21,18,UF,37,37*        CORPORATE MEETING TO RECONCILE MODIFICATIONS
PAR,1,2.,,1.25,4.*
PAR,2,.5,.25,1.*
PAR,3,.25,.25,.5*
PAR,4,24.,16.,,40.*
PAR,5,8.*
PAR,6,16.*
PAR,7,8.*
PAR,8,24.,16.,,40.*
PAR,9,8.*
PAR,10,8.*
PAR,11,24.,8.,,40.*
PAR,12,8.*
PAR,13,10.*
PAR,14,12.*
PAR,15,12.*
PAR,16,16.*
PAR,17,2.*
PAR,18,2.*
PAR,19,2.*
PAR,20,8.*
PAR,21,8.*
PAR,22,16.*
PAR,23,16.*
PAR,24,3.,,1.,,18.*
PAR,25,0.*
PAR,26,3.,,1.,,16.*
PAR,27,0.*
PAR,28,24.,8.,,40.*
PAR,29,80.,,40.,,160.*
PAR,30,2.,,1.,,8.*
PAR,31,6.,,2.,,16.*
PAR,32,0.*
PAR,33,0.*
PAR,34,0.*
PAR,35,12.,,4.,,20.*
PAR,36,40.,,20.,,80.*
PAR,37,1.,,.5,4.*
COL,1/FAV-RPTS*
HIS,1/FAV-RPTS,18,1000.,,500.*
COL,2/LOST-SAL*
COL,3/SUCCESS*
HIS,2/LOST-SAL,18,2000.,,1000.*
HIS,3/SUCCESS,10,8000.,,1000.*
FIN*
0.    11.
0.    31.
0.    51.
200.  20.
100.  12.
50.   10.
50.   10.
300.  17.
0.    20.
0.    20.
0.    10.
0.    20.
60.   20.
120.  20.
```

Figure 9-9   (Continued)

```
61.     20.
248.    20.
61.     17.
61.     17.
0.      51.
0.      20.
750.    0.
400.    31.
400.    32.
0.      73.
0.      0.
0.      73.
0.      0.
200.    20.
800.    26.
0.      73.
400.    73.
0.      0.
0.      0.
0.      0.
200.    20.
800.    26.
0.      73.
```

Figure 9-9 (cont.) Data input for sales negotiation model, Example 14.

Looking at node 12, favorable reports received, it is seen that approximately 43 percent of the potential projects result in all five reports being favorable. Thus, 57 percent of the sales negotiations are turned down for internal reasons. The time estimates indicate that it takes over 38 days to decide that negotiations should be carried beyond the internal report phase. The cost data indicate that it costs over $3050 when all favorable reports are obtained. This information can be extremely useful for an analyst who is attempting to improve the sales negotiation process, as it provides trade-off data regarding the possibility of increasing the probability of favorable reports versus the time and costs required to obtain the favorable reports. By developing alternative networks up to node 12, such trade-offs can be made. The analyst should attempt to develop procedures for detecting when unfavorable reports will be issued. Possibly sequential reporting of the engineering, production, financial, marketing and purchasing reports should be made. Since engineering and marketing have the highest probability of issuing a neg-

FINAL RESULTS FOR 500 SIMULATIONS

AVERAGE NODE STATISTICS

NODE	LABEL	PROBABILITY	AVE.	STD.DEV.	SD OF AVE	NO OF OBS.	MIN.	MAX.	STAT TYPE
22	LOST-SAL	.8440	62.1055	56.4425	2.7476	422.	22.6712	287.7906	F
23	SUCCESS	.1560	182.0164	49.1436	5.4512	78.	125.7381	425.7386	F
12	FAV-RPTS	.4340	38.1034	4.6936	.3186	217.	28.5247	50.9886	F

Figure 9-10 Summary report for times associated with sales negotiation model, Example 14.

USER STATISTICS FOR VARIABLES BASED ON OBSERVATION AT TIME 30.095 IN RUN 500

	AVE	STD DEV	SD OF AVE	MINIMUM	MAXIMUM	OBS
FAV-RPTS	3053.6797	141.4692	9.5036	2760.4418	3469.0602	217
LOST-SAL	4943.8782	3330.3886	162.1208	2475.4571	17774.4282	422
SUCCESS	11946.3841	2730.1616	309.1299	9524.0147	25238.0935	78

Figure 9-11 Summary report for costs associated with sales negotiation model, Example 14.

321

ative report, possibly these two activities should be performed prior to the other reports. If this is done, the time required to reach the decision with regard to the preliminary reports will be extended.

The summary statistics for a lost sale indicate that it takes 62 days on the average to make this determination. Since node 22 can be reached from many points in the network, this time should have a wide variability which is the case as indicated by its standard deviation of 56.4 and its range of 23 to 288. The average cost associated with a lost sale is $4944. This indicates that when the project fails more money is expended in obtaining favorable reports than is put into the negotiation effort after the reports are obtained. When the project succeeds, which occurs only 15.6 percent of the time, the negotiation process takes a lengthy 182 days and costs on the average $11,947. Other statistical quantities concerning the time and cost when the negotiation is successful are shown in Figures 9-10 and 9-11.

Figure 9-12, the time and cost histograms associated with node 22, lost sale, are presented. These histograms illustrate that the distribution function associated with node 22 has discrete breaks due to the different paths that can be used to reach node 22. For example, failed reports occurred on 283 runs. ((1-.434)*500.). The histogram for node 22 shows 283 values in the range 20 to 50; hence, this cluster of values is associated with failed reports. The other values in the histogram for node 22 are for the times when a lost sale occurred after favorable reports were received.

Figure 9-13 presents the histograms for the time and costs associated with a successful sales negotiation. These histograms can be used to monitor company time and cost data associated with successful sales ne-

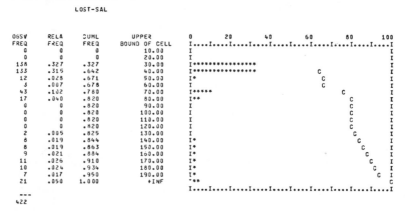

Figure 9-12 Histograms of times and costs associated with unsuccessful sales negotiation, Example 14.

LOST-SAL

```
OBSV    RELA    CUML      UPPER
FREQ    FREQ    FREQ    BOUND OF CELL    0        20       40       60       80       100
                                        I....I....I....I....I....I....I....I....I....I....I
   0       0       0     2000.0000      I                                                  I
 203    .481    .481     3000.0000      I*****************************                     I
  80    .190    .671     4000.0000      I**********                       C                I
   0       0    .671     5000.0000      I                                 C                I
  38    .090    .761     6000.0000      I*****                       C                     I
  25    .059    .820     7000.0000      I***                              C                I
   0       0    .820     8000.0000      I                                      C           I
   0       0    .820     9000.0000      I                                      C           I
  10    .024    .844    10000.0000      I*                                     C           I
  33    .078    .922    11000.0000      I****                                      C       I
  13    .031    .953    12000.0000      I**                                          C I   I
   3    .007    .960    13000.0000      I                                            C I   I
   8    .019    .979    14000.0000      I*                                             CI  I
   6    .014    .993    15000.0000      I*                                              CI I
   1    .002    .995    16000.0000      I                                               C  I
   1    .002    .998    17000.0000      I                                               C  I
   1    .002   1.000    18000.0000      I                                               C  I
   0       0   1.000    19000.0000      I                                               C  I
   0       0   1.000    20000.0000      I                                               C  I
   0       0   1.000       INF          I                                               C  I
 ---                                    I....I....I....I....I....I....I....I....I....I....I
 422
```

Figure 9-12   (Continued)

gotiations. From the histogram, we see that over 20 percent of the time, the total sales negotiation cost will be greater than $14,000. Thus, we can expect 1 time out of 5 to have this high cost, given that the sales negotiation pattern follows the one described by the Q-GERT model. By making such comparisons, the company can maintain some control over the costs involved in their sales negotiations activities.

F STAT HISTOGRAM FOR NODE   23

SUCCESS

```
OBSV    RELA    CUML      UPPER
FREQ    FREQ    FREQ    BOUND OF CELL    0        28       40       60       80       100
                                        I....I....I....I....I....I....I....I....I....I....I
   0       0       0      100.00        I                                                  I
   0       0       0      120.00        I                                                  I
  10    .128    .128      140.00        I******                                            I
  20    .256    .385      160.00        I***************     C                             I
  14    .179    .564      180.00        I*********                    C                    I
  15    .192    .756      200.00        I**********                            C           I
   4    .051    .808      220.00        I***                                   C           I
  10    .128    .936      240.00        I******                                     C I    I
   0       0    .936      260.00        I                                           C I    I
   3    .038    .974      280.00        I**                                          C I   I
   0       0    .974      300.00        I                                            C I   I
   0       0    .974      320.00        I                                            C I   I
   1    .013    .987      340.00        I*                                             CI  I
   0       0    .987      360.00        I                                             CI   I
   0       0    .987      380.00        I                                             CI   I
   0       0    .987      400.00        I                                             CI   I
   0       0    .987      420.00        I                                             CI   I
   1    .013   1.000      440.00        I*                                              C  I
   0       0   1.000      460.00        I                                              C   I
   0       0   1.000       +INF         I                                              C   I
 ---                                    I....I....I....I....I....I....I....I....I....I....I
TOTAL  78
```

Figure 9-13 Histograms of times and costs associated with successful sales negotiation, Example 14.

SUCCESS

OBSV FREQ	RELA FREQ	CUML FREQ	UPPER BOUND OF CELL	0 20 40 60 80 100
				I....I....I....I....I....I....I....I....I....I....I
0	0	0	8000.0000	I I
0	0	0	9000.0000	I I
12	.154	.154	10000.0000	I******** I
31	.397	.551	11000.0000	I******************** C I
11	.141	.692	12000.0000	I******* C I
2	.026	.718	13000.0000	I* C I
6	.077	.795	14000.0000	I**** C I
10	.128	.923	15000.0000	I****** C I
1	.013	.936	16000.0000	I* C I
0	0	.936	17000.0000	I C I
1	.013	.949	18000.0000	I* C I
4	.051	1.000	INF	I*** C
---				I....I....I....I....I....I....I....I....I....I....I
78				

Figure 9-13   (Continued

COMPUTATION OF WAITING TIMES

The average waiting time of transactions in a Q-node is calculated by the Q-GERT Analysis Program using a variant of Little's Formula (97, 129). It can be shown that the time integrated number in a Q-node is equal to the sum of the waiting times of transactions in a Q-node if no transactions reside in the Q-node when the computations are made (or, the waiting time is defined for transactions still in the Q-node as time spent in the queue up to the computation instant, say T). Using this information, it can be shown that the average waiting time, $\overline{w}$, is

$$\overline{w} = \overline{q} * \overline{t}$$

where $\overline{q}$ = average number in the Q-node, and
$\overline{t}$ = average time between arrivals to the Q-node.
   In computing $\overline{w}$ for the Q-node, NODE, at time T, the Q-GERT Analysis Program employs TINIQ (NODE) / T to estimate $\overline{q}$; and T divided by (NTC (NODE) + NREL (NODE)) to estimate $\overline{t}$. From these relations, we compute AVEWT = $\overline{w}$ as

AVEWT = TINIQ(NODE)/FLOAT(NTC(NODE) + NREL (NODE))

The value of AVEWT is printed as part of the Q-GERT Summary Report. To make the average waiting time in Q-node NODE directly available in user-written subprograms, FUNCTION AVEWT (NODE) is included as part of the Q-GERT Analysis Program.
   There are situations when it is desirable to compute the time spent in a queue by each transaction. Two methods for obtaining such statistics will now be presented.

Let d_i = departure time of ith transaction from the Q-node,
   a_i = arrival time of ith transaction to the Q-node, and
   N = number of transactions departing the Q-node

then $w_i = d_i - a_i$ is the waiting time of ith transaction at the Q-node. With these definitions, $\bar{w}$ is

$$\bar{w} = \frac{\sum\limits_{i=1}^{N} w_i}{N} = \frac{\sum\limits_{i=1}^{N} (d_i - a_i)}{N}$$

This formula requires that arrival times be associated with queue departure times, that is, d_i and a_i need to be associated with transaction i.

Method 1 obtains statistics on the waiting time by assigning the arrival time at a Q-node to be an attribute of a transaction. User statistics collection is then performed at the Q-node where d_i is available as the time the transaction is put into service. The network segment and function UF to accomplish this are shown in Figure 9-14.

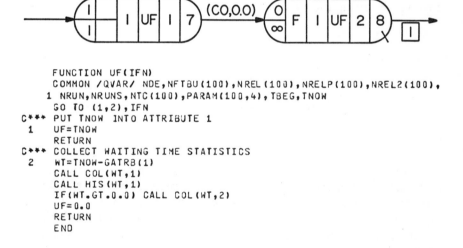

```
      FUNCTION UF(IFN)
      COMMON /QVAR/ NDE,NFTBU(100),NREL(100),NRELP(100),NREL2(100),
     1 NRUN,NRUNS,NTC(100),PARAM(100,4),TBEG,TNOW
      GO TO (1,2),IFN
C*** PUT TNOW INTO ATTRIBUTE 1
    1 UF=TNOW
      RETURN
C*** COLLECT WAITING TIME STATISTICS
    2 WT=TNOW-GATRB(1)
      CALL COL(WT,1)
      CALL HIS(WT,1)
      IF(WT.GT.0.0) CALL COL(WT,2)
      UF=0.0
      RETURN
      END
```

Figure 9-14 Network and function UF to collect waiting times, Method 1.

In Figure 9-14, user function 1 causes the time at which the transaction passes through node 7 to be assigned to attribute 1. Since the activity from node 7 to Q-node 8 has a zero time specification, attribute 1 contains the arrival time of the transaction to Q-node 8, that is, a_i. At Q-node 8, user function 2 is prescribed. When a transaction is taken from the queue (or upon arrival if the server is idle), user function 2 is invoked. The waiting time of the transaction is computed as the time it departs from the queue minus the value of attribute 1. In function UF, this is computed as WT at statement 2. User-statistics collection subprograms COL and HIS are called to record these observations of the waiting time spent in Q-node 8. Also collected in function UF is the waiting time given that the transaction waited, that is WT when WT is greater than zero. Estimates of the average and standard deviation of the waiting time and a histogram of waiting times will be printed by the

Q-GERT Analysis Program whenever a summary report is printed. In addition, the user can obtain outputs for each run by calling COLP and HISP in subroutine UO.

A second method for obtaining estimates of the average waiting time involves rewriting the equation for $\bar{w}$ as

$$\bar{w} = \frac{\sum_{i=1}^{N} d_i - \sum_{i=1}^{N} a_i}{N}$$

This formula allows $\bar{w}$ to be computed by summing queue arrival times and queue departure times separately. The network segment and user code to compute $\bar{w}$ from the above equation are shown in Figure 9-15. User function 1 is used to compute the sum of the arrival times, SARRT, and the number of arrivals, XARR. User function 2 is used to compute the sum of departure times, SDEPT, and the number of departures, XDEP. Subroutine UI initializes these values. In subroutine UO, averages are computed for interarrival, interdeparture and waiting times. Since transactions can be in Q-node 21 at the end of the run, the computation of average waiting time, AWAIT, assumes the transactions depart the queue at the end of the run, that is, for each transaction in the queue, a departure time equal to the run time is assumed. Since UO is called at the end of the run, TNOW is equal to the run time in subroutine UO. Note that this second method of obtaining the average waiting time does not require the user statistics collection routines.

```
      FUNCTION UF(IFN)
      COMMON/USER1/SARRT,XARR,SDEPT,XDEP
      COMMON /QVAR/ NDE,NFTBU(100),NREL(100),NRELP(100),NREL2(100),
     1 NRUN,NRUNS,NTC(100),PARAM(100,4),TBEG,TNOW
      GO TO (1,2),IFN
C*** ADD TNOW TO SUM OF ARRIVAL TIMES
    1 SARRT=SARRT+TNOW
      XARR=XARR+1.0
      RETURN
C*** ADD TNOW TO SUM OF DEPARTURE TIMES
    2 SDEPT=SDEPT+TNOW
      XDEP=XDEP+1.0
      RETURN
      END

      SUBROUTINE UI
      COMMON/USER1/SARRT,XARR,SDEPT,XDEP
C
C
      SARRT=0.0
      XARR=0.0
      SDEPT=0.0
      XDEP=0.0
      RETURN
      END


      SUBROUTINE UO
      COMMON/USER1/SARRT,XARR,SDEPT,XDEP
      COMMON /QVAR/ NDE,NFTBU(100),NREL(100),NRELP(100),NREL2(100),
     1 NRUN,NRUNS,NTC(100),PARAM(100,4),TBEG,TNOW
C*** COMPUTE AVERAGE TIME BETWEEN ARRIVALS (ATBA)
      ATBA=SARRT/XARR
C*** COMPUTE AVERAGE TIME BETWEEN DEPARTURES (ATBD)
      ATBD=SDEPT/XDEP
      XRINQ=XARR-XDEP
C*** AVERAGE WAITING TIME
      AWAIT=(SDEPT+XRINQ*TNOW-SARRT)/XARR
      WRITE(6,100)NRUN,ATBA,XARR,
     *      ATBD,XDEP,AWAIT
  100 FORMAT(# RUN NO. = #,I4//# AVERAGE TIME
     *         BETWEEN ARRIVALS = #F9.2/
     *       # NUMBER OF ARRIVALS = #F9.2/
     *       # AVERAGE TIME BETWEEN DEPARTURES = #F8.2/
     *       # NUMBER OF DEPARTURES = #I19/
     *       # AVERAGE WAITING TIME = #F18.2)
      RETURN
      END
```

Figure 9-15 Q-GERT network segment and user code to compute average waiting times, Method 2.

AUXILIARY ATTRIBUTE PROCESSING SUBROUTINES

To augment the attribute storage and retrieval system included in the
Q-GERT Analysis Program, three subroutines are provided to allow the
Q-GERT user to initialize and use user-defined arrays for storing attributes of transactions. The subroutines allow the user to employ different arrays for storing attributes for different types of transactions. The
number of attributes per transaction can then be set by the user. The
three subroutines included in Q-GERT are described in Table 9-2.

Table 9-2   Subroutines for Auxiliary Attribute Processing

Subroutine Name	Description
SUBROUTINE INITA (ARRAY,NEXTR, NATT, NROWS)	Initializes the two dimension array, ARRAY, which has NATT columns and NROWS rows; sets next row to store auxiliary attributes, NEXTR, to one.
SUBROUTINE STORA(ATT, ARRAY, NEXTR,NATT)	Stores NATT values of auxiliary attributes as defined in the vector, ATT, in row NEXTR of ARRAY; Resets NEXTR to the next row in ARRAY that can be used to store auxiliary attributes.
SUBROUTINE FREEA (NRFRE, ARRAY, NEXTR, NATT)	Makes row NRFRE of ARRAY available for storing auxiliary attributes; Resets NEXTR to NRFRE.

Subroutine INITA is used to initialize an array that has NROWS
rows and can accommodate up to NATT attributes. Subroutine INITA
establishes NEXTR as the first row in which a set of auxiliary attributes
will be stored.

Subroutine STORA is used to store the values of the auxiliary attributes as defined in the vector ATT into row NEXTR of the auxiliary
attribute array ARRAY. The number of attributes placed in row
NEXTR is NATT. The user, before employing subroutine STORA,
must define the vector ATT to have NATT values. In addition, the row
number should be saved in which the auxiliary attributes will be stored.
This row number can be employed as a regular attribute of a transaction
and thus a transaction's auxiliary attributes can be identified through

this pointer to the row number of ARRAY. Subroutine STORA internally changes the value of NEXTR after being called so that it is important for the user to access the value of NEXTR before the call to STORA.

Subroutine FREEA is used to free up row NRFRE of auxiliary attribute array ARRAY. Row NRFRE becomes the next row of ARRAY in which auxiliary attributes will be placed, that is, the value of NEXTR is updated to be equal to NRFRE. In this way, the rows of ARRAY are dynamically used to store auxiliary attributes of transactions.

EXAMPLES OF THE USE OF AUXILIARY ATTRIBUTE SUBROUTINES

The use of auxiliary attributes in a Q-GERT model has three fundamental advantages:

1. Storage space is saved when a transaction is routed in more than one direction, since only a pointer is contained in the regular attribute set of each transaction routed. The auxiliary attributes would all be maintained in a user-defined array, and would not need to be duplicated;
2. Transactions that have different requirements for attributes can be accommodated in the same Q-GERT model without requiring excess storage allocation to the transactions that have only a small number of attributes; and
3. Access to auxiliary attributes is direct as the user can work directly with the array in which the auxiliary attributes are stored.

Examples of the use of each of the auxiliary attribute subroutines will now be given. The initialization of two arrays for storing auxiliary attributes can be performed in subroutine UI as shown below.

```
SUBROUTINE UI
COMMON/UCOM1/CUSTA(50,3),NRCUS,XINFA(100,5),NRINF
CALL INITA(CUSTA,NRCUS,3,50)
CALL INITA(XINFA,NRINF,5,100)
RETURN
END
```

The first call to subroutine INITA initializes the array CUSTA which has 50 rows and three columns. This array could be used for storing three attributes for each of 50 customer transactions. Subroutine INITA initializes the pointer to the first row of CUSTA to be used for storing auxiliary attributes to 1, this is, NRCUS=1. The second call to subroutine INITA initializes the array XINFA which has 100 rows and 5 columns which allows the storage of 5 auxiliary attributes for as many as 100 transactions. The pointer to the first free row of XINFA is defined as the variable NRINF.

Consider now the use of subroutine STORA. The following code is written to store auxiliary attributes in the array CUSTA when user function 1 occurs. User function 1 is called from node 7 where auxiliary attributes are to be assigned. Attribute 1 is used to maintain the pointer to the row number in which the auxiliary attributes are stored.

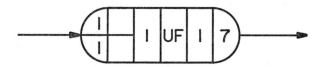

```
      FUNCTION UF(IFN)
      COMMON /UCOM1/CUSTA(50,3),NRCUS,XINFA(100,5),NRINF
      DIMENSION TATT(5),CP(4),VAL(4)
      DATA CP/0.1,0.3,0.7,1.0/
      DATA VAL/1.,2.,3.,4./
      GO TO (1,2,3,4,5),IFN
C*** DEFINE CUSTOMER ATTRIBUTES AND SET ATTRIBUTE 1 OF TRANSACTION AS
C*** A POINTER TO ROW OF CUSTA WHERE ATTRIBUTES ARE MAINTAINED
    1 TATT(1)=TNOW
      TATT(2)=DPROB(CP,VAL,4,1)
      TATT(3)=UN(1)
      UF=NRCUS
      CALL STORA(TATT,CUSTA,NRCUS,3)
      RETURN
         .
         .
         .
```

When a transaction passes through node 7, user function 1 is called to make an assignment to attribute 1. The assignment to attribute 1 will be the pointer to the row in the array CUSTA that contains the attributes assigned to the customer transaction passing through node 7. In function UF, a transfer is made to statement 1 when function number 1 occurs. The temporary attribute vector TATT is used to store three values for customer attributes. Auxiliary attribute 1 is the current time; auxiliary attribute 2 is a sample from a probability mass function as defined by the DATA statements; and auxiliary attribute 3 is a sample from a uniform distribution. Next, UF is set equal to the row number in which these auxiliary attributes will be stored in the array CUSTA. This assigns the value of NRCUS to attribute 1 of the customer transaction. A call to subroutine STORA places the values of TATT into row NRCUS of the array CUSTA. In addition, the value of NRCUS is updated to the row number that is next available for storing auxiliary customer attributes.

It is also possible to store auxiliary attributes at a user function employed at a branch. In this case, the row number in which the auxiliary attributes are to be stored is put directly into attribute 1 through the use of the following statements:

XRCUS=NRCUS
CALL PATRB(XRCUS,1)

The first statement given above is used to get a real representation of the row number in which auxiliary attributes are to be stored. The call to subroutine PATRB places this value into attribute 1 of the transaction being processed at the branch. Statements defining and storing five auxiliary attributes into the array XINFA could then be written.

When a transaction is deleted from the model and the auxiliary attributes are no longer required, the user should make the row in which the auxiliary attributes are stored available for use by other transactions. The code to accomplish this at sink node 22 is shown below.

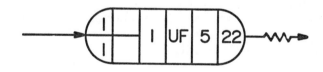

```
FUNCTION UF(IFN)
    •
    •
    •
5  NRTF=GATRB(1)
   CALL FREEA(NRTF,CUSTA,NRCUS,3)
   UF=0.0
   RETURN
    •
    •
    •
```

At statement 5, the row number used to store auxiliary attributes is obtained by getting the value of attribute 1. A call is then made to subroutine FREEA, which makes row NRTF available for storing auxiliary attributes of another transaction. UF is then set equal to zero as required by function calls in FORTRAN.

To use auxiliary attributes, the user obtains the row number associated with auxiliary attributes by using function GATRB. Decisions would then be made directly using the auxiliary attribute array. For example, if it is desired to set a variable equal to zero, if auxiliary attribute 2 of a customer transaction is less than or equal to 1, or to set the variable to 100 if the attribute is greater than 1, the following code would be used.

```
C*****  IF AUX. ATT. 2 FOR THIS XACT .GT. 1.0 SET UF=1.0,
C*****  OTHERWISE UF=0
        NPTR=GATRB(1)
        UF=0.0
        IF(CUSTA(NPTR,2).GT.1.0)UF=100.0
```

As can be seen by the above code, the array CUSTA is employed directly by the user once the row number in which the auxiliary attributes are stored is obtained. Thus, any complex decision logic based on the auxiliary attributes can be performed.

This completes the discussion of the subprograms available in the Q-GERT Analysis Program that are provided to augment the standard input, output and storage procedures.

EXERCISES

9-1. For the one server, single queue system, collect statistics and obtain a histogram on the time between arrivals and on the service time where the time between arrivals is prescribed to be exponentially distributed with a mean of 10 and the service time is prescribed to be normally distributed with a mean time of 8 and a standard deviation of 2. (Minimum = 0, Maximum = 100)

9-2. For the queueing situation described in Exercise 9-1, write subprograms employing user-collected routines to obtain statistics on the following random variables:
a. waiting time of transactions at the Q-node;
b. number of transactions in the system;

    c. waiting times of transactions in the queue for each 500 time unit interval in a simulation run of length 10,000; and

    d. a histogram on the average number of transactions in the system where each sample is taken for a 500 time unit subinterval.

9-3. For the queueing situation of Exercise 9–1, consider that the queue has a finite capacity of seven units. Transactions that balk from the queue are routed back to the queue with a two-unit time delay. Draw the Q-GERT network to obtain the average time between balkers, statistics on the number of balkers occurring on the first run and the average number of balkers occurring over 20 runs.

9-4. For the conveyor system presented in Example 4 of Chapter 4, embellish the Q-GERT network to obtain statistics on the number of transactions that are recycled to the first server.

9-5. For Example 1, Chapter 4, it is desired to run a simulation of length 4800 time units but it is desired to clear statistical storage arrays at time 480. Specify how this can be done. Embellish the Q-GERT network of Example 1 to obtain estimates of the average number of transactions (television sets) in the system during a simulation of 4800 time units. It is desired to begin collecting statistics on the number of transactions in the system at time 480.

9-6. In Example 1, Chapter 4, make the arrival rate a function of the average number of televisions in the system. If the average number of televisions in the system is greater than 3 at the time of an arrival, the time between arrivals is uniformly distributed between 4 and 8. Develop the Q-GERT network that will accommodate this change.

9-7. Develop a generalized PERT/cost simulator using the Q-GERT analysis program as the basis. The program should allow the user to input costs associated with each activity. Summary statistics on the costs for completing the project are to be printed automatically.

9-8. Evaluate the sales negotiation process of Example 14 and develop better procedures for performing the five studies. Perform a complete analysis of the negotiation process.

9-9. For the situation given in Example 1, Chapter 4, write the code for Function UF to compute and obtain a histogram of the average time a TV spends: 1) waiting for an inspector; and 2) waiting for the adjustor. Base the estimates on one run and employ the two methods presented in the text. Compare the results with the values presented in the standard Q-GERT summary report.

9–10. Write subroutine UO to obtain the average waiting times computed in Exercise 9–9 for methods 1 and 2.

9–11. Model the system described in Exercise 5–5 to allow the routing for a job to be read in from a peripheral device. The maximum number of machine groups a job is ever routed to is 9. [Hint: Use an auxiliary attribute array to store the routing and the number of machine groups the job has visited.]

Chapter 10

Q-GERT SUBNETWORKS

For complex networks, it often happens that a portion of the network is repeated, that is, subnetworks that perform a similar function appear in several locations throughout the network. Such subnetworks, sometimes referred to as modules (50) or macros (121,127), allow an analyst to build a network model using a higher level of constructs than is possible through the direct use of Q-GERT symbols. The modeling approach of first building Q-GERT subnetworks that model specific functions and then integrating the subnetworks into a total model was suggested by Halpin and Happ (50). In their work, subnetworks (modules) were developed to represent specific equipment allocation functions for use in engineer construction planning. A similar approach was taken by Auterio, Sigal, Duket and Wortman in building network models of Air Force Base Port Cargo Facilities (5,26,127).

Through subnetworks, a hierarchical network modeling approach can be taken where the levels of the hierarchy correspond to the network elements (branches and nodes), subnetworks and then networks. To support this higher level modeling capability, advanced input procedures have been included in the Q-GERT Analysis Program for defining and duplicating subnetworks throughout a Q-GERT model. In addition, editing procedures are available that enable the user to reproduce similar subnetworks. The advanced input procedures allow a subnetwork to be defined for one location in the network and then a duplicate of the subnetwork to be used in other positions in the network. The editing features allow changes to be made in the duplicated subnetwork. The procedures for defining, duplicating, editing and linking subnetworks are given in this chapter. An example illustrating the use of subnetworks to model space experiments is given at the end of this chapter.

Q-GERT SUBNETWORKS INPUT FEATURES

Through input procedures, it is possible to define a subnetwork that the Q-GERT Analysis Program can duplicate to facilitate the construction of large networks consisting of similar combinations of nodes and branches. More importantly, it facilitates the modeling of systems in terms of higher level functions which can then be duplicated throughout a network using the subnetwork input procedures. For example, in Halpin and Happ's work (50), six basic subnetworks were defined to describe earth moving operations. The functions modeled by the subnetworks were: 1) cycling of earth movers; 2) materials handling; 3) pairing resources and loading operations; 4) holding or storage operations; 5) initialization of vehicle status; and 6) traveling and dumping operations. The network modeling of earth moving operations was then performed by linking subnetworks together to describe the operation of an entire system.

Defining and Duplicating a Subnetwork

A Q-GERT subnetwork is indicated by preceding the standard Q-GERT input for a subnetwork with a DEF card and following all the input cards for the subnetwork with an ESN (end of subnetwork) card. All subnetworks have an *identification or ID number* associated with them. For example, suppose the user desired to define the subnetwork shown in Figure 10-1. The Q-GERT input cards shown in Figure 10-2 would be used. The DEF card instructs the Q-GERT Analysis Program to store all succeeding input cards until an ESN card is encountered. Note that the cards between the DEF and ESN cards completely describe the subnetwork of Figure 10-1. The Q-GERT program processes these cards in normal fashion and then makes the subnetwork available for duplication. However, the identification number on the DEF card is attached to all node and activity numbers of the subnetwork.

As an example of the use of a subnetwork specification, consider the network in Figure 10-3. Note the identification number notation for the

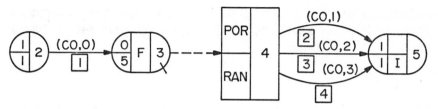

Figure 10-1 A subnetwork.

```
DEF,1*
REG,2,1,1*
QUE,3,0,5,0,(10)4*
SEL,4,POR,RAN,(7)3*
STA,5,1,1,0,I*
ACT,2,3,CO,0.,1*
ACT,4,5,CO,1.,2*
ACT,4,5,CO,2.,3*
ACT,4,5,CO,3.,4*
ESN*
```

Figure 10-2 Data input for defining a subnetwork.

defined subnetwork. In Figure 10-3, the subnetwork consisting of nodes 2, 3, 4 and 5 and activities 1, 2, 3 and 4 is repeated in two other locations in the network.

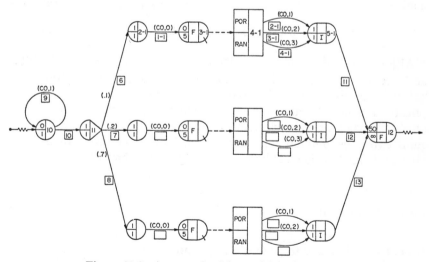

Figure 10-3 An example of the need for subnetworks.

Once the user has defined a subnetwork by enclosing its input description between a DEF and ESN card, duplication can be accomplished by the following card:

DUP,2*

The DUP card instructs the program to duplicate the last defined subnetwork. The second field of the DUP card specifies the ID number to be associated with the nodes and activities of the new, internally generated subnetwork. Specifically, the Q-GERT program defines node and activity numbers in all subnetworks by an N-I identifier where N is the number of the original node or activity appearing in the defined subnetwork and I is the ID number of the subnetwork. The data input for defining the subnetwork and generating duplicate subnetworks with ID numbers of 2 and 3 is shown in Figure 10-4. The node and activity numbers generated by this input are shown in Figure 10-5.

```
DEF,1*              DEFINE CARD TO INDICATE THE START OF A
REG,2,1,1,D*        SUBNETWORK WITH AN ID OF 1
QUE,3,0,5,D,(10)4*
SEL,4,POR,RAN,(7)3*
REG,5,1,1,D,M*
ACT,2,3,CO,0.,1*    STANDARD Q-GERT INPUT TO DEFINE
ACT,4,5,CO,1.,2*    SUBNETWORK
ACT,4,5,CO,2.,3*
ACT,4,5,CO,3.,4*
ESN*                END OF SUBNETWORK DEFINITION
DUP,2*              CREATES A DUPLICATE SUBNETWORK WITH AN ID OF 2
DUP,3*              CREATES A DUPLICATE SUBNETWORK WITH AN ID OF 3
```

Figure 10-4   Data input to define a subnetwork and to generate two duplicates.

Although it is good practice, a DUP card need not immediately follow an ESN card. Other Q-GERT input cards may be processed after a subnetwork definition and prior to duplication, as a DUP card always duplicates the last defined subnetwork. However, only after all required duplications of a particular subnetwork are accomplished may the next subnetwork be defined and duplicated. The subnetwork number on DEF and DUP cards must be unique integers less than 100.

Editing Subnetworks

It is often necessary to generate duplicates of a subnetwork which are not exactly identical to the original one. To meet the need for duplicat-

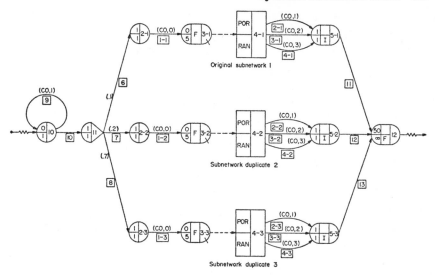

Figure 10-5   Illustration of subnetwork and duplicate subnetwork labeling.

ing similar, but not identical subnetworks, the capability of editing a duplicated subnetwork has been developed. Editing can involve deleting cards from the subnetwork definition, inserting new cards or replacing cards. Each edit instruction requires one card. The card types for editing are: DEL for deletions; INS for insertions; and REP for replacements.

If a subnetwork is to be edited, the user should provide a sequence number for the input cards in the original subnetwork definition. Field 50 is used for this purpose. For the input of the subnetwork defined in Figure 10-2, the sequence number scheme shown in Figure 10-6 is permissible. The cards must be sequenced in ascending order; however, the numbers need not be consecutive. This ordering convention facilitates the editing of subnetworks.

A third field of a DUP card is used to specify whether a duplicate is to be generated through editing. An "E" specifies editing, a blank specifies no editing (no editing is the default value). Thus, to generate a subnetwork with an ID of 2 using editing, the DUP card would be

DUP,2,E*

Edit information must follow this card directly. As an example, suppose the subnetwork defined by the input data of Figure 10-4 is to be duplicated without activity 4. To accomplish this, a DUP card with the

```
DEF,1*
REG,2,1,1,D,(50)10*
QUE,3,0,5,D,(10)4,(50)20*
SEL,4,FOR,RAN,(7)3,(50)30*
STA,5,1,1,D,I,(50)40*
ACT,2,3,CO,0.,1,(50)50*
ACT,4,5,CO,1.,2,(50)60*
ACT,4,5,CO,2.,3,(50)70*
ACT,4,5,CO,3.,4,(50)80*
ESN*
```

Figure 10-6   Data input for defining a subnetwork including sequence numbers.

edit option would be used in conjunction with a DEL card as shown below.

DUP,2,E*
DEL,80*

The second field of a DEL card contains the card number to be deleted. This card causes the network element described by the information on card 80 in the original subnetwork to be deleted for subnetwork-2. Note that card 80 in the original subnetwork definition is for activity 4, and thus, activity 4-2 in Figure 10-5 would be omitted using this edit instruction.

To insert a network element, an INS card is used. The second field of the INS card specifies the card sequence number *after* which the card is to be inserted. The remaining fields on the INS card are the standard Q-GERT fields of the particular card being inserted. For example, to insert another activity from node 2 to node 3 for subnetwork-2, the following input would be used.

INS,50,ACT,2,3,CO,0,5*

This INS card adds activity 5-2 between nodes 2-2 and 3-2.

The replacement of a card is a combination of the delete and insert edit instructions and is accomplished with a REP card. For example, to change the server selection rule of S-node 4 from RAN to POR, the edit input would be:

REP,30,SEL,4,POR,POR,(7)3*

The REP card deletes card 30 and inserts the S-node described by the

REP card. Note that the skip field option references the field number of the network element card (SEL) and not the field on the replace (REP) card.

There is no restriction on the number of edit cards. The last edit card for a particular duplication, however, must be followed by an ESN card. In addition, edit cards must be ordered such that the card numbers to be edited, specified by Field 2, are in ascending order. A final restriction on editing is that edit cards must have all their information on one card, that is, edit cards cannot be continued.

Figure 10-7 combines all of the edits discussed above to produce subnetwork-2. Note that the cards are sequenced by the value in Field 2 as required.

```
DUP,2,E*
REP,30,SEL,4,POR,POR,(7)3*
INS,70,ACT,2,3,CO,0.,5*
DEL,80*
ESN*
```

Figure 10-7   Input cards for duplicating a subnetwork with editing instructions.

It should be pointed out that any activity or node number introduced through editing which is not in the original subnetwork will cause a new activity or node number to be created. Referencing the new activity or node number outside of the duplicated subnetwork is then not possible.

Linking Subnetworks

Subnetworks are connected to nodes outside the subnetwork by activities. To specify these "linking" activities, LIN cards are required. LIN cards are special ACT cards in which the start node and end node numbers are specified by an N/I notation where N is the node number and I is the identification number. If a node is not part of a subnetwork, only the value of N is given; no slash (/) or I value is used. To illustrate the LIN card, the activity between node 11 and node 2-2 in Figure 10-5 is defined below:

LIN,11,2/2,CO,0.,7,(7)0.2*

Start node   End node   Standard ACT data for Fields 4 and higher

Using the LIN card, any node in a subnetwork can be linked to any other node of the network. The complete input for the network presented in Figure 10–5 when editing subnetwork-1 is shown in Figure 10–8.

```
GEN,SIGAL,(7)3,1,1,,,1,(21)12,13*
SOU,10,,1*
REG,11,1,1,P*
SIN,12,50*
ACT,10,110,CO,0.1,9*
ACT,10,11,CO,0.,,10*
DEF,1*
REG,2,1,1,D,(50)10*
QUE,3,0,5,D,(10)4,(50)20*
SEL,4,FOR,RAN,(7)3,(50)30*
STA,5,1,1,D,I,(50)40*
ACT,2,3,CO,0.,,1,(50)50*
ACT,4,5,CO,1.,,2,(50)60*
ACT,4,5,CO,2.,,3,(50)70*
ACT,4,5,CO,3.,,4,(50)80*
ESN*
DUP,2,E*
REP,30,SEL,4,POR,POR,(7)3*
INS,70,ACT,2,3,CO,0.,,5*
DEL,80*
ESN*
DUP,3*
LIN,11,2/1,CO,0.,,5,,,1*
LIN,11,2/2,CO,0.,,7,,,2*
LIN,11,2/3,CO,0.,,8,,,7*
LIN,5/1,12,,,,11*
LIN,5/2,12,,,,12*
LIN,5/3,12,CO,0.,,13*
FIN*
```

Figure 10-8   Data input for network of Figure 10-5 with editing.

Data Inputs for Processing Subnetworks

To process subnetworks, the user must specify the largest node number and largest activity number that he has included in the Q-GERT network. This information is specified on the GEN card in Fields 21 and 22.

As discussed in the previous sections, new card types are available for defining, duplicating, editing, and linking subnetworks. A short form for defining data input cards for user collected statistics and subnetwork definition and editing is shown in Figure 10-9. Complete information on each field for these new card types is given in Appendix 1.

Fields*

1	2	3	4	5
DEF	Subnetwork ID			
DUP	Subnetwork ID	Edit Option (E or blank)		
ESN				
LIN	Start Node Number/ Subnetwork ID	End Node Number/ Subnetwork ID	(Same as ACT Fields 4 to 11)	
REP	Card Number	(Fields 1-50 of a REG, SOU, SEL, QUE, STA, SIN, VAS, MOD or ACT card)		
INS	Card Number	(Fields 1-50 of a REG, SOU, SEL, QUE, STA, SIN, VAS, MOD or ACT card)		
DEL	Card Number			
COL	Numeric Code/Label	(Repeats of Field 2)		
TIM	Numeric Code/Label	Initial Value	(Repeats of Fields 2 and 3)	
HIS	Numeric Code/Label	Number of Cells [10]	Upper Limit of 1st Cell [0.0]	Width of Histogram Cell [1.0]

* Default values are given in brackets [ ]. If no default value is indicated, data for the field is required. Options for a field are given in parentheses ( ). A slash (/) indicates the field may contain two entries where the slash and second entry are optional.

Figure 10-9 Input short form for data describing user-collected statistics, and subnetwork definitions.

Output Reporting for Subnetworks

Whenever a node in a subnetwork is referenced in an output report, the subnetwork or N-I notation is employed. Portions of the echo check, trace and summary reports from the Q-GERT Analysis Program will be given in the next section where an example of the use of subnetworks is provided.

User Access to Node and Activity Numbers

Within the Q-GERT Analysis Program, node and activity numbers for duplicates of subnetworks are assigned. These numbers are greater than any number employed by the user. When writing user functions, it may be necessary for the user to obtain these internally used node and activity numbers. Two Q-GERT functions are available for this purpose.

Function NODCV(N,I) is a *node* number *conversion* subprogram that returns the internally used node number corresponding to node N-I. Function NATCV(N,I) is an *activity* number *conversion* subprogram that returns the internally used activity number corresponding to activity N-I. The subprograms that require the internally used numbers are referenced in the footnote to Table 7-4.

In the next section, an example is given to illustrate the use of subnetworks. Due to space limitations, the example had to be kept small and, hence, does not show the power of subnetworks in creating large networks nor in modeling using a modular higher level approach. In one situation, a network with over 900 nodes was created using this subnetwork approach (5).

EXAMPLE 15.   USING SUBNETWORKS TO ANALYZE SPACE EXPERIMENTS*

Problem Statement

The performance of experiments in space by a spacecraft crew are almost always severely constrained by time. Generally, many experiments are proposed by the scientific community. Of those proposed, a subset must be chosen for a given space mission. The sequencing of these experiments can be an important factor in determining the number of experiments that can be completed.

A Q-GERT network of the sequence of experiments will be developed that permits the assessment of the time required to perform the experiments. In addition, information regarding the successful completion of

---

* An earlier version of this example was developed by Dr. J. Ignizio in a course on GERT held at Virginia Polytechnic Institute and State University (107, 142).

experiments will be determined. By modifying the sequence of experiments (which involves modifying the Q-GERT network), an analysis can be performed on proposals for different sequencing procedures.

It will be assumed that there are three possible outcomes from the performance of an experiment: 1) successful completion; 2) failure; and 3) inconclusive results. If an experiment is successfully completed the next experiment in the sequence is performed. If a failure occurs, the experiment is scrubbed and the next experiment is then performed. If the results of an experiment are inconclusive, the experiment is repeated a prescribed number of times or until a success or failure occurs.

A schematic diagram of a sequence of three space experiments is shown in Figure 10-10. In this schematic diagram, node 2 is the source node and node 8 is the sink node. Each experiment is represented by a black box with the possible outcomes of an experiment being inconclusive results, success and failure. For this example, a Q-GERT subnetwork will be developed for one experiment which will serve as a basis for defining the other experiments. This example will be used to further illustrate the preparation of data for the Q-GERT Analysis Program when subnetworks are involved. Also, the outputs for subnetworks and a model trace will be illustrated.

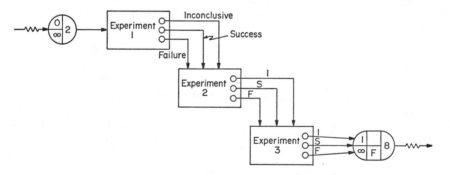

Figure 10-10 Schematic diagram of a sequence of space experiments, Example 15.

The characteristics for each experiment are given in Table 10-1.
From Table 10-1, it is seen that the time to perform an experiment is normally distributed, but for each experiment there are different parameter values. Also, the probabilities of success, failure and inconclusive results are different for each experiment. In the design to be evaluated, experiments 1 and 2 can be repeated twice and experiment 3 can be repeated once. An experiment is repeated only if inconclusive results are obtained.

Table 10-1.   Experiment Characteristics.

Experiment Number	Probability of Success	Probability of Failure	Probability of Inconclusive Results	Allowable Number of Repeats
1	0.6	0.1	0.3	2
2	0.5	0.1	0.4	2
3	0.7	0.1	0.2	1

Experiment Number	Distribution Type	Mean Time	Minimum Time	Maximum Time	Standard Deviation
1	Normal, NO	10.0	5.0	20.0	2.0
2	Normal, NO	20.0	15.0	25.0	1.0
3	Normal, NO	15.0	10.0	30.0	3.0

Q-GERT Model

A Q-GERT subnetwork defining one experiment is given in Figure 10-11. The defined subnetwork will be used to model experiment 1 and duplicates of this subnetwork will be used to model experiments 2 and 3. Node 3-1 is the starting point for the experiment and activity 1-1, the branch from node 3-1 to node 4-1, represents the time required to perform the activity that models the experiment. The time description for the activity is specified as normally distributed with parameter values in parameter set IET. Since the parameter set values change from experiment to experiment, the value of IET will have to be changed in the duplicates of the subnetwork. Throughout this discussion, variable names are given to those elements of the network that will have to be altered when the subnetwork is duplicated. This legend is given below.

Legend:
   IET = Parameter set number for experiment time
   P_I = Probability of inconclusive results
   P_S = Probability of successful experiment
   P_F = Probability of failed experiment
   NRE = Number of times experiment can be repeated

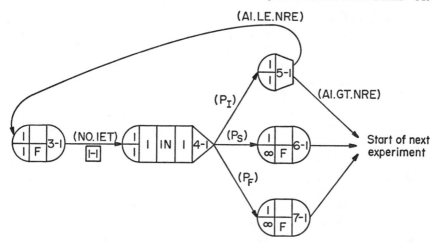

Figure 10-11 Q-GERT network defining the subnetwork for one experiment, Example 15.

Following the completion of the experiment as represented by node 4-1, attribute 1 is set equal to 1 to indicate that the next time the experiment is performed it will be repeat number 1 of the experiment. Branching from node 4-1 is done probabilistically and models the three possible outcomes from the experiment: 1) inconclusive results as represented by the branch from node 4-1 to node 5-1 with probability P_I associated with it; 2) successful results as modeled by the branch from node 4-1 to node 6-1 with probability P_S associated with it; and 3) a failed experiment as modeled by the branch from node 4-1 to node 7-1 with probability P_F associated with it. At node 5-1 the experiment is to be repeated, but only NRE repeats are allowed. Conditional-take first branching is performed at node 5-1 and the branch from node 5-1 back to node 3-1 is taken if attribute 1 is less than or equal to the number of times the experiment can be repeated.

The first time node 5-1 is reached, attribute 1 is equal to 1 and the experiment is repeated. When node 5-1 is released a second time, attribute 1 will be equal to 2 and the branch from node 5-1 to node 3-1 again will be taken. The third time node 5-1 is released, attribute 1 will be equal to 3 and the condition on the branch from node 5-1 to node 3-1 will not be satisfied. At this time, the condition on the branch from node 5-1 to the start of the next experiment (A1.GT.NRE) will be satisfied since attribute 1 will now be greater than the 2 which is the allowed number of repeats permitted for experiment number 1.

When the experiment is successfully completed, the branch from node 4-1 to node 6-1 is taken. Statistics on the time required to success-fully complete the experiment are collected at node 6-1 and branching then occurs to the start of the next experiment. When node 7-1 is re-leased, the experiment has failed. Statistics are collected on the time as-sociated with a failed experiment and branching to the start of the next experiment occurs. Note that a node has not been provided to model the starting point of the next experiment. Node 3-I will be used as the start-ing point for experiment I. Thus, the branches leading to the start of the next experiment are not really part of the subnetwork but will be de-fined on link (LIN) cards. This example was modeled in this fashion to illustrate the linking of nodes within different subnetworks. The inclu-sion of another node in the subnetwork to represent the end of an exper-iment would be an alternate and equivalent representation.

The data input that couples the three experiments and links them to the source and sink nodes illustrated in Figure 10-10 is provided in Fig-ure 10-12. On the GEN card, the largest user-given node number, 8, and activity number, 1, are placed in Fields 21 and 22. The next five cards are in standard form. The subnetwork defining experiment 1 is defined in the next set of cards between the DEF and ESN cards. In Field 50, sequence numbers are provided to allow the subnetwork to be edited. Specific values have been inserted for the variables that were included in Figure 10-11. Thus, on the card with sequence number 70, the param-eter set number is specified as 1. On cards sequenced as 80, 90 and 100, the appropriate probabilities have been inserted in Field 8. Further, on the card sequenced as 110 the number of repeats for experiment 1 is specified as 2 in Field 9.

The subnetwork with ID=2 represents experiment 2. Cards se-quenced as 70, 80 and 90 are replaced. Card number 70 is replaced in order to specify parameter set number 2 to represent the parameter values for the time to perform experiment 2. Cards 80 and 90 are re-placed to change the probabilities associated with the corresponding ac-tivities. This completes the changes required for this duplicate subnet-work, and this is indicated by an ESN card.

The changes to create a subnetwork with ID equal to 3 are given next. The first three changes are replacements similar to those given for du-plicate 2. For experiment 3, the number of repeats of the experiment is limited to one, and this new information is contained on the card se-quenced as 110. Note that the field numbers on edit cards refer to the fields prescribed for the standard Q-GERT input cards and do not in-clude the editing card type and card sequence number in the field count. The end of edits for subnetwork-3 is indicated by an ESN card.

The linkages between the source node, the nodes of the subnetworks, and the sink node are given next on the data input. First, an activity

```
GEN,PRITSKER,SPACE-EXP-15,9,13,1977,9,1,1,,1000,,,1,(17)1,2,(21)8,1*
SOU,2*                                    SOURCE NODE OF NETWORK
SIN,8/ENDEXPTS,(7)36.,5.*                 SINK NODE OF NETWORK
PAR,1,10.,5.,20.,2.*                      PARAMETER VALUES FOR EXPERIMENT 1
PAR,2,20.,15.,25.,1.*                     PARAMETER VALUES FOR EXPERIMENT 2
PAR,3,15.,10.,30.,3.*                     PARAMETER VALUES FOR EXPERIMENT 3
DEF,1*                                    START OF MACRO DEFINITION
STA,3/STARTEXP,1,1,0,F,10.,,4.,(50)10*    START NODE FOR EXPERIMENT 1
REG,4,1,1,P,(50)20*                       END NODE FOR EXPERIMENT 1
VAS,4,1,IN,1,(50)30*                      ASSIGN NUMBER OF REPEATS TO ATTRIBUTE 1
REG,5,1,1,F,(50)40*                       DECISION NODE FOR REPEATING EXPERIMENT
STA,6/SUCCESS,(7)10.,,4.,(50)50*          COLLECT STATISTICS ON SUCCESS PROBABILITY AND TIME
STA,7/FAILURE,(7)10.,,4.,(50)60*          COLLECT STATISTICS ON FAILURE PROBABILITY AND TIME
ACT,3,4,NO,1,1,(50)70*                    ACTIVITY REPRESENTING EXPERIMENT
ACT,4,5,(8)0.3,(50)80*                    BRANCH REPRESENTING INCONCLUSIVE RESULTS
ACT,4,6,(8)0.6,(50)90*                    BRANCH REPRESENTING SUCCESS
ACT,4,7,(8)0.1,(50)100*                   BRANCH REPRESENTING FAILURE
ACT,5,3,(9)A1.LE.2,(50)110*               BRANCH TO REPEAT EXPERIMENT
ESN*                                      END OF MACRO DEFINITION
DUP,2,E*                                  START OF DUPLICATE 1 OF MACRO WITH EDITING
REP,70,ACT,3,4,NO,2,1*                    REPLACE PARAMETER SET NUMBER
REP,80,ACT,4,5,(8).4*                     REPLACE REPEAT PROBABILITY
REP,90,ACT,4,6,(8).5*                     REPLACE SUCCESS PROBABILITY
ESN*                                      END OF DUPLICATE 1
DUP,3,E*                                  DUPLICATE 2 OF MACRO WITH EDITING
REP,70,ACT,3,4,NO,3,1*                    REPLACE PARAMETER SET NUMBER
REP,80,ACT,4,5,(8).2*                     REPLACE REPEAT PROBABILITY
REP,90,ACT,4,6,(8).7*                     REPLACE SUCCESS PROBABILITY
REP,110,ACT,5,3,(9)A1.LE.1*               REPLACE NUMBER OF REPEATS PERMITTED
ESN*                                      END OF DUPLICATE 2
LIN,2,3/1*                                ACTIVITY TO START FIRST EXPERIMENT
LIN,5/1,3/2,(9)A1.GT.2*                    LINK EXPERIMENT 1 TO EXPERIMENT 2
LIN,6/1,3/2*
LIN,7/1,3/2*
LIN,5/2,3/3,(9)A1.GT.2*                    LINK EXPERIMENT 2 TO EXPERIMENT 3
LIN,6/2,3/3*
LIN,7/2,3/3*
LIN,5/3,8,(9)A1.GT.1*                      LINK EXPERIMENT 3 TO SINK NODE 8
LIN,6/3,8*
LIN,7/3,8*
TRA,4/1,5/1*
FIN*
```

Figure 10-12 Data input for space experiments modeled using subnetworks, Example 15.

from source node 2 to node 3-1 is prescribed. Specifying a branch to a node in a subnetwork is done using a LIN card. As previously mentioned, the activities from nodes 5-1, 6-1 and 7-1 were not included as part of the subnetwork definition. Thus, LIN cards must be used to describe the branches from these nodes to the start node of experiment 2. The start node of experiment 2 is node 3-2. On the LIN card, following the definition of the card type, one field is used to specify the start node (5/1) and one field for the end node (3/2). The normal information for an ACT card is then given. Examples of other LIN cards are shown in Figure 10-12. The end of data is indicated by FIN card. The complete Q-GERT network corresponding to the data input presented in Figure 10-12 is presented in Figure 10-13.

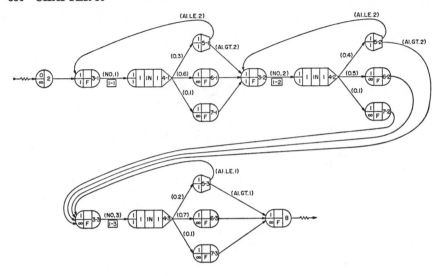

Figure 10-13   Q-GERT network of three experiments, Example 15.

Summary of Results

One thousand runs of the sequence of three space experiments were performed using the Q-GERT Analysis Program. The types of information of interest concern the success and failure probabilities associated with the performance of each experiment and the length of time required until each experiment is completed. With such information, a designer of the experimental procedure would have information for reevaluating the time allocation to each experiment and the sequencing of three experiments. Of importance for this type of problem, is that the Q-GERT model presents a vehicle by which more elaborate experimental designs can be assessed. More elaborate designs would include dependencies between experiments both with regard to time to perform the experiment and the probability of successful completion of the experiment. (See Exercises 10-5 and 10-6)

The summary report for Example 15 is shown in Figure 10-14. The average time to perform all three experiments was 63.04 time units based on 1000 simulated experiments. From the output, it is seen that there was considerable variability in the time to perform all three experiments, as the minimum time was 35.12 and the maximum was 124.90. This resulted in a standard deviation of over 18 time units.

GERT SIMULATION PROJECT SPACE-EXP-15 BY PRITSKER
DATE 9/ 13/ 1977

FINAL RESULTS FOR 1000 SIMULATIONS

AVERAGE NODE STATISTICS

NODE	LABEL	PROBABILITY	AVE.	STD.DEV.	SD OF AVE	NO OF OBS.	MIN.	MAX.	STAT TYPE
8	ENDEXPTS	1.0000	63.0409	18.0523	.5709	1000.	35.1205	124.8998	F
7-3	FAILURE	.1290	63.3476	19.7889	1.7423	129.	37.0888	111.6574	F
6-3	SUCCESS	.8250	62.3810	17.6163	.6133	825.	35.1205	123.8080	F
3-3	STARTEXP	1.0000	44.7750	16.6415	.5263	1000.	23.5570	98.3296	F
7-2	FAILURE	.1620	41.6517	14.6757	1.1530	162.	23.5570	91.3396	F
6-2	SUCCESS	.7740	43.0257	15.2519	.5482	774.	23.7146	98.3296	F
3-2	STARTEXP	1.0000	13.6856	6.8531	.2167	1000.	5.0000	37.9490	F
7-1	FAILURE	.1380	13.0074	5.8023	.4939	138.	6.1592	34.7080	F
6-1	SUCCESS	.8350	13.2701	6.4329	.2226	835.	5.0000	37.9490	F
3-1	STARTEXP	1.0000	0	0	0	1000.	0	0	F

Figure 10-14 Q-GERT summary report for space experiment analysis, Example 15.

351

The histogram describing the time to complete all three experiments is shown in Figure 10-15 and can be used to estimate the probability of completing all three experiments by a specific time. For example, an estimate of the probability of completing all three experiments by time 71 is 0.703. Thus, if 71 time units are allocated to the performance of the three experiments, in 70.3 percent of the cases, all three experiments would be completed. In 29.7 percent of the cases, sufficient time would not be available for completing all three experiments. The many peaks included in the histogram for node 8 are due to the recycling and repeating of experiments which induces a cyclic type behavior in the histogram.

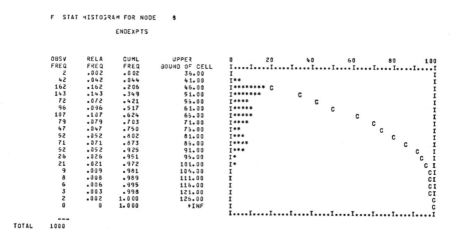

Figure 10-15   Histogram of time to complete three experiments, Example 15.

The discussion given above for the time to complete all three experiments does not relate to the outcome of each experiment. Such information is available on Figure 10-14 under the probability heading. For experiment 3, the estimate of the probability of the experiment failing is 0.129 as seen by the probability of releasing node 7-3. The probability of successfully completing experiment 3 is 0.825. By subtracting the sum of these two quantities from 1, an estimate of 0.046 is obtained as the probability of having inconclusive results on experiment 3. This probability could be decreased by increasing the number of times experiment 3 can be repeated. The success and failure probabilities associated with other experiments are shown in Figure 10-14.

Other information obtained from the Q-GERT Analysis Program involves the times to complete an experiment conditioned on the results of the experiment. Thus, the results for node 6-1 provide estimates of the time to complete experiment 1 when it was completed successfully. From Figure 10-14, this value is given as 13.27 time units. The histogram for node 6-1, shown in Figure 10-16, provides detailed information regarding the successful completion times for experiment 1. From the histogram, it is seen that experiment 1 is completed successfully within 22 time units, 89.2 percent of the time.

```
        F  STAT HISTOGRAM FOR NODE    6-1

                      SUCCESS


        OBSV     RELA     CUML     UPPER        0       20      40      60      80     100
        FREQ     FREQ     FREQ    BOUND OF CELL  I....I....I....I....I....I....I....I....I....I....I
        311     .372     .372       13.00       I******************                                I
        285     .341     .714       14.00       I******************              C                  I
         60     .072     .786       18.00       I****                                   C           I
         89     .107     .892       22.00       I*****                                       C      I
         39     .047     .939       26.00       I**                                            C    I
         17     .020     .959       30.00       I*                                              C   I
         28     .034     .993       34.00       I**                                             CI
          6     .007    1.000       38.00       I                                                 C
          0       0     1.000       42.00       I                                                 C
          0       0     1.000       46.00       I                                                 C
          0       0     1.000       50.00       I                                                 C
          0       0     1.000       54.00       I                                                 C
          0       0     1.000       58.00       I                                                 C
          0       0     1.000       62.00       I                                                 C
          0       0     1.000       65.00       I                                                 C
          0       0     1.000       70.00       I                                                 C
          0       0     1.000       74.00       I                                                 C
          0       0     1.000       78.00       I                                                 C
          0       0     1.000       82.00       I                                                 C
          0       0     1.000       +INF        I                                                 C
                                                I....I....I....I....I....I....I....I....I....I....I
        ---
TOTAL   835
```

Figure 10-16   Histogram of time to successfully complete experiment 1, Example 15.

The Q-GERT Analyst, after assessing the results obtained from the Q-GERT Analysis Program, can decide to: modify the parameters of the network to assess experimental design changes; explore possible ways of changing the design by resequencing experiments; and redeveloping the network to include more contingencies between experiments.

EXERCISES

10-1.   Redo the input for Example 15 to obtain a trace of the first 10 runs and a nodal trace of nodes 4-1, 5-2 and 6-3 on runs 6 and 7.

10-2.   Prepare the data input using subnetwork concepts for a system consisting of ten single server queueing subsystems in series. Assume, at first, that all subsystems are identical. Next, assume the queue capacity of the fourth subsystem is limited to three units. Next, assume that the sixth subsystem has a queue capacity of four and blocks the previous server.

10-3. Using subnetworks, model and prepare the data input for Example 4, Chapter 4, which deals with a conveyor system having five servers in parallel. Repeat this exercise for the situation in which 25 servers are positioned along the conveyor belt.

10-4. Model a large system for which many subsystems exist having similar structure using the subnetwork concepts of Q-GERT.

10-5. For the space experiment example, develop the Q-GERT model to make the number of times an experiment can be performed a function of the time remaining in a mission. Develop a model to select the next experiment to perform if the experiments do not have to be performed in a specified order.

10-6. For Example 15, develop a procedure for allocating time to perform an experiment and base the number of repeats allowed on this time. Develop the Q-GERT model for your procedure.

Chapter 11

RESOURCES IN Q-GERT

Throughout this book, we have modeled the flow of transactions through nodes and branches with the flow of a transaction halted when it arrived to a busy server or when it waited for the arrival of other transactions. In some situations, it may be convenient to halt the flow of a transaction until a specific resource type becomes available to be allocated to the transaction. Examples of resource types are: workspaces; technicians; and money. In this chapter, we present the concept of resources and how they can be allocated to transactions.

Resources are a complex subject. From the examples cited above, we see that resources such as workspaces and technicians are similar to service activities. However, resources have a characteristic that we normally associate with transactions. This characteristic is that a resource is allowed to be allocated at various nodes in the network, that is, a resource can be allocated to a transaction waiting in Q-node 10 and at some later time, it can be allocated to a transaction waiting in Q-node 15. Thus, conceptually a resource flows through the network. Once a resource is allocated to a transaction, it cannot be reallocated until the resource is no longer being used, that is, it is freed. When a resource is freed, an interrogation procedure is initiated to determine the next transaction to which the resource should be allocated. Due to the complex nature of resource flow, allocation and release, it is not practical to depict graphically their movement on the Q-GERT network.

More formally, a resource is defined as an entity which is required by a transaction before the transaction can proceed through the network.

Resource types are defined by the Q-GERT modeler to differentiate among different entities that may be required by a transaction. For each resource type, there is an available number of units, that is, a capacity. For example, technicians can be defined as resource type 2 and we can declare that 10 technicians are available for allocation to job transactions.

Given that resource units exist, we need a way of modeling the allocation of them to transactions. Q-GERT provides the ALLOCATE node type to achieve this task. Of course, transactions may wait for a specified number of units of a resource type. In accordance with past modeling conventions, transactions wait if necessary in Q-nodes. Thus, preceding an ALLOCATE node are one or more Q-nodes. When resource units become available, a selection of a transaction is made that requires the units. The selected transaction is routed from the Q-node through the ALLOCATE node to a user-designated node prescribed on the network model. The ALLOCATE node operates partly like an S-node in that it selects a transaction from a set of possible Q-nodes. It also operates like a MATCH node in that it matches resource units with transactions and routes a transaction from a Q-node to a prescribed node of the network. When a transaction arrives to a Q-node that precedes an ALLOCATE node and the required resource units are available, the transaction proceeds immediately to the prescribed node that follows the ALLOCATE node.

When a transaction is allocated resource units, they are taken out of an available resource pool and are not available for reallocation until they are freed. To accomplish this freeing, requires another node type which we have named the FREE node. A transaction arriving to a FREE node releases the node. Associated with the FREE node is a prescribed number of units of a specified resource type to be freed. Note that any transaction that is routed to a FREE node causes resource units to be freed. The resource units freed are then available for reallocation to transactions at ALLOCATE nodes. As will be seen, we will need to specify a sequencing procedure at FREE nodes that specifies the order in which ALLOCATE nodes are to be polled when attempting to reallocate the freed resource units.

ILLUSTRATION OF RESOURCE MODELING

To illustrate the use of resources when modeling using Q-GERT, consider the one server, single queue model. Let the server be modeled as resource type 1 of which there is only one unit available. To build the Q-GERT network, we replace the service activity with a sequence of nodes and branches to model the allocate, activity time, and resource freeing functions. This is shown below.

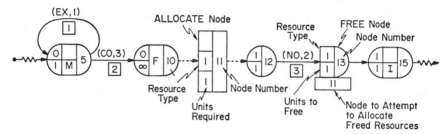

At ALLOCATE node 11, the one unit of the resource type 1 is allocated to a waiting transaction and routed to node 12. Activity 3 represents the time the resource is used by the transaction. At FREE node 13, one unit of the resource is freed which is allocated at node 11 to the first waiting transaction (as specified by the node number placed below node 13).

Clearly, this model of the one server, single queue system is more complex (3 extra nodes) than the model that employed a service activity. However, this model is easily expanded to include a set of branches to model the time the resource is held by the transaction. For example, the same server resource could be required to perform two consecutive operations as shown below.

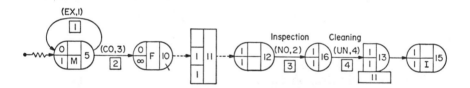

In this network, both the inspection and cleaning operations must be completed before another inspection operation can be started. This illustration demonstrates the difference between a resource and a server. Service activities are a special type of resource in which the resource stays fixed and is only allocated to a transaction during the period in which the service activity is being performed. A resource can be viewed as a floating server which is in use from the time it is allocated until it is freed. Freed resources then float through the network in an order prescribed by the sequence of ALLOCATE nodes to be polled. Q-GERT automatically computes statistics on resource utilization and resource availability which are then printed as part of the standard Q-GERT summary report.

To further preview the new node types associated with resources, we illustrate how we can make resource units unavailable. We do this, by changing the capacity, that is, the number of units of the resource available. This capacity change is accomplished at an ALTER node. For example, the server resource could be removed from operation to model the taking of breaks by altering the capacity of resource type 1. The following disjoint network shows the time of a first break to occur as soon as possible after time 3, the length of a break is 0.25 hours, and that breaks are to be taken every two hours.

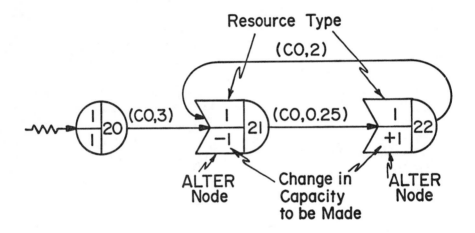

The above illustration has introduced the three node types of Q-GERT used for modeling systems employing resources. We will now define more fully the concepts of RESOURCES and ALLOCATE, FREE, and ALTER nodes.

DEFINING RESOURCE TYPES

Resource types are defined through the use of an RES data input card. No node type is used for defining resource types as transactions do not flow through resource definitions. We use a RESOURCE block on the network in the same fashion as we would use a legend on a figure. The RES card is used to provide general information regarding a resource. A separatê RES card is required to define each resource type. The field descriptions for the RES card are listed below.

Field	Description	Default Value
1	Card type, RES	None
2	Resource number/Label	None/Blanks
3	Resource capacity or number of units available	1
4–13	ALLOCATE nodes associated with resource*	No associated ALLOCATE node

*This list of ALLOCATE nodes specifies the order in which the ALLOCATE nodes are to be polled when resource units become available.

As is standard in Q-GERT, the first field provides the card type designator (RES for resources). The second field provides a numeric code to be used when referencing the resource type and a label to be used on output reports. In the third field, the user prescribes the number of units of this resource type that are to be available at the beginning of a run, that is, the initial resource capacity. In Fields 4 to 13, a list of ALLOCATE nodes is provided. The order of the ALLOCATE nodes given in Fields 4 to 13 prescribes the sequence in which the ALLOCATE nodes will be polled when resource units are freed or when a positive capacity change is made at an ALTER node.

The RES card must precede data cards that define ALLOCATE, FREE, and ALTER nodes that reference the resource type.

ALLOCATE NODES

An ALLOCATE node is used to allocate resources to transactions that arrive to or are waiting in Q-nodes that precede the ALLOCATE node. Resources are allocated when resources become available due to a transaction passing through a FREE or ALTER node. The symbol for the ALLOCATE node is shown below.

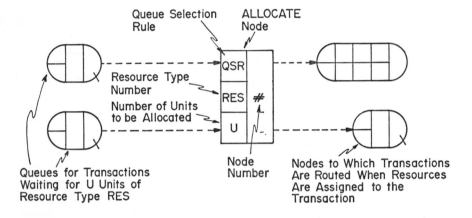

The ALLOCATE node resembles the S-node in shape and in the fact that transactions wait in Q-nodes that precede it. However, it differs from it graphically in two respects:

1) three spaces are available for information on the input side of the ALLOCATE node; and
2) dashed lines are used on both the input and output sides of the ALLOCATE node in the same fashion as the MATCH node.

An important observation is that Q-nodes preceding ALLOCATE nodes must reference ALLOCATE nodes in Field 10 and beyond in the same manner as S-nodes and MATCH nodes are referenced by preceding Q-nodes. On the input side of the ALLOCATE node, the following information is prescribed:

1) the queue selection rule (QSR) which can be any of those prescribed for an S-node except the ASM rule;
2) the resource number, RES, of the resource type to be allocated; and
3) the number of units, U, of RES to be allocated to each transaction at the ALLOCATE node.

When sufficient units of a resource can be allocated and a transaction has been selected from one of the preceding Q-nodes, the transaction is removed from the Q-node and routed to a specific node associated with that Q-node that is on the output side of the ALLOCATE node and connected to it by the dashed line. When resources are allocated at the AL-LOCATE node, they are made unavailable. Value assignments can be made at ALLOCATE nodes so that the resource type and number of units allocated can be stored as attributes of a transaction passing through the ALLOCATE node.

The field descriptions for the ALLOCATE data input card are listed below.

Field	Description	Default Value
1	Card type, ALL	None
2	ALLOCATE node number	None
3	Queue Selection Rule (See Table 5-2)	POR
4	Resource type number	1
5	Resource units to be allocated	1
6	Input Q-node number/Node number to which transaction from input Q-node is to be sent	None/No routing
7-16	Repeats of Field 6	None

As an illustration of the ALLOCATE node and its associated input card, consider node 20 shown below.

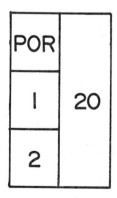

ALLOCATE , 20 , POR , I , 2, 7/27 , 8/28 ✱

Node 20 allocates 2 units of resource type 1 to transactions waiting in Q-node 7 or Q-node 8. It selects transactions from Q-node 7 first and routes these transactions to node 27. If no transactions are in Q-node 7, then available resource units are allocated to transactions waiting in Q-node 8. When either fewer than 2 units of resource 1 are available or no transactions are in Q-nodes 7 or 8, ALLOCATE node 20 has completed its function. A transaction, arriving to Q-node 7 or 8 when two units of resource 1 are available, is routed immediately.

FREE NODES

The FREE node allows transactions to make resources available. At the FREE node, the resource type and the units of the resource to be freed are prescribed. Both of these quantities can be integer or attribute numbers. Thus, the resource number and the number of units to be freed can be carried as attributes of the transaction arriving to the FREE node. Branching from a FREE node can be DETERMINISTIC, PROBABILISTIC, or CONDITIONAL. The FREE node can have associated with it, a list of ALLOCATE nodes where the resources freed are to be reallocated. The symbol for the FREE node is shown below.

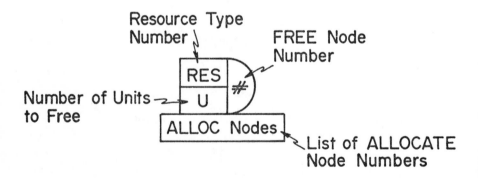

The field descriptions for the FREE input card are listed below.

Field	Description	Default Value
1	Card type, FRE	None
2	FREE node number	None
3	Branching type	Deterministic
4	Resource number: Integer or attribute number specified as Ak	1
5	Resource Units to be freed: Integer or attribute number specified as Ak	1
6–15	List of ALLOCATE nodes in the order they are to be polled to reallocate freed units*	None

*If the general list of ALLOCATE nodes as specified on the RES card is not to be checked, the last specified field should contain a negative value.

In the description of the data for Fields 4 and 5, note that an integer or attribute number can be prescribed. If an attribute number is desired then the letter A is given before the attribute number. In Fields 6–15, the ALLOCATE nodes are prescribed in the order they are to be polled. Added to this list will be any ALLOCATE nodes given in the general RES card for the resource type defined by Field 4. If it is desired not to concantenate the general list of ALLOCATE nodes then a negative value (for example, -1,) should be prescribed at the end of the ALLO-CATE node list.

As an illustration of the free node, consider the situation in which 10 units of resource type 3 are to be freed when a transaction arrives to FREE node 21. The 10 freed units are to be assigned to transactions waiting in Q-nodes before ALLOCATE nodes 16, 17, and 18. No other

ALLOCATE nodes should be considered. FREE node 21 is shown below along with its associated data input.

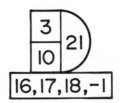

FREE, 21, D, 3, 10, 16, 17, 18, −1✱

Every transaction arriving to node 21 will free 10 units of resource type 3 for reallocation at nodes 16, 17, and 18. *Note that transactions routed to node 21 are not required to have had resources allocated to them.*

As an illustration of the use of freeing resource units based on an attribute of a transaction, consider the FREE node shown below. This node specifies that the number of units of resource 4 to be freed is given by the value in attribute 2 (A2) of the transaction arriving to node 22. Probabilistic branching is used to route the arriving transaction. Freed resources are to be allocated at ALLOCATE nodes 30 and 31. If all freed resources are not allocated, the node list given on the resource card is to be polled.

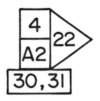

FREE, 22, P, 4, A2, 30, 31✱

ALTER NODES

The ALTER node is placed in the network at locations where it is desired for transactions to cause a change (positive or negative) in the capacity of a resource type. Each transaction that arrives to the ALTER node causes the same alteration in the resource capacity. At the ALTER node, the resource number and the change requested are prescribed as integers. Branching from an ALTER node can be DETERMINISTIC, PROBABILISITIC, or CONDITIONAL. The ALTER node has associated with it a list of ALLOCATE nodes where increases in the resource units due to a positive capacity change are to be allocated.

When the capacity of a resource type is increased, a polling of ALLO-CATE nodes is started to determine if transactions waiting at Q-nodes preceding the ALLOCATE node can use the newly available units of resource. When a capacity decrease is requested, it is satisfied immediately if a sufficient number of units are available. If this is not the case, the portion of the requested decrease not satisfied is queued. As resource units are freed at FREE nodes, any queued capacity decrease is satisfied prior to the reallocation of the freed resource units.

The symbol for the ALTER node is shown below.

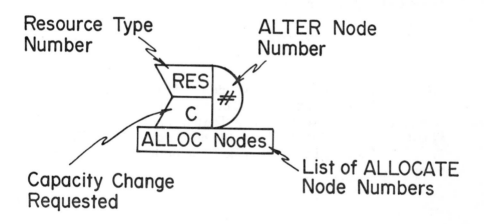

The field descriptions for the ALTER data input card are listed below.

Field	Description	Default Value
1	Card type, ALT	None
2	ALTER node number	None
3	Branching type	Deterministic
4	Resource number	1
5	Capacity change requested: A positive value indicates a capacity increase; A negative value indicates a capacity decrease.	1
6–15	List of ALLOCATE nodes in the order they are to be polled to allocate units available due to a capacity increase.*	None

*If the general list of ALLOCATE nodes as specified on the RES card is not to be checked, the last specified field should contain a negative value.

As an illustration of the ALTER node, consider the situation in which an increase of 5 units in the capacity of resource type 2 is to occur whenever a transaction arrives to node 23. The newly available units are to be allocated only at ALLOCATE nodes 18 or 17 with node 18 polled first. The ALTER node and associated data input for this situation are shown below.

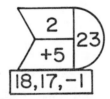

ALTER, 23, D, 2, +5, 18, 17, -1 ✳

Every transaction arriving to node 23 increases the capacity of resource 2 by 5 units. These units are allocated immediately if needed by transactions waiting in Q-nodes preceding either ALLOCATE node 18 or 17. The arriving transaction is routed deterministically from node 23.

If a decrease of 2 units is to be made in the capacity of resource 3 at node 24, it is represented by the ALTER node shown below.

ALTER,24,D,3,−2✳

If 6 units of resource 3 are available when a transaction arrives to node 24, the capacity of resource 3 is reduced by 2 units and the number of units available is changed to 4. If only 1 unit is available, the capacity is reduced by 1 and the number of units available is set to 0. When units of resource 3 are freed, 1 unit is used to satisfy the requested capacity change.

SHORT FORM FOR RESOURCE DATA INPUT

In Table 11-1, a short form is presented for the data input cards associated with resources. Complete descriptions of the data input card fields are given in Appendix 1.

Table 11-1.   Resource Input Short Form

1	2	3	4	5	6	7–49
RES	Resource number/ ---------------- Label	Resource units available [1]	Associated ALLOC nodes	(Repeats of Field 4)		
ALLOC	Node number	Queue selector rule [POR]	Resource number [1]	Resource units required by wait- ing trans- actions [1]	Q-node/ -------------- Routing node [trans- action de- stroyed]	(Repeats of Field 6)
FREE	Node number	Branching (D,P,F,A) [D]	Resource number (i,Ai) [1]	Resource units to be freed (i,Ai) [1]	Associ- ated ALLOC nodes*	(Repeats of Field 6)
ALTER	Node number	Branching (D,P,F,A) [D]	Resource number (i,Ai) [1]	Resource capacity change (i,Ai) [1]	Associ- ated ALLOC nodes*	(Repeats of Field 6)

*If last field is negative, do not concatenate general list of ALLOCATE nodes from RES definition card.

FUNCTIONS FOR ACCESSING RESOURCE INFORMATION

Five functions are included in the Q-GERT Analysis Program for accessing resource related information. These functions are given below.

Function Name	Definition
ICSRA(NRES)	Integer-value of Current Status of Resource-type NRES Availability, that is, the number of units of NRES not in use (allocated).
ICSRU(NRES)	Integer-value of Current Status of Resource-type NRES being Used.
ICCR(NRES)	Integer-value of Current Capacity of Resource-type NRES.
TIRA(NRES)	Time-Integrated Number of Resources Available of resource type NRES.
TIRU(NRES)	Time-Integrated Number of Resources Used of resource type NRES.

The first three functions in the above table can be used to make decisions based on the current status of the model of the system. Attribute values can be assigned based on the current status and transactions routed according to the attribute values. Also, transactions can be put into the network using subroutine PTIN when prescribed conditions are detected. For example, if 10 units are available, route a transaction to an ALTER node to decrease the capacity by 5 units.

The functions for obtaining the time-integrated values associated with resource availability and utilization allow average values to be computed by dividing the time-integrated values by the time period over which statistics have been collected (TNOW-TBEG). In this way, decisions based on average use and average availability can be included in a model.

SUBPROGRAMS FOR PERFORMING RESOURCE OPERATIONS

Three subprograms are included in the Q-GERT Analysis Program for allocating, freeing, and altering resources directly from a user function. These subprograms are given below.

SUBPROGRAM NAME	DEFINITION
FUNCTION IALOC(NRES, NUNIT)	Attempts to allocate NUNIT units of resource type NRES to the current transaction. If the units are allocated, IALOC is set to 1. If the units are not allocated, IALOC is set to 0.
SUBROUTINE FREE(NRES, NUNIT,NODES)	Frees NUNIT units of resource type NRES to be allocated at the ALLOCATE nodes specified in the vector NODES($\cdot$).
SUBROUTINE ALTER(NRES, NUNIT,NODES)	Alters the capacity of resource type NRES by NUNIT units. If NUNIT is greater than 0, capacity is increased and the newly available units are attempted to be allocated at ALLOCATE nodes specified in the vector NODES($\cdot$).

Function IALOC is used to allocate resource units to the transaction passing through the node for which the user function was called. The value returned from Function IALOC should be checked to determine if the units requested were available for allocation. When IALOC is returned with a value of 1, the units were allocated to the current transaction. Otherwise, the units were not allocated.

Subroutines FREE and ALTER perform the identical functions as the FREE and ALTER nodes, respectively. These subroutines are included to enable the freeing and altering of resource units within a user-written program insert. The vector NODES which is the third argument to both subroutines corresponds to the ALLOCATE node list as placed below the FREE and ALTER nodes. When a zero value is encountered for an ALLOCATE node number, the general list of ALLOCATE nodes given in the RESOURCE block is polled. Thus, if NODES(1) equals zero, the ALLOCATE nodes prescribed in the RESOURCE block are polled. To avoid polling the ALLOCATE nodes in the RESOURCE block, a -1 should be placed after the last ALLOCATE node given in the vector NODES. When using subroutines FREE and ALTER in function UF, the user must provide a dimensioned array corresponding to the vector NODES($\cdot$).

EXAMPLES USING RESOURCES

Three examples of models that use resources are presented. Example 16 presents a model of the truck hauling situation presented in Example 8. This example illustrates how resources can be used in place of assembly operations. A complete set of reports for this example is given to illustrate the data input and resource outputs obtained from the Q-GERT Analysis Program.

Example 17 involves a set of tankers that berth at loading docks. A tugboat is required for berthing and deberthing operations. This model illustrates the reallocation of a resource when it is freed to prescribed ALLOCATE nodes. In this example, storms are modeled as transactions that prohibit tugs to start any new operation until the storm is over. This is accomplished through the use of the ALTER node.

Example 18 is an elaboration of Example 1: the model of inspection and adjustment operations on a TV production line. The model includes two inspectors with different levels of capability. One of the inspectors is prohibited from inspecting TV sets that have been adjusted. The other inspector is permitted to assist the adjustor when no TV sets are waiting to be inspected.

EXAMPLE 16. MODELING TRUCK HAULING USING RESOURCES

Problem Statement

This example uses resources to model the situation described in Example 8 where a bulldozer produces two loads which are loaded onto a truck by a manual loader. In Example 8, separate transactions are used to model trucks, loaders, and loads. Each type of transaction waits in a separate Q-node until a transaction of each type can be assembled. At that time, the loading operation is performed by a service activity. After the service activity, the loader transaction is routed through an activity representing a five-minute break. The truck transaction is routed through hauling, dumping, and travel operations.

An alternative view of this situation is to model trucks and loaders as resources and to have the loads be modeled as transactions that wait for the allocation of each resource type.

Q-GERT Model

In this example, resource type 1 is defined as LOADERS. The initial capacity is 2. Resource type 2 is defined as TRUCKS which has an initial capacity of 4. When two loads are made available through the bulldozing operations, one transaction is created that requires one unit of the resource LOADERS and one unit of the resource TRUCKS. The Q-GERT model of this situation with resources is shown in Figure 11-1. In Figure 11-1, node 23 is an ALLOCATE node which is used to allocate one unit of resource type 2 (TRUCKS). A transaction representing two loads waits for a truck at Q-node 5. When a truck is allocated, a load transaction is routed to node 22. Node 22 is a Q-node which precedes ALLOCATE node 21 where one unit of resource type 1 (LOADERS) is required before the transaction in Q-node 22 can be routed to node 25. When the load transaction reaches node 25, one unit of the loader resource and one unit of the truck resource have been allocated and, hence, loading can begin. Loading is represented by the activity from node 25 to node 8. At ALTER node 8, the capacity of the loader resource is reduced by one, and a transaction is routed to node 14 where a loader is freed. An ALTER node is used before the FREE node since the loader is not available during the five minute break. If the break time

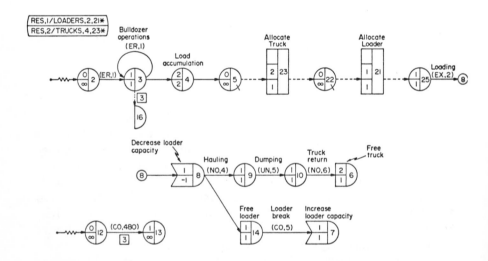

Figure 11-1   Q-GERT model of a truck hauling system with resources, Example 16.

should be included in the utilization statistics, then no ALTER node should be used. The branch from node 14 to node 7 represents the five minute break required for a loader following a loading operation. At ALTER node 7, the capacity of resource type 1 is increased by one and made available for reallocation. From the resource definition of LOADERS, they are reallocated at ALLOCATE node 21. Since no branching occurs from node 7, the transaction arriving to node 7 is destroyed.

The transaction routed from node 8 to node 9 represents a truck hauling a load. Following the hauling activity, there is a dumping activity and a truck return activity. Eventually, the transaction arrives to FREE node 6 where one unit of the truck resource is made available. Any truck resource that is freed is reallocated at ALLOCATE node 23 to a load that is waiting in Q-node 5. If no transaction is waiting at Q-node 5, the truck is made available to process the next transaction that arrives to Q-node 5.

The transaction that arrived at FREE node 6 is destroyed since no activities emanate from node 6. The data input echo for the truck hauling situation using resources is shown in Figure 11–2. The warning message shown in Figure 11–12 is due the omission of a specified stopping condition. Each run is to be made until all events are processed.

Summary of Results

The outputs from the Q-GERT Analysis Program for this example are shown in Figures 11–3 and 11–4. The echo check shown in Figure 11–3 illustrates the information on resources used in the example. Figure 11–4 presents the first run summary report. These values can be compared to the values given for Example 8 in Table 6–5. Note that the loader utilization is obtained from the utilization of resource type 1 and the number of loaders waiting corresponds to the number of units of resource type 1 available. The average number of trucks idle is obtained from the average availability of resource type 2. Care is required in interpreting the statistics on the TRUCK resource. Trucks are allocated to loads when a truck is available and a load transaction is waiting. Thus, a truck resource waiting for a loader in Q-node 22 is considered as being in use. When multiple resources are to be allocated to a transaction, care is required in modeling and in interpreting the output statistics.

```
*** INPUT CARDS ***

GEN,PRITSKER,HAULING-16,7,3,1977,,,,C,,5,C*
  ** INPUT ERROR NUMBER    11:-*
   **CHECK FIELD  10 AND SUBSEQUENT FIELDS OF THE ABOVE CARD**
SOU,2*                       START NODE FOR BULLDOZING OPERATIONS
ACT,2,3,ER,1*                FIRST BULLDOZER ACTIVITY
PAR,1,4,3,100,2*             PARAMETER VALUES FOR LOAD GENERATION
REG,3,1,1*                   GENERATION OF LOAD TRANSACTIONS
ACT,3,3,ER,1*                SUBSEQUENT BULLDOZER ACTIVITIES
ACT,3,4*                     INFORMATION TRANSFER
REG,15*                      REPLACEMENT NODE TO STOP TRANSACTION GENERATION
REG,4,2,2*                   ACCUMULATION OF TWO LOADS FOR HAULING
ACT,4,5*                     INFORMATION TRANSFER
QUE,5/LOAD-Q,(10)23*         QUEUE FOR LOADS READY FOR LOADING
RES,2/TRUCKS,4,23*
ALL,23,,2,1,5/22*
QUE,22/TRK+LOAD,(10)21*      TRUCK + LOAD WAITING FOR LOADER
RES,1/LOADERS,2,21*
ALL,21,,1,1,22/25*
REG,25,1,1*
ACT,25,8,EX,2*
PAR,2,14,0,100*              PARAMETER VALUES FOR LOADING TIME
ALT,8,,1,-1*                 COMPLETION OF LOADING
ACT,8,14*
FRE,14,,1,1*
ACT,8,9,NO,4,,1*            HAULING ACTIVITY
PAR,4,22,0,100,3*           PARAMETER VALUES FOR HAULING TIME
ACT,14,7,CO,5*              BREAK TIME FOR LOADER
ALT,7,,1,1*
REG,9,1,1*                  END OF HAULING
ACT,9,10,UN,5*              DUMPING ACTIVITY
PAR,5,,2,8*                 PARAMETER VALUES FOR DUMPING TIME
REG,10,1,1*                 END OF DUMPING
ACT,10,6,NO,6*              TRUCK TRAVEL TIME
PAR,6,18,0,100,3*           PARAMETER VALUES FOR TRUCK TRAVEL TIME
FRE,6,,2,1*
SOU,12*                     START OF TIMING SUBNETWORK
ACT,12,13,CO,480,3*         ONE DAY INFORMATION TRANSFER
REG,13*                     END OF DAY NODE
MOD,3,3,16*
FIN*
*** ERROR COUNT    C-FATAL ERRS ***
                   1-WARNINGS
*** EXECUTION WILL BE ATTEMPTED ***
    ON RUN    1 SIMULATION ENDED DUE TO COMPLETION OF ALL ACTIVITIES AT TIME   554.4393
```

Figure 11-2   Q-GERT input for hauling problem, Example 16.

** QUEUE NODES **

NODE	LABEL	INITIAL NO. IN QUEUE	MAXIMUM NO. ALLOWED	OUTPUT TYPE	PRIORITY SCHEME	MAY BLOCK INCIDENT SERVERS	NODE FOR BALKERS	FOLLOWING NODES
5	LOAD-Q	3	9999	D	FIFO	NO	0	23
22	TRK+LOAD	0	9999	D	FIFO	NO	0	21

** RESOURCES **

RESOURCE NUMBER	LABEL	UNITS AVAILABLE	ASSOCIATED ALLOCATE NODES
1	LOADERS	2	21
2	TRUCKS	4	23

** RESOURCE ALLOCATE NODES **

NODE	SELECTION RULE	RESOURCE NUMBER	UNITS SEIZED	B-NODE/ OUTPUT NODE
23	POR	2	1	5/ 22
21	POR	1	1	22/ 25

** FREE RESOURCE NODES **

NODE	OUTPUT TYPE	RESOURCE NUMBER	UNITS FREED	ASSOCIATED ALLOCATE NODES
6	D	2	1	1
14	D	1	1	1

** ALTER RESOURCE NODES **

NODE	OUTPUT TYPE	RESOURCE NUMBER	UNITS CREATED OR DESTROYED	ASSOCIATED ALLOCATE NODES
7	D	1	-1	

Figure 11-3   Echo check from Q-GERT for resources, Example 16.

```
GERT SIMULATION PROJECT HAULING-16   BY PRITSKER
             DATE   7/  8/ 1977

    **FINAL RESULTS FOR FIRST SIMULATION**

       TOTAL ELAPSED TIME =    554.4393


       **NUMBER IN Q-NODE**                    ** WAITING TIME **
                                                  IN QUEUE

 NODE   LABEL      AVE.    MIN.  MAX.    CURRENT      AVERAGE
                                        NUMBER

   5    LOAD-Q     .7850    0    3.         0         13.6015
  22    TRK+LOAD   .0762    0    2.         0          1.3210


       **RESOURCE UTILIZATION**

RESOURCE  LABEL     NOW     AVE.     MAX.      NOW        AVE.       MAX.
                  IN USE   IN USE   IN USE  AVAILABLE  AVAILABLE  AVAILABLE

   1    LOADERS     0      .794      2          2        .918        2
   2    TRUCKS      0     3.442      4          4        .558        4
```

Figure 11-4   Final results for first run, Example 16.

EXAMPLE 17. OIL TANKER ACCOMMODATION AT A PORT

Problem Statement

This problem is extracted from Schriber (121). A port consists of three berths and one tugboat. Tugboats are used to berth tankers so that tankers can be loaded. Tugboats will only begin to berth a tanker if a berth is available. When a tanker is loaded, a tug is required to deberth the tanker before the berth can be reemployed. The berthing and deberthing operations require one hour of tugboat time.

The port currently services three types of tankers, each of which requires a different amount of time to load. All loading times are uniformly distributed. Information on the tankers is given in Table 11–2.

The values given in Table 11–2 indicate that 25 percent of the arriving tankers require a loading time that is uniformly distributed between 16 and 20. Fifty-five percent of the tankers (type 2) require between 21 and 27 hours, uniformly distributed. Type 3 tankers, representing the remaining 20 percent, require between 32 and 40 hours to load, uniformly distributed. The interarrival time between tankers of all three types is between 4 and 18 hours, uniformly distributed.

A proposal is being considered that would contract for the port to service five additional tankers that require between 18 and 24 hours to load. These five tankers would return periodically to the port with the time from the end of deberthing until they return being uniformly distributed between 216 and 264 hours.

Table 11-2.   Tanker Type, Relative Frequency and Loading Time.

Type	Relative Frequency	Loading Time,* Hours
1	0.25	(16,20)
2	0.55	(21,27)
3	0.20	(32,40)

*Loading times are uniformly distributed in the range (A,B).

One additional complication regarding port operation is the occurrence of storms. Storms occur frequently and the time between the end of one storm and the onset of the next storm follows an exponential distribution with a mean time of 48 hours. The duration of a storm is uniformly distributed between 2 and 6 hours. When a storm occurs, tugs cannot be assigned to the berthing or deberthing operations. However, tugs in the process of berthing or deberthing continue until the operation is completed.

Q-GERT Model

The modeling strategy will be to model the tug as a resource (resource type 1) and to model the three berths as a second resource (resource type 2). Tankers are modeled as transactions that require both a berth and a tug resource to be loaded. A storm is modeled by a disjoint network that alters the capacity of the tug resource.

The Q-GERT model of the oil tanker accommodation at a port system is shown in Figure 11–5. The RESOURCE block shows that resource type 1 is for the TUG, and resource type 2 models the BERTHS. At node 1, tankers of type 1, 2, and 3 are generated. Attribute 1 is set equal to 0 for these tankers. At source node 2, the five proposed tankers are generated and attribute 1 for each of these tankers is set equal to an integer value from 1 to 5. The time between releases of node 2 is modeled by the duration of the activity from node 2 to node 2 and represents an offset time for arrivals of the proposed tankers. Q-node 3 represents the queue for tankers awaiting a berth. At ALLOCATE node 5, berths are allocated one unit at a time to tankers waiting in Q-node 3. The

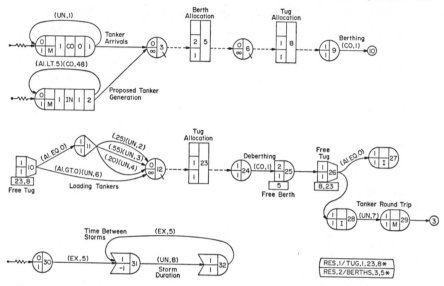

Figure 11-5 Q-GERT model of oil tanker accommodation at a port, Example 17.

tanker transactions are routed to Q-node 6 when a berth is allocated. ALLOCATE node 8 allocates a tug to a tanker. The berthing operations are represented by the activity from node 9 to node 10. Node 10 is a FREE node where one unit of the tug resource is freed. First, the tug is attempted to be allocated at ALLOCATE node 23 and then at ALLO-CATE 8. Since the tug is in the port, this order of allocation spec-ifies that a deberthing should be performed prior to a berthing if a tanker is waiting for deberthing. From FREE node 10, the tankers are segregated based on attribute 1. If attribute 1 equals 0, it is a regular tanker and if attribute 1 is greater than 0, it is one of the proposed tank-ers. At node 11, the regular tankers are segregated according to the rela-tive frequencies in which they occur. Thus, the three branches from node 11 to Q-node 12 each represent a different type of tanker. Proba-bilistic branching from node 11 causes the tankers to be loaded accord-ing to the prescribed relative frequency. At Q-node 12, the tankers wait for a tug to be allocated from ALLOCATE node 23. When a tug is allo-cated for the deberthing operation, the tanker is routed over the activity from node 24 to 25 which requires one hour. At FREE node 25, a berth is freed and made available for allocation at ALLOCATE node 5. At FREE node 26, a tug is freed and ALLOCATE nodes 8 and 23 are polled in that order. Since a deberthing operation was just finished, the tug should be allocated to a berthing operation if a tanker is waiting. Thus, ALLOCATE node 8 is listed first. From FREE node 26, regular tankers are routed using conditional, take-first branching to STATISTICS node 27 to get the amount of time the tanker spent in the port. If the tanker is a newly proposed one, it is routed from FREE node 26 to node 28 where statistics are collected on the proposed time in the port for the tanker. The proposed tanker is then routed back to node 29 to be marked after incurring the anticipated round trip time. It is then sent to Q-node 3 to wait for port operations.

The disjoint network representing storms is modeled by nodes 30, 31, and 32. At source node 30, the first storm is scheduled to occur in an exponentially distributed time. When the storm occurs, it is processed at ALTER node 31 which decreases the capacity of the tug resource by 1. This change will only occur when one unit of the tug resource is available. The storm duration is modeled by the activity from node 31 to node 32. Following the storm duration, the tug capacity is increased by 1. This tug, if needed, is to be allocated from node 23. If not required at node 23, an attempt to allocate it from node 8 should be made. This order presumes that the tug would go to port during the storm and a deberthing operation should be performed if one is ready to be performed. The activity from node 32 to node 31 represents the time between storms and the time until the tug capacity should again be decreased by 1. Figure 11–6 shows the input corresponding to the Q-GERT network model presented in Figure 11–5.

Summary of Results

Figure 11–7 illustrates selective outputs from the Q-GERT Analysis Program. A detailed analysis of these results will not be given. From the outputs we see that one tug is more than sufficient for servicing 3 berths. With the addition of the proposed tankers, the average number of tankers waiting for a berth is 1.65 and the waiting time is over 15 hours. This long waiting time indicates that further analysis is required before agreeing to process the proposed tankers at the port.

EXAMPLE 18. EMBELLISHED INSPECTION AND ADJUSTMENT MODEL

Problem Statement

This example is an elaboration of Example 1 involving the inspection and adjustment of television sets on a production line. The problem in-

```
GEN,PRITSKER,TANKER,11,16,1977,2,,,876C,(14)1*
SOU,1,,1*
VAS,1,1,CO,0*
ACT,1,1,UN,1*
ACT,1,3*
SOU,2,,1,A*
VAS,2,1,IN,1*
ACT,2,2,CO,48,(9)A1.LT.5*
ACT,2,3,*
QUE,3/BERTH-Q,(10)5*               WAIT FOR BERTH
RES,2/BERTH,3,5*
ALL,5,,2,,3/6*                     ALLOCATE BERTH
QUE,6/TUGIN-Q,(10)8*               WAIT FOR TUG
RES,1/TUG,1,23,8*                  ALLOCATE TUG TO DEBERTH THEN TO BERTH
ALL,8,(6)6/9*                      ALLOCATE TUG FOR BERTHING
REG,9,,1*
ACT,9,10,CO,1*                     BERTHING ACTIVITY
FRE,10,F,,,23,8*                   FREE TUG TO DEBERTH THEN TO BERTH
ACT,10,11,(9)A1.EQ.C*              LOADING OPERATIONS
ACT,10,12,UN,6,(9)A1.GT.0*
REG,11,,1,P*
ACT,11,12,UN,2,(8).25*
ACT,11,12,UN,3,(8).55*
ACT,11,12,UN,4,(8).2C*
QUE,12/TUGOUT-Q,(10)23*            WAIT FOR TUG
ALL,23,(6)12/24*                   ALLOCATE TUG FOR DEBERTHING
REG,24,,1*
ACT,24,25,CO,1*                    DEBERTHING ACTIVITY
FRE,25,,2,,5*                      FREE BERTH
ACT,25,26*
FRE,26,F,,,8,23*                   FREE TUG TO BERTH THEN DEBERTH
ACT,26,27,(9)A1.EQ.C*
ACT,26,28,(9)A1.GT.0*
STA,27/REGTANK,,1,,I*
STA,28/PROPTANK,,1,,I*
ACT,28,29,UN,7*
REG,29,,1,,M*
ACT,29,3*
SOU,30,0,1*
ACT,30,31,EX,5*                    OCCURRENCE OF FIRST STORM
ALT,31,,,-1*                       TUG CAPACITY DECREASED
ACT,31,32,UN,8*                    STORM
ALT,32,,,1*                        TUG CAPACITY INCREASED
ACT,32,31,EX,5*                    TIME BETWEEN STORMS
PAR,1,,4,18*
PAR,2,,16,20*
PAR,3,,21,27*
PAR,4,,32,40*
PAR,5,48*
PAR,6,,18,24*
PAR,7,,216,264*
PAR,8,,2,6*
FIN*
```

Figure 11-6 Q-GERT input for port accommodation problem, Example 17.

GERT SIMULATION PROJECT TANKER   BY PRITSKER
                DATE 11/ 16/ 1977

          FINAL RESULTS FOR FIRST SIMULATION

          TOTAL ELAPSED TIME =   876C.0000

                NODE STATISTICS

NODE	LABEL	AVE.	STD.DEV.	NO OF OBS.	STAT TYPE
28	PROPTANK	37.8661	13.9254	157.	I
27	REGTANK	42.4232	15.6326	794.	I

          NUMBER IN Q-NODE   ** WAITING TIME **
                                                      IN QUEUE

NODE	LABEL	AVE.	MIN.	MAX.	CURRENT NUMBER	AVERAGE
3	BERTH-Q	1.6463	0	7.	2	15.0852
6	TUGIN-Q	.0255	0	2.	0	.2344
12	TUGOUT-Q	.0226	0	2.	0	.2077

                RESOURCE UTILIZATION

RESOURCE	LABEL	NOW IN USE	AVE. IN USE	MAX. IN USE	NOW AVAILABLE	AVE. AVAILABLE	MAX. AVAILABLE
1	TUG	1	.217	1	0	.719	1
2	BERTH	3	2.889	3	0	.111	3

Figure 11-7 Summary Report for Run 1, Example 17.

volves television sets arriving to 2 inspectors for an inspection operation. Eighty-five percent of the inspected TV sets are sent directly to packing and fifteen percent require an adjustment operation. An adjustor performs the adjustment operation. Television sets are reinspected after they are adjusted.

For this example, one of the two inspectors is a new trainee who only inspects TV sets that have not been adjusted. The other inspector, who is referred to as the "master inspector", can inspect any TV set and, in addition, can perform the adjustment operation. The master inspector only performs the adjustment operation if no TV sets are waiting for inspection.

Q-GERT Model

To model this situation, we use resources to allow the master inspector to perform either the inspection operation or the adjustment operation. Three resource types are used: resource type 1 represents the trainee inspector; resource type 2 represents the master inspector; and resource type 3 represents the adjustor. Only one unit of each resource type is available. In this model, the time to perform the inspection and adjustment operations are assumed to be independent of the resource type performing the operation.

The Q-GERT network for this situation is shown in Figure 11–8. The arrival of TV sets is modeled using SOURCE node 1. After arrival, the TV sets wait in Q-node 2. Q-node 2 has two ALLOCATE nodes associated with it. ALLOCATE node 10 is used to allocate one unit of resource type 1 (the trainee inspector) to an arriving TV set. If the new trainee is busy, then the TV set can be processed by resource type 2, the master inspector. This priority of the trainee inspector over the master inspector is indicated on the data card by the order in which the ALLO-CATE nodes are placed on the Q-node input description. In this case, ALLOCATE node 10 has preference over ALLOCATE node 17. At AL-LOCATE node 10, one unit of resource type 1 would be allocated to waiting transactions in Q-node 2. When a unit is allocated, the transaction from Q-node 2 is routed to node 11. The transaction that is routed has a value of 1 assigned to attribute 1 of the transaction. This assignment specifies that resource type 1 is used to inspect the TV set.

ALLOCATE node 17 allocates one unit of resource type 2 (the master inspector). Two Q-nodes precede ALLOCATE node 17 since the master inspector can process TV sets that have been adjusted or newly arriving TV sets. A preferred order, POR, rule is used to select transactions from the Q-nodes preceding ALLOCATE node 17. The preferred node is Q-node 16 first, then Q-node 2. This gives priority to TV sets that have been adjusted and are waiting in Q-node 16. At ALLOCATE node 17, the resource type number is assigned to attribute 1 of the transaction passing through node 17. Transactions taken from either Q-node 16 or Q-node 2 are routed to node 11 for the inspection activity.

The end node of the inspection activity is FREE node 3. At FREE node 3, one unit of the resource type defined by attribute 1 is made available, that is, the resource that performed the inspection operation is made available to be allocated to waiting transactions. Since the resource type freed is based on an attribute value, the order in which AL-LOCATE nodes are to be polled cannot be specified at the FREE node. In this situation, the order as specified on the RESOURCE definition is used. The trainee inspector is always allocated from node 10 as he can only inspect newly arriving TV sets. The master inspector is prescribed to perform inspections before adjustments and is reallocated at ALLO-CATE node 17 before being considered at ALLOCATE node 13 to help the adjustor.

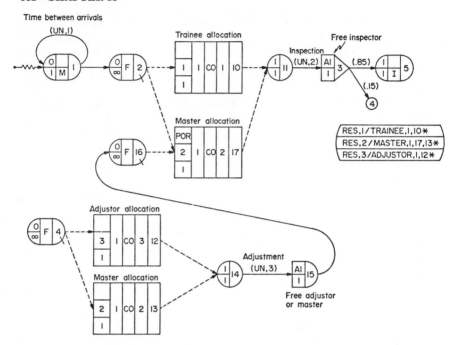

Figure 11-8   Q-GERT model of TV inspection and adjustment using resources, Example 18.

From FREE node 3, 85 percent of the TV sets are routed to packing (node 5) where time-in-the-system statistics are collected. Fifteen percent of the TV sets are routed to Q-node 4 which precedes the adjustment operation. Since adjustment can be performed by either the adjustor or the master inspector, two ALLOCATE nodes follow Q-node 4. ALLOCATE node 12 allocates one unit of resource type 3 (the adjustor) to a transaction requiring adjustment. The value of attribute 1 of a transaction passing through ALLOCATE node 12 is assigned a value of 3 to indicate that the adjustor performed the adjustment operation. If the master inspector is assigned to perform the adjustment operation at ALLOCATE node 13, a value of 2 is assigned to attribute 1. Transactions taken from Q-node 4 are routed to node 14. The activity from node 14 to node 15 represents the adjustment operation. Node 15 is a FREE node which makes one unit available of the resource type defined by attribute 1. Again, the order for polling ALLOCATE nodes at FREE node 15 cannot be specified as the resource type is taken from an attribute value. Transactions finishing the adjustment operation are routed to Q-node 16 to await re-inspection by the master inspector.

This example illustrates how Q-GERT can model a complex resource allocation problem involving complex procedures for allocating a resource, the master inspector, to a set of operations. Also included in the example are detailed rules for re-allocating freed resources. The data input to describe the network of Figure 11-8 to the Q-GERT Analysis Program is shown in Figure 11-9.

```
GEN,PRITSKER,TV-INS-ADJ-R,11,22,1977,1,C,3,48C,,1G,(14)1*
RES,1/TRAINEE,1,1C*
RES,2/MASTER,1,17,13*                ALLOC TO INSP. THEN ADJ.
RES,3/ADJUSTOR,1,12*
SOU,1,0,1*
ACT,1,1,UN,1*
PAR,1,,3.5,7.5*
ACT,1,2*
QUE,2/FRST INSQ,(10)10,17*           TRY TRAINEE THEN MASTER
ALL,10,POR,1,1,2/11*                 ALLOC TRAINEE
VAS,10,1,CO,1*                       ASSIGN TRAINEE RESOURCE TYPE(1)
REG,11,1,1*
ACT,11,3,UN,2,1*                     INSPECTION ACTIVITY
PAR,2,,6,12*
FRE,3,P,A1,1*                        FREE TRAINEE(A1=1) OR MASTER(A1=2)
ACT,3,5,(8)0.85*
ACT,3,4,(8)0.15*
STA,5/SYS-TIME,1,1,,I,5.,,5.*
QUE,4/ADJ-QUE,(10)12,13*             TRY ADJUSTOR THEN MASTER
ALL,12,POR,3,1,4/14*                 ALLOC ADJUSTOR
ALL,13,POR,2,1,4/14*                 ALLOC MASTER FOR ADJUSTING
VAS,12,1,CO,3*                       ASSIGN ADJUSTOR RESOURCE TYPE(3)
VAS,13,1,CO,2*                       ASSIGN MASTER RESOURCE TYPE(2)
REG,14,1,1*
ACT,14,15,UN,3,2*                    ADJUSTMENT ACTIVITY
PAR,3,,2J.,,40.*
FRE,15,,A1,1*                         FREE MASTER(A1=2) OR ADJUSTOR(A1=3)
ACT,15,16*
QUE,16/Q-REINSP,(10)17*
ALL,17,POR,2,1,16/11,2/11*           ALLOC MASTER FOR INSPECTION
VAS,17,1,CO,2*
FIN*
```

Figure 11-9 Q-GERT input for inspection and adjustment stations model, Example 18.

Summary of Results

The results from 10 runs of the Q-GERT Analysis Program for 480 time units are shown in Figure 11-10. Comparing the results for this model with the results from Example 1 shows a decrease in the utilization of the adjustor as expected and an increase in the use of the inspectors.

GERT SIMULATION PROJECT TV-INS-ADJ-R BY PRITSKER
DATE 11/ 22/ 1977

FINAL RESULTS FOR   10 SIMULATIONS

AVERAGE NODE STATISTICS

NODE	LABEL	PROBABILITY	AVE.	STD.DEV.	SD OF AVE	NO OF OBS.	MIN.	MAX.	STAT TYPE
5	SYS-TIME	1.0000	25.3211	6.2681	1.9822	10.	14.1835	34.6288	I

AVERAGE NUMBER IN Q-NODE / **NUMBER IN Q-NODE**

NODE	LABEL	AVE.	STD.DEV.	SD OF AVE	MIN.	MAX.	MAX.
2	FRST INS	1.5700	.5940	.1878	.4077	2.2890	6.0000
4	ADJ-QUE	.6081	.6057	.1915	0	1.8236	5.0000
16	Q-REINSP	.1653	.0557	.0176	.0767	.2472	2.0000

AVERAGE RESOURCE UTILIZATION / **AVERAGE WAITING TIME** / **NUMBER OF RESOURCES**

RESOURCE	LABEL	AVE.	STD.DEV.	SD OF AVE	NO. OF OBS.	MIN.	MAX.	AVE.	STD.DEV.	SD OF AVE	MAX.
1	TRAINEE	.9467	.0205	.0065	10.	.9062	.9799	8.6142	3.3086	1.0463	1.
2	MASTER	.9384	.0259	.0082	10.	.8801	.9659	17.9269	15.1974	4.8059	1.
3	ADJUSTOR	.6420	.1912	.0605	10.	.3014	.8954	6.9117	1.2962	.4399	1.

AVERAGE RESOURCE AVAILABILITY / **NUMBER OF RESOURCES**

RESOURCE	LABEL	AVE.	STD.DEV.	SD OF AVE	NO. OF OBS.	MIN.	MAX.	MAX.
1	TRAINEE	.0533	.0205	.0065	10.	.0201	.0938	1.
2	MASTER	.0616	.0259	.0082	10.	.0341	.1199	1.
3	ADJUSTOR	.3580	.1912	.0605	10.	.1046	.6986	1.

Figure 11-10   Results for ten runs of Q-GERT Analysis Program, Example 18.

Surprisingly, the trainee inspector is busier than the master inspector. This occurs because the trainee inspector processes the newly arriving TV sets even if the master inspector is also idle. It is interesting to note that the average time required for inspection and adjustment of TV sets has increased from 19.5 (Example 1) to 25.3 time units shown in Figure 11–10. This increase is due primarily to the increased waiting time at the inspection station.

EXERCISES

11–1. Describe the procedures and choices with regard to the disposition of a resource unit when it becomes available due to a transaction arrival at a FREE node. Specify the assumptions inherent in the Q-GERT reallocation procedure. Discuss the reallocation of a resource in a system with which you are familiar.

11–2. Specify a rationale for the omission of the ASM queue selection rule from the list of rules allowed for the ALLOCATE node.

11–3. Model the truck hauling situation of Examples 8 and 16 using resources to model loaders and transactions to model trucks. Perform an analysis of the network and compare your results with the results obtained from Examples 8 and 16.

11–4. Model the following embellishments to the TV inspection and adjustment model, Example 18:
   (a) Make the inspection and the adjustment times dependent on the resource allocated to perform the operations;
   (b) Require the master inspector to perform immediately the adjustment operation when a TV set he has inspected is classified as requiring adjustment;
   (c) Allow the adjustor to inspect TV sets that have been adjusted.

11–5. Use resource concepts to solve Exercise 8–9.

11–6. Use resource concepts to solve Exercise 8–11.

11–7. Use resource concepts to solve Exercise 8–10. Embellishments:
   (a) If a caller balks two or more times because he cannot access a talk (GI) line, he places two consecutive calls when he does gain access to a talk line.
   (b) With probability 0.2, a caller gets a busy signal in which case he relinquishes his talk line and tries to call again in 15 minutes. With probability 0.1, he gets no answer in which case he doesn't try again.

(c) The company has decided to add a second dial line that is a high speed line for which dialing time is exponentially distributed with a mean of .15 a minimum of .075 and a maximum of 4.0. The high speed line should be used whenever possible.

(d) A new policy has been introduced that allocates two talk lines for data communications during the last 10 minutes of every hour. These two lines are, thus, not available to callers during this time. The lines are assigned to data communication functions as soon as possible during the last 10 minutes of every hour.

A CONCLUDING NOTE

This book makes two fundamental contributions to modeling and simulation. First and foremost, it documents Q-GERT: a new language for modeling procedural systems. Second, a method for analyzing Q-GERT models with a simulation program is detailed. Further discussion of these developments would be superfluous. However, a few more words about problem solving seem in order.

In modeling and simulation, what is important is relative. Models are built to be explanatory devices; analysis vehicles; design assessors; or crystal balls. The purpose for which the model is built should be reflected in the amount of detail included in the model. By knowing the purpose for which a model is built, the relative worth of including specific details can be assessed. Only those elements that could cause significant differences in decision making resulting from the outputs of the model need be considered.

Since Q-GERT models are easily extended and embellished, it behooves the Q-GERT problem solver to start small and to provide quick feedback to his client or sponsor. Starting small could mean developing an aggregate model that crudely approximates the total system under study. Starting small could also mean picking the critical part of the system and modeling it. In either case, interaction with the client is necessary.

A good modeler draws his client into problem solving activities for three reasons: to insure that a proper problem formulation has been developed; to assist in determining the system details that can be omitted from the model; and to set the stage for implementing the results of the analysis. In this light, an analyst should consider reformulating the purpose for which the model was built and, if necessary, rebuild the model. Q-GERT is designed to be used in this mode. Clearly, such iterative and evolutionary Q-GERT model-building activities could go on forever. With this thought in mind, this book is ended.

REFERENCES AND BIBLIOGRAPHY

1. Abramowitz, M. and I. A. Stegum, Eds., *Handbook of Mathematical Functions*, Applied Mathematics Series 55, Washington, D.C.; National Bureau of Standards, 1964.
2. American National Standards Institute, *American National Standard FORTRAN*, ANSI X3.9–1966.
3. Archibald, R. D. and R. L. Villoria, *Network-Based Management Systems (PERT/CPM)*, New York: John Wiley & Sons, Inc., 1968.
4. Arisawa, S. and S. E. Elmaghraby, "Optimal Time-Cost Trade-Offs in GERT Networks", *Management Science*, Vol. 18, No. 11, July 1972, pp. 589–599.
5. Auterio, V. J., "Q-GERT Simulation of Air Terminal Cargo Facilities", *Proc. Pittsburgh Modeling and Simulation Conference*, Vol. 5, 1974, pp. 1181–1186.
6. Auterio, V. J. and S. D. Draper, "Aerial Refueling Military Airlift Forces: An Economic Analysis Based on Q-GERT Simulation", Material Airlift Command, Presented at Chicago ORSA Conference, 1974.
7. Ayoub, M. A., R. J. Smillie et al, "A Computerized Approach for the Assessment and Evaluation of Job Performance Aids," *Proc. Human Factors Society Meeting*, 1976, pp. 466–478.
8. Bellas, C. J., and A. C. Samli, "Improving New Product Planning with GERT Simulation", *California Management Review*, Vol. XV, No. 4, Summer, 1973, pp. 14–21.
9. Bird, M., E. R. Clayton, and L. J. Moore, "Sales Negotiation Cost Planning for Corporate Level Sales", *Journal of Marketing*, Vol. 37, No. 2, April, 1973, pp. 7–13.
10. Bird, M. M., E. R. Clayton, and L. J. Moore, "Industrial Buying: A Method of Planning for Contract Negotiations", *Journal of Economics and Business*, 1974.

11. Branson, M. H. and B. Shah, "On GERT Modeling of a Class of Finite Queueing Processes", *AIIE Transactions,* Vol. 4, No. 1, 1972, pp. 43–48.

12. Brounstein, S. H., "An Adjudication Research Simulation Model (ARSM)", Institute of Law and Social Research Paper, Washington, D.C., 1975.

13. Burgess, R. R., "GERTS Models of a University" M.S. Thesis, Virginia Polytechnic Institute, Blacksburg, Virginia, 1970.

14. Burt, J. M., Jr., and M. Garman, "Monte Carlo Techniques for Stochastic Network Analysis", *Fourth Conference on the Applications of Simulation,* 1970, pp. 146–153.

15. Burt, J. M., D. P. Gaver, and M. Perlas, "Simple Stochastic Networks: Some Problems and Procedures," Nav. Res. Logist. Quart., Vol. 17, December 1970, pp. 439–460.

16. Byers, J. K., "Application of GERT to Reliability Analysis", Ph.D. Dissertation, The University of Arkansas, 1970.

17. Clayton, E. R., and L. J. Moore, "GERT vs. PERT" *Journal of Systems Management,* Vol. 22, No. 2, 1972, pp. 11–19.

18. Clymer, A. B., "The Modeling of Hierarchical Systems," *Proc. Conference on Applications of Continuous System Simulation Languages,* 1969, pp. 1–16.

19. Cooper, R. B., *Introduction to Queueing Theory,* New York, Macmullen, 1972.

20. Crowston, W. and G. L. Thompson, "Decision CPM: A Method for Simultaneous Planning, Scheduling and Control of Projects", *Operations Research,* Vol. 15, No. 3, 1967, pp. 407–426.

21. Dabaghian, L., Y. Akiba, and W. W. Happ, "Network Modules to Simulate Quantized Entity Flow," Joint Automatic Control Conference, Austin, Texas, June 19, 1974.

22. Dabaghian, L., Y. Akiba, and W. W. Happ, "Simulation and Modeling Techniques Using GERTS IIIQ: An Introductory Account for Prospective Users," Seventh Asilomar Conference on Circuits, Systems and Computers, Monterey, California, November 27–29, 1973.

23. Davis, E. W., "Project Scheduling Under Resource Constraints—Historical Review and Categorization of Procedures", *AIIE Transactions,* Vol. 5, No. 4, 1973, pp. 297–313.

24. Devor, R. E., G. L. Hogg, and M. Handwerker, "Analysis of Criminal Justice Systems with GERTS IIIQ: A Case Study", *Proc. Pittsburgh Modeling and Simulation Conference,* Vol. 5, 1974, pp. 1193–1199.

25. Drezner, S. H., and A. A. B. Pritsker, "Network Analysis of Countdown", The RAND Corporation, RM-4976-NASA, March, 1966.

26. Duket, S. and D. Wortman, "Q-GERT Model of the Dover Air Force Base Port Cargo Facilities", MACRO Task Force, Material Airlift Command, Scott Air Force Base, Illinois, 1976.

27. Eisner, H., "A Generalized Network Approach to the Planning and Scheduling of a Research Project", *Operations Research,* Vol. 10, No. 1, 1962, pp. 115–125.

28. Elmaghraby, S. E., "An Algebra for the Analysis of Generalized Activity Networks", *Management Science,* Vol. 10, No. 3, 1964, pp. 494–514.

29. Elmaghraby, S. E., *The Design of Production Systems,* New York: Reinhold Publishing Corporation, 1966.

30. Elmaghraby, S. E., "On Generalized Activity Networks", *Journal of Industrial Engineering,* Vol. 18, No. 11, 1976, pp. 621–31.

31. Elmaghraby, S. E., "On the Expected Duration of PERT Type Networks", *Management Science,* Vol. 13, No. 5, 1967, pp. 299–306.

32. Elmaghraby, S. E., *Network Models in Management Science,* Springer-Verlag Lecture Series on Operations Research, 1970.

33. Elmaghraby, S. E., "Theory of Networks and Management Science: I and II", *Management Science,* Vol. 17, Nos. 1 and 2 1970, pp. 1–34, No. 1, and pp. B-54–B71.

34. Emshoff, J. R., and R. L. Sisson, *Design and Use of Computer Simulation Models,* New York: The Macmillan Company, 1970.

35. Enlow, R. A., "An Application of GERT Network Techniques to the Selection and Management of Research and Development Projects", PhD Dissertation, Arizona State University, 1970.

36. Evans, G. W., II, G. F. Wallace, and G. L. Sutherland, *Simulation Using Digital Computers,* Englewood Cliffs, N.J.: Prentice-Hall, Inc., 1967.

37. Federal Power Commission Exhibit EP-237, "Risk Analysis of the Arctic Gas Pipeline Project Construction Schedule", Vol. 167, Federal Power Commission, 1976.

38. Feller, W., *An Introduction to Probability Theory and Its Applications,* New York: John Wiley and Sons, Inc., Vol. I, 1957.

39. Feller, W., *An Introduction to Probability Theory and Its Applications,* New York: John Wiley and Sons, Inc., Vol. II, 1972.

40. Fishman, G. S., *Concepts and Methods in Discrete Event Digital Simulation,* New York: John Wiley and Sons, Inc., 1973.

41. Fox, B. L., *Notes on Operations Research-5,* Operations Research Center, University of California, ORC 66–13, Berkeley, CA., 1966.

42. Freeman, R. J., "A Generalized PERT", *Operations Research,* Vol. 8, No. 2, 1960, p. 281.

43. Fulkerson, D. R., "Expected Critical Path Lengths in PERT Networks", *Operations Research,* Vol. 10, No. 6, 1962, pp. 808–817.
44. Gallagher, D. J., "A GERT Network Approach to the Study of Queueing Phenomena", Ph.D. Dissertation, Arizona State University, 1970.
45. Gordon, G., System Simulation, Englewood Cliffs, N.J.: Prentice-Hall, Inc., 1969.
46. Gordon, G., *The Application of GPSS V to Discrete Systems Simulation,* Englewood Cliffs, N.J.: Prentice-Hall, Inc., 1975.
47. Grant, F. H., III, and A. A. B. Pritsker, "GERT Network Model of Burglary Resistance," NSF Grant No. GI 34978, Purdue University, December, 1973.
48. Hahn, G. J. and S. S. Shapiro, *Statistical Methods in Engineering,* New York: John Wiley & Sons, Inc., 1967.
49. Halpin, D. W., "An Investigation of the Use of Simulation Networks for Modeling Construction Operations", Ph.D. Dissertation, University of Illinois, 1973.
50. Halpin, D. W. and W. W. Happ, "Digital Simulation of Equipment Allocation for Corps of Engineering Construction Planning", U.S. Army, CERL, Champaign, Illinois, 1971.
51. Hartley, H., and A. Wortham, "A Statistical Theory for PERT Critical Path Analysis", *Management Science,* Vol. 12, No. 10, June 1966, pp. 470–473.
52. Hebert, J. E. III, "Critical Path Analysis and a Simulation Program for Resource-Constrained Activity Scheduling in GERT Project Networks", Ph.D. Dissertation, Purdue University, 1975.
53. Hill, T. W., "System Improvement: A Sensitivity Approach Using GERT", Master's Engineering Report, Arizona State University, 1966.
54. Hogg, G. L., "An Analysis of Labor Limited Queueing Systems with a GERT's Simulation", Ph.D. Dissertation, University of Texas, Austin, 1971.
55. Hogg, G. L. et al, "GERTS QR: A Model of Multi-Resource Constrained Queueing Systems Part I: Concepts, Notations, and Examples", *AIIE Transactions,* Vol. 7, No. 2, 1975, pp. 89–99.
56. Hogg, G. L. et al, "GERTS QR: A Model of Multi-Resource Constrained Queueing Systems Part II: An Analysis of Parallel Channel, Dual Constrained Queueing Systems with Homogeneous Resources", *AIIE Transactions,* Vol. 7, No. 2, 1975, pp. 100–109.
57. Horowitz, J., *Critical Path Scheduling,* New York: The Ronald Press Co., 1976.
58. Jöhnk, M. D., "Erzeugung von Betaverteilten und Gammaverteilten Zufallszahien", *Metrika,* Vol. 8, 1964, pp. 5–15.

59. Kaimann, R. A., "Coefficient of Network Complexity", *Management Science,* Vol. 21, No. 2, October 1974, pp. 172–177.
60. Kamins, M., Two Notes on the Lognormal Distribution, RM-3781-PR, The Rand Corporation, Santa Monica, California, 1963.
61. Kase, S. and H. Ohta, "An Application of Sampling Inspection to Correcting Plan for Semi-Markov Production Process," *AIIE Transactions,* Vol. 6., No. 2, 1974, pp. 151–158.
62. Kay, Ira M., "An Over-the-Shoulder Look at Discrete Simulation Languages," *AFIPS Conference Proceedings 40,* 1972, pp. 791–798.
63. Kiviat, P. J., "Development of Discrete Digital Simulation Languages," *SIMULATION,* Vol. 8, February 1967, pp. 65–70.
64. Kiviat, P. J. Digital Event Simulation: Modeling Concepts, The Rand Corporation, RM-5378-PR, Santa Monica, California, 1967.
65. Kiviat, P. J., Digital Computer Simulation: Computer Programming Languages, The Rand Corporation, RM-5883-PR, Santa Monica, California, 1969.
66. Kleijnen, J. P. C., *Statistical Techniques in Simulation, Parts I and II,* New York: Marcel Dekker, Inc., 1974.
67. Kleindorfer, G. B., "Bounding Distributions for a Stochastic Acylic Network", *Operations Research,* Vol. 19, No. 7, 1971, pp. 1586–1601.
68. Knuth, D. E., *The Art of Computer Programming, Vol. 2, Seminumerical Algorithms,* Reading, Mass.: Addison Wesley, 1969.
69. Lee, C., and L. P. McNamee, "A Stochastic Network Model for Air Cargo Terminals," Ninth Annual Allerton Conference on Circuit and Systems Theory, 1971, pp. 1140–1150.
70. Lawrence, K. D., and C. E. Sigal, "A Work Flow Simulation of a Regional Service Office of a Property and Casualty Insurance Company with Q-GERT," *Proc. Pittsburgh Modeling and Simulation Conference,* Vol. 5, 1974, pp.1187–1192.
71. Lewis, T. G., *Distribution Sampling for Computer Simulation,* Lexington, Mass.: Lexington Books, 1975.
72. MacCrimmon, K. R. and C. A. Ryavec, "An Analytical Study of the PERT Assumptions," *Operations Research,* Vol. 12, 1964, pp. 16–38.
73. Maggard, M. J., W. G. Lesso, et al, "Network Analysis with GERTS IIIQR," *Industrial Engineering,* Vol. 6, No. 5, May, 1974, pp. 24–29.
74. Maggard, M. J., W. G. Lesso, et al, "GERTS IIIQR: A Multiple Resource Constrained Network Simulation Model", *Management Datamatics,* Vol. 5, No. 1, 1976, pp. 5–14.

75. Malcolm, D. G., J. H. Rosenbloom, C. E. Clark and W. Fazer, "Application of a Technique for Research and Development Program Evaluation," *Operations Research,* Vol. 7, 1959, pp. 616–669.
76. McMillan, C. and R. F. Gonzalez, *Systems Analysis: A Computer Approach to Decision Models,* Homewood, Illinois: Richard D. Irwin, Inc., 1973.
77. McNamee, L. P. and C. Lee, "Development of a Standard Data Base and Computer Simulation Model for an Air Cargo Terminal", U.S. Army, CERL, Champaign, Ill., 1973.
78. Meier, R. C., W. T. Newell, and H. L. Pazer, *Simulation in Business and Economics,* Englewood Cliffs, N.J.: Prentice-Hall, Inc., 1969.
79. Meyer, H. A., "Symposium on Monte Carlo Methods", New York: John Wiley & Sons, Inc., 1956.
80. Mihram, G. A., *Simulation: Statistical Foundations and Methodology,* New York: Academic Press, 1972.
81. Mize, J. H., and J. G. Cox, *Essentials of Simulation,* Englewood Cliffs, N.J.: Prentice-Hall, Inc., 1968.
82. Mize, J. H., "Multiple Sequence Random Number Generators", *Proc. Winter Simulation Conference,* 1973, pp. 67–76.
83. Moder, J. J. and C. R. Phillips, *Project Management with CPM and PERT* (Second Edition), New York: Van Nostrand Reinhold Company, 1970.
84. Moder, J., R. A. Clark, and R. S. Gomez, "Applications of a GERT Simulator to a Repetitive Hardware Development Type Project", *AIIE Transactions,* Vol. 3, No. 4, 1971, pp. 271–280.
85. Moder, J. J. and E. G. Rodgers, "Judgement Estimates of the Moments of PERT Type Distributions", *Management Science,* Vol. 15, No. 2, Oct. 1968, pp. B76–83.
86. Moore, L. J., "Business Systems Analysis with GERTS IIIZ," Proc. *Pittsburgh Modeling and Simulation Conference,* Vol. 5, 1974, pp. 1177–1179.
87. Moore, L. J. and E. R. Clayton, *Introduction to Systems Analysis with GERT Modeling and Simulation,* New York: Petrocelli Books, 1976.
88. Moore, L. J., D. F. Scott, and E. R. Clayton, "GERT Analysis of Stochastic Systems," *Akron Business and Economic Review,* 1974, pp. 14–19.
89. Morris, W., "On the Art of Modeling", *Management Science,* Vol. 13, No. 12, 1967, pp. B707–717.
90. Morrison, K. R., "A Heuristic Algorithm for Multi-project, Limited Resource Compressible Activity Networks", Ph.D. Dissertations, Virginia Polytechnic Institute and State University, 1973.

91. Naylor, T. H., J. L. Balintfy, D. S. Burdick, and K. Chu, *Computer Simulation Techniques*, New York: John Wiley and Sons, Inc., 1965.

92. Parzen, E., *Modern Probability Theory and Its Applications*, New York: John Wiley & Sons, Inc., 1960.

93. Perry, C. and Greig, I. D., "Estimating the Mean and Variance of Subjective Distributions in PERT and Decision Analysis", *Management Science*, Vol. 21, No. 12, August 1975, pp. 1477–1480.

94. Phillips, D. T., *Applied Goodness of Fit Testing*, AIIE Monograph Series, AIIE-OR-72-1, Atlanta, Georgia, 1972.

95. Phillips, D. T. and R. F. Slovick, "A GERTS IIIQ Application to a Production Line", *Proc. 1974 AIIE National Conference*, pp. 307–318.

96. Phillips, D. T. and A. A. B. Pritsker, "GERT Network Analysis of Complex Production Systems" *International Journal of Production Research*, Vol. 13, No. 3, 1975, pp. 223–237.

97. Phillips, D. T., A. Ravindrin and J. Solberg, *Introduction to Operations Research*, New York: John Wiley and Sons, Inc., 1976.

98. Polito, J., Jr., and C. C. Petersen, "User's Manual for GRASP", Purdue Laboratory for Applied Industrial Control, Report Number 75, April 1976.

99. Porte, H. A., and W. W. Happ, "Activity Networks to Model Transportation Systems Subject to Facility Constraints," *Ninth Annual Allerton Conference on Circuit and Systems Theory*, 1971, pp. 1151–1160.

100. Pritsker, A. A. B., "Applications of Multichannel Queueing Results to the Analysis of Conveyor Systems," *Journal of Industrial Engineering*, Vol. 17, No. 1, 1966, pp. 14–21.

101. Pritsker, A. A. B., GERT: Graphical Evaluation and Review Technique, The Rand Corporation, RM-4973-NASA, Santa Monica, California, April 1966.

102. Pritsker, A. A. B., and W. W. Happ, "GERT: Graphical Evaluation and Review Technique, Part I. Fundamentals," *Journal of Industrial Engineering*, Vol. 17, No. 5, 1966, pp. 267–74.

103. Pritsker, A. A. B., and G. E. Whitehouse, "GERT: Graphical Evaluation and Review Technique, Part II. Applications," *Journal of Industrial Engineering*, Vol. 17, No. 5, 1966, pp. 293–301.

104. Pritsker, A. A. B., "GERT Networks", *The Production Engineer*, 1968, pp. 499–506.

105. Pritsker, A. A. B. and P. J. Kiviat, *Simulation with GASP II*, Englewood Cliffs, N.J.: Prentice-Hall, Inc., 1969.

106. Pritsker, A. A. B., "The Status of GERT", in H. Lombaers (Ed.), Project Planning by Network Analysis, North-Holland Publishing Co., Amsterdam-London, 1970, pp. 147–53.

107. Pritsker, A. A. B., and R. R. Burgess, "The GERT Simulation Programs: GERTS III, GERTS IIIQ, GERTS IIIC, and GERTS IIIR," NASA/ERC Contract NAS-12-2113, Virginia Polytechnic Institute, May, 1970.

108. Pritsker, A. A. B., *The GERTE User's Manual,* Pritsker & Associates, Inc., Lafayette, IN., 1974.

109. Pritsker, A. A. B., *The Precedence GERT User's Manual,* Pritsker & Associates, Inc., Lafayette, IN., 1974.

110. Pritsker, A. A. B., *The Q-GERT User's Manual,* Pritsker & Associates, Inc., Lafayette, IN., 1974.

111. Pritsker, A. A. B., *The GASP IV Simulation Language,* New York: John Wiley and Sons, Inc., 1974

112. Pritsker, A. A. B., D. B. Wortman, G. P. Chubb, D. J. Seifert, "SAINT: Systems Analysis of Integrated Networks of Tasks," *Proc. Pittsburgh Modeling and Simulation Conference,* 1974, pp. 1201–1205.

113. Pritsker, A. A. B. and C. E. Sigal, *The GERT IIIZ User's Manual,* Pritsker & Associates, Lafayette, IN, 1974.

114. Randolph, P. H., and R. D. Ringeisen, "A Network Learning Model with GERT Analysis," *Journal of Mathematical Psychology,* VOl. II, No. 1, 1974, pp. 59–70.

115. Raju, G. V. S., "Sensitivity Analysis of GERT Networks", *AIIE Transactions,* Vol. III, No. 2, 1971, pp. 133–141.

116. Roberts, S. D. and T. E. Sadlowski, "INS: Integrated Network Simulator", *Proc. Winter Simulation Conference,* 1975, pp. 575–586.

117. Saaty, T. L., *Elements of Queueing Theory,* New York: McGraw Hill Book Co., Inc., 1961.

118. Sauls, E., "The Use of GERT", *Journal of Systems Management,* Vol. 23, No. 8, 1972, pp. 11–21.

119. Samli, A. C., and C. Bellas, "The Use of GERT in the Planning and Control of Marketing Research", *Journal of Marketing Research,* Vol. VIII, August, 1971, pp. 335–39.

120. Schmidt, J. W., and R. E. Taylor, *Simulation and Analysis of Industrial Systems,* Homewood, Illinois: Richard D. Irwin, Inc., 1970.

121. Schriber, T., *Simulation Using GPSS,* New York: John Wiley & Sons, Inc., 1974.

122. Settles, F. S., "GERT Network Models of Production Economics", *Proc. 1969 AIIE National Conference,* pp. 383–94.

123. Seum, C. S., "The Addition of Queue Nodes and Server Nodes to Precedence GERT", Master's Thesis, Purdue University, 1975.

124. Shannon, R. E., "Simulation: A Survey with Research Suggestions", *AIIE Transactions,* Vol. 7, No. 3, 1975, pp. 289–301.
125. Shannon, R. E., *System Simulation: The Art and Science,* Englewood Cliffs, N.J.: Prentice-Hall, Inc., 1975.
126. Sigal, C. E., and A. A. B. Pritsker, "SMOOTH: A Combined Continuous-Discrete Network Simulation Language," *Simulation,* Vol. 22, March 1974, pp. 65–73.
127. Sigal, C. E., S. Duket and A. A. B. Pritsker, "New Additions to Q-GERT, Pritsker & Associates, Inc., Lafayette, Ind., 1976.
128. Smith, R. L., "Stochastic Analysis of Personnel Movement in Formal Organizations", Ph.D. Dissertation, Arizona State University, 1968.
129. Stidham, S., Jr., "A Last Word on L=λW", *Operations Research,* Vol. 22, No. 2, 1974, pp. 417–421.
130. Taha, H. A. *Operations Research: An Introduction,* New York: The Macmillan Company, 1971.
131. Teichrow, D., J. Lubin, and D. Truitt, "Discussion of Computer Simulation Techniques and Comparison of Languages", *SIMULATION,* Vol. 9, October 1967, pp. 181–190.
132. Tocher, K. D., *The Art of Simulation,* New York: D. Van Nostrand Company, 1963.
133. Townsend, T., "GERT Networks with Item Differentiation Capabilities", Master's Thesis, Purdue University, 1973.
134. VanSlyke, R. M., "Monte Carlo Methods and the PERT Problem", *Operations Research,* Vol. XI, September-October 1963, pp. 839–860.
135. Vanston, J. H., Jr., "Use of the Partitive Analytical Forecasting (PAF) Technique for Analyzing of the Effects of Various Funding and Administrative Strategies on Nuclear Fusion Power Plant Development", University of Texas, TR ESL-15, Energy Systems Laboratory, 1974.
136. Watters, L. J., and M. J. Vasilik, "A Stochastic Network Approach to Test and Checkout", *Proc. Fourth Conference of Application of Simulation,* 1970, pp. 113–123.
137. Weist, J. and F. Levy, *Management Guide to PERT-CPM,* Englewood Cliffs, N.J.: Prentice-Hall, Inc., 1969.
138. White, J. A., J. W. Schmidt and G. K. Bennett, *Analysis of Queueing Systems,* New York: Academic Press, 1975.
139. Whitehouse, G. W., "Extensions, New Developments, and Applications of GERT: Graphical Evaluation and Review Technique", Ph.D. Dissertation, Arizona State University, 1966.
140. Whitehouse, G. E., "The Choice Between GERTS and Simulation

Modeling for Industrial Systems", *Proc. Pittsburgh Modeling and Simulation Conference,* Vol. 5, 1974.

141. Whitehouse, G. E., "GERT, A Useful Technique for Analyzing Reliability Problem", *Technometrics,* February, 1970.
142. Whitehouse, G. E., *Systems Analysis and Design Using Network Techniques,* Englewood Cliffs, N.J.: Prentice-Hall, Inc., 1973.
143. Whitehouse, G. E., and A. A. B. Pritsker, "GERT: Part III — Further Statistical Results: Counters, Renewal Times, and Correlations", *AIIE Transactions,* Vol. 1, No. 1, March, 1969, pp. 45–50.
144. Wortman, D. B., C. E. Sigal et al., *New SAINT Concepts and the SAINT Simulation Program,* AMRL-TR-75, Aerospace Medical Research Laboratory, Wright-Patterson Air Force Base, April 1975.
145. Wortman, D. B., S. D. Duket and D. J. Seifert, "Simulation of a Remotely Piloted Vehicle/Drone Control Facility Using SAINT", *Proc. Summer Computer Simulation Conference,* San Francisco, 1975.

Appendix 1

DATA INPUT DESCRIPTION

This appendix includes all the information required to prepare the input cards (records) for the Q-GERT Analysis Program. Throughout the book, descriptions of the various input fields have been given. The purpose of this appendix is to provide one reference location for detailed information concerning data input.

In subsequent pages, the following information is presented.

1. A short form, Figure A1, for input data fields for each card type (except the GEN card) and a listing of the various code options, Table A1, for defining function types, parameter values, branching conditions codes and selection rules;

2. A description of the sequencing rules for card types and the procedures for defining fields in a column-free format on the input cards (records); and

3. A detailed description of each card type including default values, editing performed and associated error codes.

Fields*

	1	2	3	4	5	6	7	8	9	10
REG or SOU		Node number	Initial number to release [1]	Subsequent number to release [∞]	Branching (D,P,F,A) [D]	Marking (M) [M if SOU, no M if REG]	Choice criterion (F,L,S,B) [L]/ Attribute [M]			
SIN or STA		Node number/ label	Initial number to release [1]	Subsequent number to release [∞]	Branching (D,P,F,A) [D]	Statistics desired (F,A,B,I,D) [F]	Upper limit of first cell [N]	Width of histogram cell [N]	Choice criterion (F,L,S,B) [L]/ Attribute [M]	
QUE		Node number/ label	Initial number in queue [0]	Capacity of Q-node [∞]	Branching (D,P) [D]	Ranking (F,L,S,B) [F]/ Attribute [M]	Block or node number for balkers (B) [balkers destroyed]	Upper limit of first cell [N]	Width of histogram cell [N]	Following S-nodes or match nodes or allocate nodes
SEL		Node number/ label	Queue selection rule [POR]	Server selection rule [POR]	Choice criterion (S, B) [B]/ Attribute [M]	Block or node number for balkers (B) [balkers destroyed]	Associated Q-nodes	(R e p e a t s o f F i e l d 7)		
MAT		Node number	Matching attribute	Q-node/ Routing node	(R e p e a t s o f F i e l d 4)					

Figure A1 Q-GERT input short form.

400

Fields*

1	2	3	4	5	6	7	8	9	10
SEE	Stream number	Seed[0]/ ----- Initialization (I, N) [N]		Parameter set [0]	(Repeats of Fields 2 and 3)	(Repeats of Fields 3, 4 and 5)			
VAS	Node number	Attribute number [1]	Distribution type (CO)	Parameter set [0]					
PAR	Parameter set number	Parameter 1 [0]	Parameter 2 [-10^{20}]	Parameter 3 [10^{20}]	Parameter 4 [0]	Stream number [10]			
ACT	Start node	End node	Distribution or function type [CO]	Parameter set or constant [0.0]	Activity number/ label	Number of parallel servers [1]	Probability or attribute number or order [.5]	Condition code	
								[Ni.R] i = start node	
MOD	Activity number	Node out	Node in	(Repeats of Fields 3 and 4)					
TRA	Node number/ subnetwork ID	(Repeats of Field 2)							

* Default values are given in brackets [ ]. If no default is indicated, data for the field is required. Options for a field are given in parentheses ( ). A slash (/) and dashed line indicate the field may contain two entries where the slash and second entry are optional.

Figure A1 Q-GERT Input Short Form. (Continued)

Fields

1	2	3	4	5
DEF	Subnetwork ID			
DUP	Subnetwork ID	Edit Option (E or blank)		
ESN				
LIN	Start Node Number/ Subnetwork ID	End Node Number/ Subnetwork ID	(Same as ACT Fields 4 to 11)	
REP	Card Number	(Fields 1–50 of a REG, SOU, SEL, QUE, STA, SIN, VAS, MOD, or ACT card)		
DEL	Card Number			
INS	Card Number	(Fields 1–50 of a REG, SOU, SEL, QUE, STA, SIN, VAS, MOD or ACT card)		
COL	Numeric Code/Label	(Repeats of Field 2)		
TIM	Numeric Code/Label	Initial Value	(Repeats of Fields 2 and 3)	
HIS	Numeric Code/Label	Number of Cells [10]	Upper Limit of 1st Cell [0.0]	Width of Histogram Cell [1.0]

Figure A1   (continued)

Table A1. Code Options for Q-GERT Specifications

Distribution and Function Types (See Table 2-1)		Parameter Values* (See Figure 3-2)			
Code	Key	1	2	3	4
AT	Attribute	–	–	–	–
BE	Beta	μ	a	b	σ
BP	Beta PERT	m	a	b	–
CO	Constant	μ	–	–	–
ER	Erlang	μ/k	a	b	k
EX	Exponential	μ	a	b	.
GA	Gamma	μ	a	b	σ
IN	Incremental	–	–	–	–
LO	Lognormal	μ	a	b	σ
NO	Normal	μ	a	b	σ
PO	Poisson	μ–a	a	b	–
TR	Triangular	m	a	b	–
UF	User Function	–	–	–	–
UN	Uniform	–	a	b	–

* —→not used; $\mu\to$ mean; $\sigma\to$ standard deviation; m → mode; a → minimum or optimistic time; b → maximum or pessimistic time.

Branching Condition Codes (See Table 5-1)		Queue Selection Rules (See Table 5-2)		Server Selection Rules (See Table 5-3)	
Code	Key	Code	Key	Code	Key
T.R.V.	Time .R. Value	POR	Preferred order	POR	Preferred order
T.R.Ak	Time .R. Attribute k	CYC	Cyclic	CYC	Cyclic
Aj.R.V.	Attribute j.R. Value	RAN	Random	RAN	Random
Aj.R.Ak	Attribute j.R. Attribute k	LAV	Largest average number	LBT	Largest busy time
where $R=\{$LT;LE;EQ;NE;GT; or GE$\}$		SAV	Smallest average number	SBT	Smallest busy time
		LWF	Longest waiting of first	LIT	Longest idle time
Ni.R	Node i Released	SWF	Shortest waiting of first	SIT	Shortest idle time
Ni.N	Node i Not Released	LNQ	Largest number in queue	PFS	Probabilistic from
NAj.R	Node Aj Released	SNQ	Smallest number in queue		free servers
NAj.N	Node Aj Not Released	LNB	Largest number of balkers		
		SNB	Smallest number of balkers		
		LRC	Largest remaining capacity		
		SRC	Smallest remaining capacity		
		ASM	Assembly mode		

CARD TYPE SEQUENCING RULES

Listed below are the sequencing rules for input data that must be followed. Rules 4 through 8 pertain to subnetwork processing, and Rule 9 pertains to the input to obtain nodal traces.

1. A GEN card must be first.
2. Start nodes of branches must be defined before they are referenced on ACT cards or LIN cards.
3. Nodes and activities must be defined before they appear on MOD cards.
4. Only the following cards are allowed between a DEF card and an ESN card:

REG	STA	VAS	MAT
SOU	QUE	ACT	
SIN	SEL	MOD	

   If a card number is specified in Field 50 on these cards for editing purposes, the order of the cards must be from low number to high number.
5. A DUP card references the subnetwork defined between the DEF and ESN cards that most recently precedes the DUP card.
6. A DUP card with an edit option must be immediately followed by all edit cards, that is, INS, DEL, REP type cards.
7. Edit cards must be followed by an ESN card.
8. Edit cards must be arranged so that the card numbers to which edits are being made as specified by Field 2 are in ascending order.
9. A TRA card to specify node numbers for a nodal trace must not be placed between a DEF card and an ESN card or between a DUP card and an ESN card. If a TRA card contains subnetwork node numbers, the definition of the subnetwork must precede the TRA card.

FREE FORM INPUT FEATURES

1. *Blanks*—Blanks are ignored except in the analyst name field. Hence information may be punched in any column of the input card.
2. *Field Termination*—All fields on a card except the last are terminated by commas.

3. *Multiple Values in a Field*—Selected fields may require two inputs. These inputs are separated by a slash (/). In basic Q-GERT, multiple values are used to assign labels to nodes and activities.

4. *Continuation Cards*—Continuation cards are permitted. If the last nonblank character of a card is a comma, it is assumed that additional fields of the input record are contained on the card which follows. Fields may *not* be split between cards. A continuation card contains no card ID and the additional fields may be punched anywhere on the card. Continuation cards may themselves be continued. However, an input record may not exceed 50 fields.

5. *Record Termination*—An asterisk should be punched after the last field of an input card. If no asterisk is present and the last nonblank character in the card is *not* a comma, then an end of input record is assumed. The use of an asterisk is preferred since it reduces scanning time. Also, comments can be placed on the data card following the asterisk.

6. *Alphanumeric Information*—Alphanumeric fields may be of any length that will fit on a single card. *Parentheses, asterisks, slashes, periods and commas are used for punctuation purposes and are not permitted in alphanumeric fields.* Characters not significant are ignored.

7. *Numeric Information*—Any numeric information may be input as an integer or as a real number.
   a. If an integer is input for a field specified as real, the real equivalent of the integer value is used.
   b. If a real is input for a field specified as integer, the decimal portion of the real field is truncated and the integer equivalent of the truncated result is used.

8. *Default values*—Default values are defined for all nonessential input fields. To indicate that the default value is to be used for a certain field (or that a field is not applicable in a given context), the user should do one of the following:
   a. *Omit the field*—Omission of a field is indicated by a comma or by blanks followed by a comma.
   b. *Skip to the next user specified input field*—If the user lists the number (enclosed in parentheses) of the next field for which he wishes to specify information, all intermediate fields will be bypassed and will assume default values.

   For example, if the following card is input

   QUE, 3/CUSTQ, (8)1.*

these assumptions will be made

Field 1 = QUE
Field 2 = 3 with label CUSTQ
Field 3 through 7 will assume default values
Field 8 = 1.

c. *Terminate the card* before giving a value for the field. For instance, in the preceding example, Field 9 assumes a default value since nine fields are associated with card type QUE and no values were specified after Field 8.

Note: A field left blank is not automatically assumed to contain the value zero (unless zero is the established default value for the field); therefore, when a zero value is intended, it should actually be specified.

9. *Error Checking*—Each input card will be read, listed, and scanned for errors. Default values will be assumed for fields containing errors. Nonfatal errors will be flagged as warnings and will *not* prevent execution. Errors flagged as fatal *will* cancel execution.

DETAILED DESCRIPTION OF DATA CARD TYPES

On the following pages, a detailed description of each data card type is provided. For each field of each data card type, an explanation is provided of: the description of the field; its value type or expected input; the Q-GERT default value assigned if the field is not prescribed; the Q-GERT editing performed; and any error codes associated with the field. Each data card description is presented in the order they appear on the Q-GERT short form (Figure A1). For convenience, each data card type is assigned a number to facilitate the locating of the description. An alphabetic listing of the data card types and their associated number is given below.

Card Code Name	Brief Description	Card Code Number
ACT	*Act*ivity description	10
ALL	*Allo*cate node definition	26
ALT	*Alt*er node definition	28
BEG	*Beg*in network analysis	12
COL	*Col*lect user statistics	22

DEF	*Def*inition of subnetwork	15
DEL	*Del*ete card from subnetwork	20
DUP	*Dup*licate last subnetwork defined	16
ESN	*E*nd *s*ub*n*etwork definition	17
FIN	*Fin*ish of all Q-GERT input	13
FRE	*Fre*e node definition	27
GEN	*Gen*eral project and network data	1
HIS	*His*togram data for user statistics	24
INS	*Ins*ert a card in a subnetwork	21
LIN	*Lin*k a subnetwork node to network	18
MAT	*Mat*ch node description	6
MOD	*Mod*ification of network data	11
PAR	*Par*ameter data values	9
QUE	*Que*ue node description	4
REG	*Reg*ular node description	2
REP	*Rep*lace a card in a subnetwork	19
RES	*Res*ource type definition	25
SEE	*See*ds for random number streams	7
SEL	*Sel*ector node description	5
SIN	*Sin*k node description	3
SOU	*Sou*rce node description	2
STA	*Sta*tistics node description	3
TIM	*Tim*e persistent variable data	23
TRA	*Tra*ce of specific nodes	14
VAS	*V*alue *as*signment to attributes	8

1. GEN - general project information

Field Number	Description	Value	Default	Editing	Associated Errors
1	Card type	GEN	(Required)	= 'GEN'	8101
2	Analyst name	Alpha field (up 12 significant characters)	12 blanks	If present, first character must be alphabetic (only first 12 characters are processed)	102
3	Project name or number	Alpha field	12 blanks	(see previous field)	103
4	Month	Integer	1	Integer between 0 and 12	104
5	Day	Integer	1	Integer between 0 and 31	105
6	Year	Integer	2001	Integer between 1970 and 2001	106
7	Number of STAtistics nodes	Integer	0	Integer between 0 and maximum number of nodes	107
8	Number of SINk nodes	Integer	0	Integer between 0 and maximum number of nodes	108
9	Number of SINk node releases to end a run	Integer	value in Field 8	Integer	109
10	Time to end one run of the network	Real	1.E20	Positive real	110
11	Number of runs of the network	Integer	1	Positive integer	111
12	Indicator for output reports in addition to the final summary report	First Run, Each Run, Cumulative & Each Run, Summary Only	First	= 'F' or 'E' or 'C' or 'S'	112

408

13	Time from which statistics will be kept on each run	Real	0	Non-negative real	113
14	Maximum number of attributes with each transaction flowing through the network	Integer	0	Non-negative integer	114
15	Run number for beginning of event tracing	Integer	0→no tracing	Integer between 0 and value of Field 11	115
16	Run number for ending of event tracing (this run will be traced)	Integer	Value of Field 15	Integer between value of Field 15 and value of Field 11	116
17	Run number for beginning of nodal tracing	Integer	0→no tracing	Integer between 0 and value in Field 11	115
18	Run number for ending of nodal trace (this run is traced)	Integer	Value in Field 17	Integer between value in Field 17 and value in Field 11	116
19	Indicator that only input cards with errors are to be listed	Errors only All cards	All input cards listed	= 'E'	119
20	Execution option	E1 — No execution E2 — No execution if any input discrepancies E3 — No execution if fatal input discrepancy	E3	= 'E1', 'E2', 'E3', or 'E4' (E4 — Echo suppressed)	120
21	Largest node number defined by user. (Specify only when including subnetworks.)	Integer	MXNOD	Integer	
22	Largest activity number defined by user. (Specify only when including subnetworks.)	Integer	MXNPO	Integer	

2. *REG*-regular node description   or   *SOU*-source node description

Field Number	Description	Value	Default	Editing	Associated Errors
1	Card type	*REG* or *SOU*	(Required)	= 'REG' or 'SOU'	8000
2	Node number	Integer	(Required)	Integer between 1 and maximum number of nodes	8002
3	Initial number of incoming transactions to release the node.	Integer	1 if *REG* 0 if *SOU*	Non-negative integer (0 if and only if *SOU*)	8003
4	Subsequent number of incoming transactions to release the node (after the first release)	Integer (to specify infinite, use default)	Infinite	Positive integer	8003
5	Output characteristics of node	*P*robabilistic *D*eterministic *F*irst (conditional, take first) *A*ll (conditional, take all)	Deterministic	= 'P', 'D', 'F', or 'A'	205

		Mark		
6	Indicator that this node is to mark		M if SOU No M if REG = 'M'	206
7	Criterion for associating an attribute set with a transaction passing through a node/	Hold the attribute set of the transaction arriving *F*irst *L*ast or hold attribute set of the transaction with the *S*mallest value in a given attribute *B*iggest value in a given attribute	*L*ast = 'F', 'L', 'S', or 'B'	207
	If *S*mall or *B*ig specified, the number of the attribute to be used or 'M' for mark time	Integer or 'M'	*M*ark Time Integer between 1 and maximum number of attributes specified for a transaction or 'M'	7207

411

3. *SIN* - *sink node description* or *STA* - *statistics node description*

Field Number	Description	Value	Default	Editing	Associated Errors
1	Card type	SIN or STA	(Required)	= 'SIN' or 'STA'	8000
2	Node number/Label for output identification	Integer/8 characters	(Required)/ Blanks	Integer between 1 and maximum number of nodes	8002
3	Initial number of incoming transactions to release the node	Integer	1	Positive integer	8003
4	Subsequent number of incoming transactions to release the node (after the first release)	Integer (to specify infinite, use default)	Infinite	Positive integer	8003
5	Output characteristics of node	*Probabilistic* *Deterministic* *First* (conditional, take first) *All* (conditional, take all)	*Deterministic*	= 'P', 'D', 'F', or 'A'	205
6	Statistical quantities to be collected	*First* (time of first release) *All* (time of all releases) *Between* (time between releases) *Interval* (time interval from most recent marking of transaction to release of this node) *Delay* (delay from first arriving transaction until the node is released)	*First*	= 'T', 'A', 'B', 'I', or 'D'	306

3. (continued)

Field Number	Description	Value	Default	Editing	Associated Errors
7	The upper limit of the first cell for the histogram to be obtained for this node. The first cell of the histogram will contain the number of times the statistic of interest at this node had a value less than or equal to the value given in this field.	Real or 'N'	N → no reporting of statistics	Real or 'N'	
8	The width of each cell of the histogram. Each histogram contains 20 cells. The last cell will contain the number of times the statistic of interest at this node had a value greater than the upper limit of the first cell (Field 7) plus 18 x cell width (Field 8).	Real or 'N'	N → no reporting of statistics	Positive real or 'N'	
9	Criterion for associating an attribute set with a transaction passing through a node / transaction arriving	Hold the attribute set of the *First* *Last* or hold attribute set of the transaction with the *Smallest* value in a given attribute *Biggest* value in a given attribute	*Last*	= 'F', 'L', 'S', or 'B'	206
	If *Small* or *Big* specified, the number of the attribute to be used or 'M' for mark time	Integer or *Mark* Time	*Mark* Time	Integer between 1 and maximum number of attributes specified for a transaction or 'M'	7207

413

4. *QUE* - queue node description

Field Number	Description	Value	Default	Editing	Associated Errors
1	Card type	QUE	(Required)	= 'QUE'	8000
2	Node number/Label for output identification	Integer /8 characters	(Required)/ Blanks	Integer between 1 and maximum number of nodes	8002
3	Initial number in queue	Integer	0	Non-negative integer	403
4	Maximum number permitted in queue	Integer (to specify infinite, use default)	Infinite	Non-negative integer	404
5	Output characteristics of node	*D*eterministic *P*robabilistic	*Deterministic*	= 'P' or 'D'	205
6	Ranking procedure for Q-node/	*F*IFO-first in-first out *L*IFO-last in-first out *S*mall value first (based on attribute value) *B*ig value first (based on attribute value)	*FIFO*	= 'F', 'L', 'S', or 'B'	406
	For Q-nodes ranked by *S*mall or *B*ig, the number of the attribute on which the ranking is based	*Integer or Mark Time*	*Mark Time*	Integer between 1 and maximum number of attributes or 'M'	7207

4. QUE - (cont.)

Field Number	Description	Value	Default	Editing	Associated Errors
7	Balking or blocking information	*Blocking* or Integer = node number to which balkers are sent	Balkers are lost to system	= 'B' or integer between 1 and maximum number of nodes	407 8407 8408 8409
8	The upper limit of the first cell for the histogram to be obtained for this node.	Real or 'N'	N → no reporting of statistics	Real or 'N'	
9	The width of each cell of the histogram. Each histogram contains 20 cells.	Real or 'N'	N → no reporting of statistics	Positive Real or 'N'	
10–31	Selector nodes or the MATCH node on output side of Q-node (if any) (but not if a service activity emanates from the Q-node) When more than one S-node is specified, the order of appearance in these fields determines the priority given to the associated S-nodes.	Integer	No S-node or MATCH node node on output side of Q-node	Integer between 1 and maximum number of nodes	8410 8411

415

5. *SEL* - selector node description

Field Number	Description	Value	Default	Editing	Associated Errors
1	Card type	*SEL*	(Required)	= 'SEL'	8000
2	Node number/Label for output identification	Integer/8 characters	(Required)/Blanks	Integer between 1 and maximum number of nodes	8002
3	Queue selection rule	3 character ID from list of queue selection rules (Table A1)	*POR*	= 3 character ID from Table A1	503
4	Server selection rule	3 character ID from list of server selection rules (Table A1)	*POR*	= 3 character ID from Table A1	504
5	For assembly nodes (field 3 = ASM), criterion for associating an attribute set with a transaction passing through the node/	Hold attribute set with the *S*mallest value in a given attribute *B*iggest value in a given attribute	*B*iggest	= 'S' or 'B'	207
	For assembly nodes (field 3 = ASM), the number of the attribute to be used or 'M' for mark time	Integer or M for *M*ark Time	*M*ark Time	Integer between 1 and maximum number of attributes for this simulation or 'M'	7207
6	Balking and blocking information	*B*locking or Integer = node number to which balkers are sent	Balkers are lost to system	= 'B' or integer between 1 and maximum number of nodes	407 8407 8409
7-16	Q-nodes associated with this selector. (Up to 10 fields may be entered.) When more than one Q-node is specified, the order of appearance in these fields determines the preferred order for selecting Q-nodes.	Integer	(At least one required)	Integer between 1 and maximum number of nodes	8507

6. *MAT* - *mat*ch node description

Field Number	Description	Value	Default	Editing	Associated Errors
1	Card Type	*MAT*	(Required)	= 'MAT'	8000
2	Node Number	Integer	(Required)	Integer between 1 and maximum number of nodes	8002
3	Matching attribute Number or M for mark time	Integer or Mark Time	Mark Time	Integer between 1 and maximum number of attributes for the simulation or 'M'	7207
4	Q-nodes containing transactions to be matched by this match node (up to 5 Q-nodes are allowed)/	Integer		at least 2 Q-nodes associated with the Match node	8604
	Node number to which a matched transaction from Q-node is to be routed	Integer	No routing		
5–8	Repeats of Field 4. At least 1 repeat required and at most 4 repeats allowed.				8605

7. SEE - Random number *seed* initialization (required only if seed values or reinitialization of seed values are desired)

Field Number	Description	Value	Default	Editing	Associated Errors
1	Card Type	SEE	(Required)	= 'SEE'	8000
2	Stream Number	Integer	MXSTR=10	Positive Integer less than or equal to MXSTR	702
3	Random Number seed for stream specified in previous field/	Integer	Internal seed value	Integer	
	Reinitialization of stream	I→Initialize seed to same value for each run N→No resetting of seed	N		
4–21	Repeats of Fields 2 and 3.				

8. **VAS** - value assignments to attributes of transactions

Field Number	Description	Value	Default	Editing	Associated Errors
1	Card type	VAS	(Required)	= 'VAS'	8000
2	Node number at which assignment is to be made	Integer	(Required)	Integer between 1 and maximum number of nodes	8802 8812
3	Number of the attribute to which the assignment is to be made	Integer	1	Integer between 1 and maximum number of attributes	8803
4	Distribution or function type for the assignment	2 character ID chosen from list of distribution types (Table A1)	CO	= 2 character ID from Table A1	804
5	Parameter set number for the assignment	Integer or Real	0.0	Integer or Real	805
6–26	(Repeat Fields 3, 4, and 5 to specify up to 7 additional assignments. Use only 1 VAS input card for each node at which assignments take place)				806 8807

9. *PAR* - *parameter set description*

Field Number	Description	Value	Default	Editing	Associated Errors
1	Card type	PAR	(Required)	= 'PAR'	8000
2	Parameter set number	Integer	(Required)	Integer between 1 and maximum number of parameter sets	8902
3	Parameter 1	Real	0.	Real	903
4	Parameter 2	Real	-10^{20}	Real	903
5	Parameter 3	Real	10^{20}	Real	903
6	Parameter 4	Real	0.	Real	903
7	Random Number Stream	Integer	MXSTR=10	Integer	903

A sample is obtained from a distribution such that if a sample is less than the minimum value, the sample value is given the minimum value. Similarly, if the sample is greater than the maximum value, the sample value is assigned the maximum value. This is not sampling from a truncated distribution but sampling from a distribution with a given probability of obtaining the minimum and maximum values.

The parameters required to sample from the distributions are described below. The parameter values for the lognormal (LO), triangular (TR), beta (BE), gamma (GA), and beta PERT (BP) are modified to simplify random sampling. Thus, parameter sets for these distributions must not be used for any other distributions, i.e., a parameter set for a lognormal distribution must only be used for sampling from a lognormal distribution.

For COnstants, no PAR card is used. The value of the constant is taken as the value given to parameter set specification.

For NOrmal, LOgnormal, BEta, and GAmma distributions

Parameter 1	The mean value
Parameter 2	The minimum value
Parameter 3	The maximum value
Parameter 4	The standard deviation

For UNiform distribution

Parameter 1	Not used
Parameter 2	The minimum value
Parameter 3	The maximum value
Parameter 4	Not used

For EXponential distribution

Parameter 1	The mean value
Parameter 2	The minimum value
Parameter 3	The maximum value
Parameter 4	Not used

For ERlang distribution

Parameter 1	The mean time for the Erlang variable divided by the value given to Parameter 4
Parameter 2	The minimum value
Parameter 3	The maximum value
Parameter 4	The number of exponential deviates to be included in the sample obtained from the Erlang distribution

For POisson distribution

Parameter 1	The mean minus the minimum value
Parameter 2	The minimum value
Parameter 3	The maximum value
Parameter 4	Not used

Care is required when using the POisson since it is not usually used to represent an interval of time. The interpretation of the mean should be the mean number of time units per time period.

For BP and TRiangular distribution

Parameter 1	The most likely value m
Parameter 2	The optimistic value a
Parameter 3	The pessimistic value b
Parameter 4	Not used

10. *ACT* - Activity description

Field Number	Description	Value	Default	Editing	Associated Errors
1	Card Type	ACT	(Required)	= 'ACT'	8000
2	Start node	Integer	(Required)	Number of an existing node	9002
3	End node	Integer	(Required)	Number of an existing node (not an assembly node)	9003
4	Distribution or function type	2 character ID chosen from list of distribution types (Table A1)	CO	= 2 character ID from Table A1	1004
5	Parameter set number or value of constant	Integer or Real	0.0		1005
6	Activity number/	Integer	System-assigned	Integer between 0 and maximum number of activity numbers	1006 9006 9105
	Label for server identification	8 characters	Blank		
7	The number of servers represented by this branch	Integer	1	Non-negative integer	1007 9007

8	Probability (only applicable if start node has 'P' branching or start node is a SELector using RFS rule)	Real number between 0. and 1. or attribute number where probability is stored	0.5	Real number between 0. and 1. or non-negative integer	1008
or					9008
8	Order of testing conditions (only applicable if start node has 'F' branching* or start node is a SELector using POR rule**)	Non-negative number (integer or real)	0 (= conditions tested in order of input)	Non-negative number	9008
9	Condition code (only applicable if start node has 'F' or 'A' branching)	See Condition Codes List***	Start node released (Ni:R).		1009 9009 9010 9011

* For each activity emanating from a start node with F (conditional, take first) output, an order value should be specified. When the start node is released, conditions on associated branches will be tested in ascending order (low values first) based on this value.

** The "preferred order" for selection from free servers is ascending order (low value first) based on this value.

*** Condition codes allowed are:

T.R.V	Time .R. Value
T.R.Ak	Time .R. Attribute k
Aj.R.V	Attribute j.R.Value
Aj.R.Ak	Attribute j.R.Attribute k

where R={LT;LE;EQ;NE;GT; or GE}

Ni.R	Node i Released
Ni.N	Node i Not Released
NAj.R	Node Aj Released
NAj.N	Node Aj Not Released

423

11. *MOD* - *node modification information* (required only if network contains nodes to be modified)

Field Number	Description	Value	Default	Editing	Associated Errors
1	Card type	*MOD*	(Required)	= 'MOD'	8000
2	Activity number	Integer	(Required)	Integer between 1 and maximum number of activities	9102
3	*Node to be replaced* (number of node to be replaced when the activity given in Field 2 is completed)	Integer	(Required)	Number of existing node	9103
4	*Replacement node* (number of node to be inserted into the network in place of the specified node in the preceding field when the activity in Field 2 is completed)	Integer	(Required)	Number of existing node not equal to value in Field 3	1104 9103
5–24	(If multiple replacements are to occur upon completion of activity prescribed by Field 2, then Fields 3 and 4 should be repeated for each additional replacement. The limit of replacements is 11.				1105 9105

12. *BEG* - *beginning of new network* (only required if there are additional networks)

Field Number	Description	Value	Default	Editing	Associated Errors
1	Card type	*BEG*	(Required)	= 'BEG'	1201 8000

13. *FIN* - *finish* of all networks

Field Number	Description	Value	Default	Editing	Associated Errors
1	Card type	*FIN*	(A blank card may be used in lieu of *FIN* card)	Blank card or = 'FIN'	1301 8000

14. *TRA* - nodal *trace*

Only one TRA card is permitted. If subnetwork nodes are to be traced, the TRA card must follow the ESN card associated with the subnetwork containing the node definition.

Field Number	Description	Value	Default	Editing	Associated Errors
1	Card type	TRA	(Required)	= 'TRA'	8000
2	User-defined node numbers to be traced/	Integer	No user-defined nodes are to be traced	Integer and less than 50 nodes to be traced	1402
	Subnetwork ID number	Integer	No ID number		
3-49	Repeats of Field 2				1403

15. DEF - Defining a subnetwork

Field Number	Description	Value	Default	Editing	Associated Errors
1	Card Type	DEF	(Required)	= 'DEF'	8000
2	Subnetwork identification number to be appended to all nodes and activity numbers defined in the subnetwork.	Integer	MXNMC	Positive Integer less than or equal to MXNMC	9502

Note: On the cards that follow a DEF card and precede the next ESN card, Field 50 is used to assign card numbers to cards. These card numbers are referenced by edit cards (DEL, REP, INS) during subnetwork generation. If Field 50 is not specified, the cards will be numbered internally in a consecutive order starting with the number 1.

16. DUP - Duplicating a Subnetwork

Field Number	Description	Value	Default	Editing	Associated Errors
1	Card Type	DUP	(Required)	= 'DUP'	9600
2	Number to be appended to all nodes and activity numbers of this subnetwork.	Integer	(Required)	Positive integer less than or equal to MXNMC	9601 9602
3	Indicator to specify whether this subnetwork generation involves editing	E - Editing	No Editing	'E' or blank	9603

17. ESN - End of Subnetwork definition or editing for duplication of subnetwork

Field Number	Description	Value	Default	Editing	Associated Errors
1	Card Type	ESN	(Required)	= 'ESN'	8000

426

18. *LIN* - Link Activity Descriptions

Field Number	Description	Value	Default	Editing	Associated Errors
1	Card Type	LIN	(Required)	= 'LIN'	8000
2	Node Number of Start Node/	Integer	(Required)	Number of an existing node	9002 9802
	Subnetwork Number of Start Node	Integer		Non-integer	9802
3	Node Number of End Node/	Integer	(Required)	Number of existing node	9003 9802
	Subnetwork Number of End Node	Integer			
4	Distribution or function type	2 character ID chosen from Table A1	CO	= 2 character ID from Table 2	1004
5	Parameter set number or value of constant	Integer or Real	0.0	Integer or real	1005
6	Activity number/	Integer	System-assigned if service activity	Integer between 0 and maximum number of activity numbers	1006
	Label for server identification	8 characters	Blanks		
7	The number of servers represented by this branch	Integer	1		

18. *LIN - Link Activity Descriptions (cont.)*

Field Number	Description	Value	Default	Editing	Associated Errors
8	Probability (only applicable if start node has 'P' branching or start node is a SELector using RFS rule)	Real number between 0. and 1. or attribute number where probability is stored	0.5	Real number between 0. and 1. or non-negative integer	9008
or 8	Order of testing conditions (only applicable if start node has 'F' branching* or start node is a SELector using POR rule**)	Non-negative number (integer or real)	0 → conditions tested in order of input	Non-negative number	9008
9	Condition code (only applicable if start node has 'F' or 'A' branching)	See Condition Codes List***	Start node released (Ni:R).		9009

* For each activity emanating from a start node with F (conditional, take first) output, an order value should be specified. When the start node is released, conditions on associated branches will be tested in ascending order (low values first) based on this value.

** The "preferred order" for selection from free servers is ascending order (low value first) based on this value.

*** Condition codes allowed are:

T.*R*.V	Time .*R*. Value
T.*R*.Ak	Time .*R*. Attribute k
Aj.*R*.V	Attribute j.*R*.Value
Aj.*R*.Ak	Attribute j.*R*.Attribute k

where *R* = {LT; LE; EQ; NE; GT; or GE)

Ni.R	Node i Released
Ni.N	Node i Not Released
NAj.R	Node Aj Released
NAj.N	Node Aj Not Released

428

19. *REP - Replace a card during generation of a duplicate of a subnetwork*

Field Number	Description	Value	Default	Editing	Associated Errors
1	Card Type	*REP*	(Required)	= 'REP'	8000 9901
2	Number of the card to be replaced in the last defined subnetwork	Integer	(Required)	Integer	9902
3-52	Input fields of the replacing card.				

20. *DEL - Delete a card during generation of a duplicate of a subnetwork*

Field Number	Description	Value	Default	Editing	Associated Errors
1	Card Type	DEL	(Required)	= 'DEL'	8000
2	Number of the card to be deleted from the last defined subnetwork	Integer	(Required)	Integer	9902

21. *INS - Insert a card during generation of a duplicate of a subnetwork*

Field Number	Description	Value	Default	Editing	Associated Errors
1	Card Type	INS	(Required)	= 'INS'	8000
2	Card number in the last defined subnetwork, after which the information on this card is to be inserted	Integer	(Required)	Integer	9902
3-52	Input fields of the card to be inserted.				

429

22. COL = Collect statistics based on observation (required only if calls to subroutine COL are employed in UF)

Field Number	Description	Value	Default	Editing	Associated Errors
1	Card type	COL	(Required)	= 'COL'	8000
2	Numeric code, I, used to identify the statistics resulting from calls to subroutine COL(X,I) with the same second argument. This code must be unique among all COL statistics/	Integer	(Required)	Non-negative integer less than or equal to MUCOL	9222
	Alphanumeric label for identification of COL statistics	Alphanumeric	Blanks	Alphanumeric	
3–9	(Repeat Field 2 to specify up to 7 COL type statistics per COL card. Additional COL cards may be used				

23. *TIM* - *Time*-persistent statistics (required only if calls to subroutine TIM are employed in UF)

Field Number	Description	Value	Default	Editing	Associated Errors
1	Card type	TIM	(Required)	= 'TIM'	8000
2	Numeric code, II, used to identify all statistics resulting from calls to subroutine TIM(XX,II) with the same second argument. This code must be unique among all TIM statistics/	Integer	(Required)	Non-negative integer less than or equal to MUTIM	9222
	Alphanumeric label for identification of TIM statistics	Alphanumeric	Blanks	Alphanumeric	
3	Initial value for the variable associated with the numeric code in Field 2.	Real	0.	Real	9223
4-15	(Repeat Fields 2 and 3 to specify up to 7 TIM type statistics per TIM card. Additional TIM cards may be used.)				

431

24. *HIS* - *His*togram information (required only if calls to subroutine HIS are employed in UF)

Field Number	Description	Value	Default	Editing	Associated Errors
1	Card type	HIS	(Required)	= 'HIS'	8000
2	Numeric code, J, used to identify the observations resulting from calls to subroutine HIS(X,J) with the same second argument. This code should be uique among all HIS specifications/	Integer	(Required)	Non-negative integer less than or equal to MUHIS	9222
	Alphanumeric label for identification of the histogram.	Alphanumeric	Blanks	Alphanumeric	
3	Number of interior cells in the histogram.	Integer	10	Non-negative integer	9223
4	The upper limit of the first cell for this histogram.	Real	0.	Real	9223
5	The width of each cell of the histogram.	Real	1.	Positive real	9223
6-29	(Repeat Fields 2, 3, 4, and 5 to specify up to 7 histograms per HIS card. Additional HIS cards may be used.				

25. *RES* - resource type definition

Field Number	Description	Value	Default	Editing	Associated Errors
1	Card Type	RES	(Required)	= 'RES'	8000
2	Resource Number/	Integer	(Required)	Nonnegative integer $\leq$ MXRES	8002
	Label	8 characters	Blanks		
3	Number of units of this resource type available	Integer	1	Positive Integer	
4-13	Resource ALLOCATE nodes to be polled when resource is freed	Integer	No ALLO-CATE nodes associated with resource definition	Integer between 1 and maximum number of nodes	

26. *ALL* - *allocate node description*

Field Number	Description	Value	Default	Editing	Associated Errors
1	Card type	ALL	(Required)	= 'ALL'	8000
2	Node number	Integer	(Required)	Integer between 1 and maximum number of nodes	8002
3	Queue selection rule	3 character ID from list of queue selection rules (Table A1)	POR	= 3 character ID from Table A1	503
4	Resource number	Integer	1	Integer between 1 and max. number of resources	
5	Resource units required by waiting transactions at associated Q-nodes	Integer	1		
6	Q-node in which transaction is waiting for resources/	Integer	(At least 1 required)	Integer between 1 and maximum number of nodes	
	Node number to which transaction is to be routed when resources are allocated	Integer	No routing	Integer between 1 and maximum number of nodes	
7-16	(Repeats of Field 6)				

27. FRE - *free* node description

Field Number	Description	Value	Default	Editing	Associated Errors
1	Card type	FRE	(Required)	= 'FRE'	8000
2	Node number	Integer	(Required)	Integer between 1 and max. number of nodes	8002
3	Output characteristics	P, D, F, A	D	= 'P', 'D', 'F', or 'A'	
4	Resource number	Integer or Ak where k is an attribute number	1		
5	Resource units to be freed	Integer or Ak where k is attribute number	1		
6–15	ALLOCATE nodes in the order to be polled to allocate freed resource units	Integer	Use ALLOC list given in RES card for resource number	List of ALLOC nodes concatenated to list provided unless a negative value is given after list	

28. *ALT* - *alter* node description

Field Number	Description	Value	Default	Editing	Associated Errors
1	Card type	ALT	(Required)	= 'ALT'	8000
2	Node number	Integer	(Required)	Integer between 1 and max. number of nodes	8002
3	Output characteristics	P, D, F, A	D	= 'P', 'D', 'F', or 'A'	
4	Resource number	Integer or Ak	1		
5	Resource units to be freed	Integer or Ak	1		
6–15	ALLOCATE nodes in the order to be polled to allocate freed resource units	Integer	Use ALLOC list given in RES card for resource number	List of ALLOC nodes concatenated to list provided unless a negative value is given after list	

Appendix 2

Q-GERT ANALYSIS PROGRAM ERROR MESSAGES

Checks for error conditions are made throughout the Q-GERT Analysis Program. Errors that occur during a simulation run have been coded with error message numbers less than 100. General input errors also have codes less than 100. Data input errors associated with specific fields of a data card have been assigned codes greater than 100. Data input errors can result in a warning message or in the cessation of program execution. These latter errors are referred to as fatal errors. Fatal data input errors have code numbers of 8000 or higher.

In general, the data input error codes have been constructed so that the first two digits provide a reference to a card type and the last two digits refer to a field number on a card.* The card type number, as defined in Appendix 1, is multiplied by 100, added to the field number and then added to 0 or 8000 depending on the severity of the error. For example, error code 407 is a warning error that Field 7 on card type 4 (QUE card) has unrecognizable data in it. Another example is error code 9009 which indicates a fatal error in Field 9 of card type 10 (ACT card). The specific type of error is determined by examining the table of error messages presented in this appendix. For error code 9009, the error message is "Invalid condition code".

_____

*When the same error can occur on various cards, the smallest card number was used to construct the error code.

ERROR CODE	CONDITION
9	Incorrect card sequencing.
10	Invalid stream number of zero.
12	Cyclic queue encountered without starting point.
14	Insufficient space available to store attributes of transactions.
15	Too many entries in auxiliary attribute array.
16	Storage array for user time-persistent variables was initialized at a time greater than last statistics collection time.
18	COLP called with argument out of specified range.
20	Negative number of observations.
22	Invalid reference to an activity.
23	COLC called with argument out of specified range.
24	Too many transactions in Q-nodes
25	Number of sink nodes incorrectly specified.
26	COL called with argument out of specified range.
27	TIMC called with argument less than 0.
28	TIM called with argument out of specified range.
29	TIMP called with argument out of specified range.
30	HIS called with argument out of specified range.
31	HISP called with argument out of specified range.
32	HISC called with argument less than 0.
33	Invalid integer.
34	Invalid condition code.
40	Number of fields input exceeds maximum — remaining fields are ignored.
50	Multiple decimal points in field — first decimal point was used.
60	Invalid character in numeric field — end of card assumed.
70	Malformed skip request — default values assumed for remainder of card.
75	Invalid resource type specified by attribute value.
87	Insufficient storage space for activity descriptions.
88	Insufficient storage space for end-of-activity events.
90	Number of resource units requested to be freed is greater than number of units in use.
91	Attribute number too large.
92	Request for status of nonexistent server.
93	Request made to start a nonexistent activity.
94	Attempt to decrease time associated with a transaction below current simulation time.

ERROR CODE	CONDITION
95	Insufficient storage space for events.
96	Attempt was made to remove a nonexistent event.
97	Insufficient storage space in blocked transaction files.
102	Nonalphanumeric analyst name field.
103	Invalid project name.
104	Invalid month.
105	Invalid day.
106	Invalid year.
107	Invalid number of nodes for statistics.
108	Invalid number of sink nodes.
109	Invalid number of sinks to realize network.
110	No sink nodes specified and no time limit set. Run will end when no events are scheduled.
111	Invalid number of simulations.
112	Invalid reporting of results request.
113	Invalid start time for statistics collection.
114	Invalid number of attributes per transaction.
115	Invalid trace start run.
116	Invalid trace end run.
119	Invalid input for Field 19 of GEN card.
120	Invalid execution option.
205	Invalid branching type.
206	Invalid mark indicator.
207	Unrecognizable choice criterion.
306	Invalid statistics type.
309	Invalid mark indicator.
403	Invalid initial number in queue.
404	Invalid queue capacity.
405	Invalid branching type.
406	Invalid ranking procedure.
407	Unrecognizable blocking/balking information.
503	Invalid queue selection rule.
504	Invalid server selection rule.
702	Invalid stream number on SEED card.
703	Negative random number stream specified.
751	Sum of probabilities not one when DPROB called.
804	Invalid distribution or function type on VAS card.
805	Invalid parameter specification on VAS card.
806	Too many assignments requested on VAS card.
903	Invalid parameter value.
907	Invalid random number stream specified on PAR card.
1002	Invalid server numbers.

ERROR CODE	CONDITION
1004	Invalid distribution or function type.
1005	Invalid parameter specification.
1006	Invalid activity number.
1007	Invalid number of parallel servers specified for non-service activity.
1008	Invalid probability or order.
1009	Numeric data in condition field.
1103	Nonexistent node referenced.
1104	Replacement node same as node to be replaced.
1105	Number of replacement pairs exceeds 11.
1201	Unrecognizable characters on BEG card.
1301	Unrecognizable characters on FIN card.
1402	Subnetwork node number could not be identified.
1403	Excess number of nodes specified for nodal trace on TRA card.
1503	Largest user defined node number out of range on GEN card.
1504	Largest user defined activity number out of range on GEN card.
7003	Invalid number of resource units specified at the beginning of a run.
7207	Invalid attribute for choice criterion or queue ranking.
7309	Invalid attribute for choice criterion or queue ranking.
8000	Invalid card ID.
8002	Invalid node number.
8003	Invalid number of requirements.
8004	Invalid ALLOCATE node specified for polling.
8005	Invalid number of resource units to be freed or altered.
8006	Error in node pairs associated with an ALLOCATE node.
8060	Insufficient space for resource related variables. Redimensioning required.
8101	GEN card missing or misspelled.
8102	Invalid RESOURCE type specified.
8105	Invalid number of resource units specified.
8407	QUE or SEL card specifies a nonexistent balk node.
8408	Transaction to balk to an S-node with emanating servers.
8409	Invalid blocking of a nonservice activity.
8410	Invalid selector node number.
8411	S-node specification exceeds allowable range.

ERROR CODE	CONDITION
8507	SEL card references a nonexistent queue node.
8604	The number of Q-nodes associated with the Match node is less than 2.
8605	One of the MAT cards references a node that has not been defined.
8802	Invalid node number.
8803	Invalid attribute number on VAS card.
8804	Non-existent resource type referred to.
8807	Excess number of assignments and/or conditional branching specifications.
8812	Value assignment requested at nonexistent node.
8888	End node of an activity invalid.
8902	Invalid parameter specification on PAR card.
9002	Invalid start node.
9003	Invalid end node.
9006	Two branches from a Q-node with the same activity number but Q-node does not have probabilistic branching.
9007	The blocking of an activity representing parallel servers is prohibited.
9008	Invalid probability (or order) value.
9009	Invalid condition code.
9010	Invalid conditional variable.
9011	Invalid conditional threshhold value.
9102	Invalid activity number on MOD card.
9105	Number of servers and/or number of modifications too large.
9502	Invalid subnetwork number.
9600	Continue card not allowed for editing.
9601	Subnetwork assigning a node number which is too large.
9602	Subnetwork assigning an activity number which is too large.
9603	Invalid subnetwork edit command.
9802	Invalid start node or end node on LIN card.
9901	Invalid condition in editing a subnetwork.
9902	Card number not defined for editing.
9222	User-statistics code exceeds allowed limit.
9223	Invalid user-statistics code.
9910	Statistics requested exceed storage space allocated. Redimensioning required.

Appendix 3

Q-GERT ANALYSIS PROGRAM OPERATIONAL INFORMATION

Technical documentation regarding the loading and compiling of the Q-GERT Analysis Program is available. Such documentation is continually updated and hence is not included in this book. It is made available when the program is purchased. In this appendix, brief discussions are provided of equipment requirements, overlay organization, program sizing, random number generators and running times.

The Q-GERT Analysis Program is written in ANSI Standard FORTRAN IV and can be run on any computer that has a FORTRAN IV compiler. The program is constructed in three parts: a main stem; a data input overlay; and a simulation overlay. Since overlay procedures vary depending on the machine, special handling to load the program on particular machines is required. Peripheral devices* 5, 6 and 7 are used in Q-GERT. All input to the program is obtained from device 5. Device 7 is used for input manipulations and to store nodel trace information. Device 6 is used for recording output information only.

Versions of the program to accommodate 100, 200 or 1000 node networks have been developed. Improved file storage procedures are continually being evaluated as are data packing methods. The standard Q-GERT Analysis Program is for 100 nodes of which 50 can be Q-nodes or S-nodes. This version employs no data packing and requires 32,000 words of core storage. Increasing the size of the problems that can be

*Reference in the program is made to logical devices and these could be assigned as card readers, printers, tapes or disk units.

run involves tailoring the COMMON storage areas to meet specific needs. Such information is included in the technical documentation.

The random number generator function is the only machine-dependent subprogram included in the Q-GERT Analysis Program. *The author recommends that a random number generator be selected that is in common use at your computing facility or one that has met your statistical standards.* Figure A2 is the FORTRAN listing of the random number generator function, DRAND, that was used in preparing the examples presented in this book. Function DRAND is an adaptation of the standard CDC 6500 random generator function to allow for 10 streams and for the reinitialization of seed values for each run. Conversion of a random number generator to the form presented for DRAND in Figure A2 should be straight-forward.

```
      FUNCTION DRAND(IX)
C
C****IF MXSTR IS GREATER THAN 10, THE DIMENSION AND DATA
C****STATEMENTS MUST REFLECT THIS INCREASE.
C
      DIMENSION L(10),LL(10)
C
      COMMON /QVAR/ NDE,NFTBU(100),NREL(100),NRELP(100),NREL2(100),NRUN,
     1NRUNS,NTC(100),PARAM(100,4),TBEG,TNOW
      COMMON/PARM/ ISTRM,JTRIB(6),NPRMS,IPAR(100),SCALE,
     1IISED(10),SSEED(10)
      DIMENSION ATRIB(1)
      EQUIVALENCE (ATRIB(1),JTRIB(6))
C
      DATA K/5536458/
      DATA ZERO/0.0/
      DATA LL/1274321477413155B,3427613512461323B,
     1        5317432515413621B,5324162421767241B,
     2        1463257432456157B,7021367742322501B,
     3        6672501452313577B,1254240657211345B,
     4        5303714101433663B,2054070571661247B/
C
      IF(IX)102,101,105
  101 CALL EROR2 (10)
  102 ISTRG=-IX
  103 ISEED=IISED(ISTRG)
      IF(ISEED)107,108,104
  108 IISED(ISTRG)=LL(ISTRG)
      GO TO 103
  104 L(ISTRG)=(ISEED.A.7777777777777776).0.1
      GO TO 107
  105 ISTRG=IX
  106 L(ISTRG)=L(ISTRG)*K
  107 DRAND=(L(ISTRG).0.1717000000000000000B)+ZERO
      RETURN
      END
```

Figure A2 FORTRAN listing of Function DRAND.

The computer time required for running the Q-GERT Analysis Program is a complex subject since it can involve loading, compiling (Q-

GERT and/or user subprograms), data input processing, simulating and output reporting. It has been found that input and output can contribute significantly to the execution time required for a program operation. In particular, excessive run tracing can increase execution times. Table A2 presents a summary of the run conditions for each example presented in this book and the time to process the example on the CDC 6500 computer operating in a multiprogramming environment.

TABLE A2. Computational Times for Examples on the CDC 6500 Computing System.

Example Number	Input Cards	Run Length*	Number of Runs	Load & Compile	Input & Echo Check	Simulation & Output	Total
1	16	480T	10	0.7	1.8	3.8	6.3
1A	16	4800T	5	0.8	1.8	17.7	20.3
2	17	480T	5	0.8	1.9	4.1	6.8
3	8	6240T	1	0.8	1.6	5.5	7.9
4	30	200X	10	0.7	2.1	14.3	17.1
5	14	300T	1	0.8	1.8	3.3	5.9
6	26	R	400	0.8	1.9	10.8	13.5
7	33	300X	5	1.0	2.2	8.8	12.0
8	34	N	1	0.9	2.2	2.3	5.4
9+	49	480T	20	0.8	2.4	28.8	32.0
10	32	R	400	1.7	2.0	9.5	13.2
11	21	6000T	5	1.4	1.9	3.9	7.2
12	15	52T	1	1.5	1.9	1.5	4.9
13	15	1000T	1	1.4	1.8	0.9	4.1
14	109	R	500	2.4	3.1	20.8	26.3
15	42	R	1000	0.8	2.3	27.6	30.7
16	38	N	5	0.8	3.0	2.4	6.2
17	53	8760T	1	0.7	3.3	10.2	14.2
18	32	480T	10	0.8	2.9	5.0	8.7

*T→time units; X→number of transactions; R→sink node releases; N→No events
+ For Example 9, a total of 22.0 seconds of computer time was required if the event and nodal traces were not requested.

INDEX

ACT card, 422
  Field 8, 149, 154
  Input, 58, 193
Activities, definition, 3, 46
  halting, 262
  numbers, 20, 264
  regular, 30
  service, 20, 30
  starting, 262
  stop next, 263
Activity time, attribute, 138
  distributions, 196
  extending, 263
ALL card, 434
All statistics, 67
ALLOCATE node, 359
  symbol, 360
ALT card, 436
ALTER, 369, 370
ALTER node, 364
  branching, 365
Analysis Program, operation, 53
ANSI FORTRAN, 443
Applications, cargo 7
  insurance, 7
  pipeline, 8
  workflow, 7
Arisawa S., 13
Arizona State University, 13

Arrivals, modeling, 21
Assembly, symbol, 160
Assembly mode, selection, 160
  use, 218
Assigning attribute values, 133, 223
  addition, 136
  Subtraction, 136
Attribute, activity time, 138, 280
Attribute assignment, 223
Attribute assignments,
  examples, 134
  S-nodes, 168
Attribute-based ranking, 142
Attributes, 29, 133
  assignments, 133
  conditional branching, 145
  selection, 39, 46
  use, 133, 136
Auterio, V., x, 335
Auxilary attributes, 328
Auxilary attributes subroutines,
  examples, 329
  list, 328
AVEWT, 257
  computation, 324

Balking, definition, 46
  example, 212

illustration, 116
S-node, 164
statistics, 70, 216
symbol, 35, 164
Balking rate, interpretation, 112
Banking system example, 209
Bartkus, D., x
Basic concepts, summary, 45–48
BEG card, 192, 424
Beta distribution, definition, 202
Beta-PERT distribution,
definition, 202
Between statistics, 67
use, 211
Blocking, 40
definition, 46
illustration, 116
restriction, 42
S-node, 165
statistics, 71
symbol, 165
Book, organization, viii, 16
plan, x
Branch, 3
definition, 19, 46
nonsolid, 34
Branching, conditional, 281
condition codes, 146
definition, 46
deterministic, 21, 29, 37, 46
probabilistic, 36, 47, 93˙
probabilistically-on-attribute,
153
Branson, M., 13
Burns, R., 13
Busy time, maximum, 111
Byers, J., 13

Capacity change, 365
CAPQ, 260
Card, definition, 9

CDC, 250
Cells, 76
Central limit theorem, 201
Change of parameters, 252
Chi-square test, 196
Choice criterion,
definition, 39, 46
Chubb, J., 15
Clayton, E., 5, 310
CLEAR, 304
Clearing statistics, 214
Code options, 193, 403
COL, 297
use, 308
COL card, 299, 430
Code options, 193, 371
COL, 297
use, 308
COMMON, 243, 444
Common random numbers, 216
Computation times, 445
Concepts, basic, 28
Conditional branching, 145
example, 225
input, 149
order, 147, 149
use, 281
Condition code message, 148
Condition codes, 146, 193
Conditions, testing order, 147,
149
Conveyor example, 107
Costs, 315
CPBE, use, 317
CPM, 12
Cramér-Von Mises test, 196
Criterion choice, use, 274
Criticality indices, 272
Crowston, W., 12
Cumulative probability distribu-
tion, 251
Cumulative report option, 213

Cumulative run reports, 194
Cumulative statistics, 217

Data input, 55, 189, 400
  code definitions, 193
  short forms, 58, 190
  subnetworks, 343
DATA statement, 290
Decision-CPM, 12
Decisions, definition, 46
DEF card, 336, 426
  use, 348
Delay statistics, 67
DEL card, 429
Deletions, DEL, 339
Deviate generators, 250
Discrete density function, 251
Distribution types, 27, 193, 250
  numeric codes, 249
Dotted lines, 179
DPROB, 251, 330
DRAND listing, 444
Drezner, S., 13
DuBrock, C., x
Duket, S., x, 15, 335
Dummy subprograms, 267
DUP card, 338, 426
Duration, activity, 26

Each-run report, 194
Echo check suppression, 409
Editing, 339
  deletions, 339
  insertions, 339
  replacements, 339
Eisner, H., 12
Elmaghraby, S., 5, 12
Erlang distribution,
  definition, 202, 216
  use, 216, 281
Error code 87, 268
Error messages, 437

ESN card, 336, 426
  use, 348
Estimated processing times, 231
Event, 46, 53
  processing, 54
  tiebreaking, 54
Event trace, 194, 222
  input, 226
Examples, list, xxi
Exponential distribution,
  definition, 198
  use, 107, 114, 223

FABID, see statistics
Feller, W., 205
Fields, default, 56
  options, 56
FIN card, 425
First release, 22
First-run report, 194
First statistics, 67
FRE card, 363, 435
FREE, 369, 370
FREE node, 362
  branching, 362
  symbol, 362
FREE node input, 363
FREEA, 328
Freeman, R., 12
Function DPROB, 251
Function DRAND, 250, 444
Function type, 26, 248
  list, 27
  numeric codes, 249
  significance, 30
Function UF, 238
  format, 239
Functions for sampling, 250

Gallagher, D., 13
Gantt, H. 11

Gamma distribution,
  definition, 202
GASP IV, 196
GATRB, 254
  use, 275, 331
Gaussian distribution, 200
GEN card, 195, 408
GERT, definition, vii
  history, 11
GERTE, 13
GERTS IIIR, 14
GERTS IIIQ, 14
GERTS IIIQR, 15
GERTS IIIZ, 14
GETAT, 258
Goodness-of-fit, 196
GPSS, viii
  terminology, 159
Grant, F., x, 15
Grant, M., x, 15
GRASP, 15

Hahn, G., 196
Halpin, D., 216, 335
HALTA, 262
Happ, W., 13, 216; 335
Headings, definition, 77
Hebert, J., 15
Hill, T., 13
HIS, 303
  use, 308
  use for plotting, 303
HIS card, 432
HISC, 303
HISP, 303
  use, 308
Histogram, cells, 76
Histogram, default, 87
  explanation, 112
Histogram outputs, definition, 87
Histograms, 302
Hogg, G., 15

IALOC, 369, 370
ICCR, 368, 369
ICSRA, 368, 369
ICSRU, 368, 369
Ignizio, J., 344
Incremental assignment,
  example 137
  use, 223
Industrial sales negotiation
  example, 310
INITA, 328
Initialize auxiliary arrays, 328
Input, cards, 28
  card types, 55, 406
  examples, 62, 64–65
  fields, 58–59
  free form, 56, 404
  sequencing rules, 55, 403
  shortform, 58, 190, 400
  subnetwork, 343
Input devices, 443
Input requirements, 55
INS, 15
Insertions, INS, 339
  Input, 429
Inserts, location, 236
  programming, 236
Interval statistics, 67
  use, 212
Inventory example, 286
Inventory position, 286
Ishmael, P., 13
ISTUS, 265
ITRAC, 194

Kolmogorov-Smirnov test, 196

Late finish time, 127
Late start time, 127
Lesso, W., 15
LIN card, 427
  use, 348

Line, dash, 156, 182
  dash-dot, 34, 182
  dot, 179
  squiggly, 23
Linking, LIN, 341
Little's formula, 326
Logistic distribution, 205
Lognormal distribution,
  definition, 201
  use, 211

Machine breakdown example, 278
Machine dependency, 250
Machine tool example, 139
Macros, 335
Maggard, M., 15
Marking, 24, 29
Mark time, 133
MAT card, 417
Match node, examples, 171
  input, 171
  input example, 172
  restriction, 171
  symbolism, 170, 182
Mellin Transforms, 13
Mixed distribution, 208
MOD card, 392
Model, definition, 1, 2
  execution, 28
  first cut, 235
  purpose, x, 2, 387
Modeling, hierarchial, 3
Modeling strategy, 235, 387
Modification, 173
Modules, 335
Moore, L., 5, 310
Multiple network analysis, 192
Multiple runs, 66
Multiple servers, input, 63
  restriction, 164

use, 103
NACTY, 264
  use, 275
NATCV, 344
NDE, 243–4
Nelson, A., 13
Network, definition, 46
Network modification, example, 212, 221
NFTBU, 243–4
Nodal trace, 192, 194
  input, 226
NODCV, 344
Node, definition, 4, 47
  mark, 24
  numbers, 20
  probability, 68
  release, 22
  sink, 23
  source, 22
  statistics, 67
  types, 46
Node modification, 173, 261
  examples, 175, 212, 221
  input, 175
  multiple, 176
  restriction, 174
  serial, 178
  symbol, 174
  terminology, 180
NODMOD, 261
NOFQ, 260
Normal distribution, definition, 200
  use, 218
Notation, see symbol
NREL, 244–5
  definition, 240
  statistics, 245
NREL2, 244–5
  definition, 240
NRELP, 244–5

NRUN, 244–5
    use, 276, 316
NRUNS, 244–5
    use 276
NTC, 244, 246
Number in queue, 240, 260
    initial, 32
    maximum, 33

Output devices, 443
Output report options, 194
Output reports, 77

PACTY, 257
PAF, 15
Paint shop example, 98
PAR card, 420
Parallel servers, 20
PARAM, 244, 247
PARAM array, use, 315
Parameter changes, 252
Parameter identifier, 26, 236
Parameter set, 26
Parameters, definition, 27, 60
PATRB, 258
    use, 331
Peripheral devices, 443
PERT, 12
    analysis, 126
    assumptions, 121
    cost, 315
    example, 118
    expected value, 272
    probabilistic, 12
    time estimates, 127
PERT criticality index, 272
Petersen, C., 15
P-GERT, 15
Phillips, D., 5, 15
Poisson distribution,
    definition, 199

Polito, J., 15
Precedence Diagramming, 12
Precedence GERT, 14
Prerequisites, viii
Pritsker & Associates, Inc., viii,
    15
Probabilistic branching, 36
    illustration, 211
Probability distribution, 250
Probability mass function, 251
Process, approach, 4
    definition, 18, 47
Programming inserts, 236
Project analysis, 317
Pseudorandom number,
    definition, 45, 250
PTIN, 259
    error, 268
    use, 282
PUTAT, 258

Q-GERT Analysis Program, viii,
    52
Q-GERT applications, 5
    approach, 387
    contributions, 387
    design, 8, 11
    error messages, 437
    history, 11
    input, 55
    intermediate concepts, 132
    modeling, 9
    operational information, 443
    running times, 444
    structure, 236
    symbols, 48
    time estimates, 127–128
Q-GERT symbols,
    intermediate, 181
Q-GERT variables,
    definition, 243

Q-node, 19,46
  attribute assignment, 141
  average number, 260
  balking, 33
  blocking, 40
  capacity, 33
  definition, 25
  initial status, 32
  input, 63
  multiple S-nodes, 166
  no capacity, 107
  number in, 260
  ranking, 39, 42, 282
  remaining capacity, 260
  selecting from, 157
  statistics, 68
  symbol, 21
  TINIQ, 261
Quarry operations example, 222
QUE card, 414
Queue, ranking, 47
Queue capacity, 206
Queue ranking,
  attribute value, 225
  illustration, 143
Queue selection rules, 158
Queueing, 19
QVAR, 243, 259

Raju, G., 13
Random, 45
Random number generator, 250, 444
Random number seed, 192
Random number stream 192, 251
Random sampling, 196
Random selection, 251
Ranking rule, 24
RCAPQ, 260
Recursive calls, 267
REG card, 410
Regular nodes, 46

Reinitialization, seeds, 192
Remaining service time, 265
REMST, 265
REP card, 429
Replacements, REP, 339
Release, 29
  first, 22
  subsequent, 22
Replications, 66
Reports, 77
  Options, 194
RES card, field description, 359
  restriction, 359
Resource, blocks, 358
  capacity change, 365
  definition, 358
  functions, 368
  modeling, 356
  types, 355
Resource block card, 433
Resource functions, 368–9
  ICCR, 368
  ICSRA, 368
  ICSRU, 368
  TIRA, 368
  TIRU, 368
Resource input, short form, 367
Resource subprograms, 369–71
  ALTER, 369, 370
  FREE, 369, 370
  IALOC, 369, 370
Resources, 355
  example, 371
  inspection, 378
  oil tanker, 375
  truck hauling, 371
Results, confidence, 101
Risk analysis, 8
Roberts, S., 15
Routing, 21
  definition, 46
  parallel queues, 156

Run,
  alternative specifications, 66
  definition, 62, 66
  specification, 52
Run-out of transactions, 220
Run statistics, 217
Run time options, 194
Runs, multiple, 66

Sabuda, J., x, 15
Sadlowski, T., 15
SAINT, 15
Sample generators, 250
SCHAT, 148
Schriber, T., 91, 103, 184, 375
Schulaker, R., 15
SEE card, 418
  example, 192
Seeds, random number, 192
Seifert, D., 15
SEL card, 416
Selection, servers, 161
Selection rules,
  numeric codes, 248
Selector nodes, 154
Server, statistics, 70, 265
  status, 18, 265
  stopping, 266
Server selection rules, 162
Servers, alternatives, 42, 45
  as transactions, 218
  initial status, 32
  multiple, 30, 31, 211
  parallel, 20
  selection, 161
Service, blocking, 40
Service activities,
  subprograms, 264
Service activity, 47
Service time, attribute value, 225
  remaining, 265
Sewing machine example, 103
Shah, B., 13

Shapiro, S., 196
Shapiro-Wilk test, 196
Short form, 58, 190, 343
Sigal, C. E., χ, 15, 335
Simulation program, 53
SIN card, 412
Sink, 23
Sink nodes, 46
Skeith, R.. 13
SMOOTH, 15
SNACT, 244
  use, 316
SNAP, 12
S-node, 154
  assembly, 160
  attribute assignments, 168
  balking, 164, 210
  blocking, 165
  choice criterion, 161
  getting transactions, 157
  input, 168
  multiple servers, 164
  Q-nodes, 166
  queue selection rules, 158
  restriction, 164, 169
  server selection, 161, 162
  symbol, 155–161
Source node, 22, 25, 46
  marking, 133
Space experiment example, 344
STA card, 412
STAGO, 266
  error, 268
  use, 282
Standridge, C., x
STARTA, 262
  error, 268
  use, 289
Statistics, 30
  collection, 24, 66
  example, 71
  interval, 24
  nodes, 46

observations, 298
  user collected, 297
STORA, 328
STSER, 266
  error, 268
Subinterval sampling, 308
Subinterval statistical collection,
  example, 304
Subnetwork, definition, 336
  duplication, 338
  editing, 339
  identification number, 336
  input form, 344
  linking, 341
  numbers, 344
  outputs, 343
  use, 346
Subprograms, activities, 261
  dummy, 267
  Q-nodes, 259
  restriction, 268
  service activities, 265
  table, 255-7
  transactions, 254
Subroutine CPBE, 252
Subroutine CPBP, 252
Subroutine CPGA, 252
Subroutine CPLO, 252
Subroutine CPTR, 252
Subroutine UI, 253
  data input, 253
Subroutine UO, 254
Subroutines, auxilary attributes,
  328
  statistics collection, 298
Summary report, 194
  headings, 77
Symbol, assembly, 160, 182
  attribute assignment, 135
  attribute branching, 181
  balking, 35, 164, 182
  blocking, 40, 165, 182
  conditional specification, 181

conditional take-all, 145
conditional take-first, 145
dashed lines, 156, 182
dash-dotted lines, 34, 182
dotted lines, 179
match node, 170, 182
probabilistic branching, 36
Q-node, 21
queue ranking, 181
S-node, 155-161, 181
user function, 237
value assignment, 181
Systems, procedural, 1
Systems approach, viii, 387

Tables,
  Auxiliary Attributes (9-2), 343
  Basic Concepts (2-2), 46
  Branching Options (6-1), 193
  Code Options (7-2), 249
  Distribution types (2-1), 27
  GEN card (6-2), 195
  Input Short form, 58, 190, 343,
    400
  Parameter Values, 60
  Probability Functions (7-3),
    250
  Q-GERT Variables (7-1), 244
  Resources, 368-70
  User Statistics (9-1), 298
  User Subprograms (7-4),
    255-7
TBEG, 244, 248
Thompson, G. L., 12
TIM, 299
  use, 301
TIM card, 431
TIMC, 299
Time, see Activity time
Time-persistence statistics, 299
  input, 301
TIMP, 299

TINIQ, 261
  use, 306
TIRA, 368, 369
TIRU, 368, 369
TISS, 265
  use, 282, 307
TMARK, 259
TNOW, 244, 283
  definition, 240
  restriction, 248
  use, 326
Townsend, T., x, 14
TRA card, 425
Trace, 194, 222, 229
  example, 123
  input, 192
Trace, user starting, 194
Transactions, accumulation, 38
  arrival, 36
  assembly, 160
  attributes, 4, 18, 133
  balking, 33
  blocking, 40
  definition, 3, 18, 47
  marking, 24
  multiple types, 223
  rerouting, 266
  routing, 29
  run out, 220
  selection, 39, 46
  type, 5
Triangular distribution,
  definition, 197
Truck hauling example, 216
Truncated, distribution, 208
TV inspection example, 91

UF, 267
  error, 268
  use, 281, 289, 301, 305, 315
  value assigned, 253

UI, 248, 253
  use, 281–2, 301, 308, 317
Uniform distribution,
  definition, 196, 267
  use, 92, 98, 211, 218
UO, 254, 267
  use, 275, 282, 290, 302
UOBV array, 299
US, 27, 134, 237, 243
User collected statistics, 297
  input, 299
  list, 298
User function, example, 237
  number, 236
  symbolism, 237
User histograms, 302
  input, 303
User input, use, 316
User statistics, clearing, 304
UTCLR array, 304
UTPV array, 300

Value assignment (VAS), 134
  input, 138
Vanston, J., 15
VAS card, 419

Waiting times, computation, 324
Washam, W., x, 14
Whitehouse, G., 5, 13
Wilson, J., x
Work stations, example, 114
Wortman, D., 15, 335

XNINQ, 260
XTEND, 263